QUANTUM MECHANICS IN CHEMISTRY

PHYSICAL CHEMISTRY
MONOGRAPH SERIES

Edited by Walter Kauzmann, Princeton University

MELVIN W. HANNA, *University of Colorado*
QUANTUM MECHANICS IN CHEMISTRY

WALTER KAUZMANN, *Princeton University*
THERMAL PROPERTIES OF GASES

QUANTUM MECHANICS IN CHEMISTRY

Melvin W. Hanna

University of Colorado

W. A. BENJAMIN, INC.

New York   Amsterdam   1965

QUANTUM MECHANICS IN CHEMISTRY

Copyright © 1965 by W. A. Benjamin, Inc.

Library of Congress Catalog Card Number 65–16457

MANUFACTURED IN THE UNITED STATES OF AMERICA

The manuscript was put into production on October 9, 1964; this volume was published on August 9, 1965

W. A. BENJAMIN, INC.
New York, New York 10016

Editor's Foreword

ANYONE responsible for teaching a one-year introductory course in physical chemistry must make difficult decisions in the selection of topics he will present to his students. In the past thirty years developments in molecular physics and quantum mechanics have made these areas essential to the student's background in physical chemistry. Yet nearly all of the topics in physical chemistry as taught thirty years ago continue to be of importance not only to physical chemists but also to those in other fields of chemistry, not to mention biologists, geologists, metallurgists, engineers, and medical scientists. Since the time available in the course is limited, important subjects must either be discussed very briefly or passed over entirely, the teacher hoping that the student will be able to pick up omitted material for himself should he need it later in his career.

The same difficulty is faced by the writer of a textbook in physical chemistry. Sometimes it is dealt with by increasing the size of the book, but more often authors compress or eliminate topics they feel to be unimportant. Furthermore, it is becoming more and more difficult for one author to write with authority about all areas of physical chemistry.

The situation cannot be dealt with by arbitrarily choosing a limited number of topics in the hope that they will be recognized universally as suitable for a one-year course in modern physical chemistry. Physical chemistry textbooks should, rather, be designed and written in such a way that flexibility is possible in choosing the topics to be taught in any given year. Different teachers will have valid reasons for emphasizing different aspects of physical chemistry, and any one teacher may want to be able to change his emphasis from one year to the next.

The present text-monograph series is an attempt to deal with this problem. The basic series will consist of about nine volumes, of 150 to 200 pages apiece, each dealing at an introductory level with important topics in physical chemistry. The texts will be written in such a way that the student will be able to learn for himself about those topics that may not have been presented in the particular physical chemistry course he may have taken. It is also intended that in each volume some more advanced material can be included which will stimulate the interest of the students and give some indication of the present status of physical chemistry, not only as a branch of chemistry but also as a foundation for other areas of science.

The total size of the basic series will be greater than that of the average introductory textbook (the basic series will have about 1,500 pages as compared with typical texts having 700 to 900 pages and covering the same topics), but it is expected that, since not all of the texts will be used in any given course, the financial and intellectual burden on the student will not be excessive. Indeed, the intellectual burden on the student should be less than that imposed by any of the introductory texts now in wide use; because of the greater number of pages available in the series, it should be possible to explain difficult points in more detail and yet to reach at least as high an intellectual level as that aimed for by conventional texts.

The basic series will be supplemented by volumes that consider special topics of current physical chemical interest and are written at a level suitable for students in the first year of their exposure to physical chemistry.

WALTER KAUZMANN

Princeton, New Jersey
January, 1965

Preface

THIS book was developed in an attempt to introduce undergraduates at the University of Colorado to some aspects of quantum mechanics, spectroscopy, and the electronic structure of atoms and molecules. The author believes that organic chemists have long had an advantage over physical chemists in that good students can read organic research material after a one-year introductory course. In physical chemistry, any adequate discussion of quantum phenomena is usually reserved for graduate school. As a result, many good students are not able to catch some of the excitement inherent in the areas of physical chemistry dealing with quantum phenomena. In addition, students desiring to do research in the fields of quantum mechanics and molecular structure have had to spend their first year (and sometimes a second year) in graduate school, developing the necessary background knowledge. Putting a fairly complete introduction to quantum phenomena at the undergraduate level gives these graduate students a chance to begin research earlier. There is the additional advantage that good students can do an undergraduate research project in these areas in their senior year.

To put any kind of adequate discussion of quantum phenomena into the undergraduate physical chemistry course requires that certain areas of "classical" physical chemistry be left out. The argument about whether such a procedure is justified or not will, no doubt, go on for some time. The author feels, however, that there is one compelling argument for the inclusion of quantum phenomena. Any discussion of quantum mechanics requires an extensive new vocabulary and mode of symbolism. Since physical chemistry is now so broad a field that something must be left out of an undergraduate course, it seems most logical to leave out those subjects that the student with a normal background can study and learn on his own. Because of the new language and symbolism, quantum mechanics, spectroscopy, and electronic structure are *not* fields which fall into this category. The main purpose of the present book is to allow instructors to develop quantum ideas in an undergraduate course in conjunction with some selection of topics from classical physical chemistry. (At the University of Colorado, one semester is spent on classical thermodynamics and kinetics. The second semester is devoted to the material covered in this book.)

This book has been written for students with a wide variety of mathematical backgrounds. For students who have had only calculus, Chapter 1 provides an introduction to the mathematical fundamentals that are used throughout the text. (Students with very good mathematical backgrounds may wish to skip Chapter 1 entirely.) Additional mathematics are then introduced as needed in conjunction with specific problems. The author believes that quantum mechanics can most logically be introduced to under-graduates, who usually know very little about the physics of wave motion, by the postulational approach. This approach begins with the classical Hamiltonian and then transforms to the appropriate quantum mechanical operators as is done in the Schrödinger formalism. For this reason, the student is introduced to certain features of classical mechanics in Chapter 2. The main point of this chapter is to teach the student how to write the classical Hamiltonian for any problem of interest. In addition, the student is introduced to the idea of generalized coordinates, conservative and nonconservative systems, and the separation of the motion of the center of mass in a many-particle system where the potential energy depends only on the internal coordi-nates of the system.

With this introduction, the postulates of quantum mechanics are presented in Chapter 3 after a discussion of the historical events showing the necessity for a new mechanics. The postulates are then applied to the specific example of a particle in a one-dimensional box. A discussion follows of vibrational and rotational energy levels and vibration-rotation spectroscopy, atomic structure, molecular structure and spectra, the electronic structure of conjugated systems, and electron and nuclear magnetic resonance spectroscopy. These subjects are developed in a logical sequence. The treatment of each depends on conclusions and relations which have been previously developed.

Problems are inserted at various points in the text to illustrate ideas which have been discussed. These problems from an integral part of the text and should be worked by the student before going to the next point. In many instances, algebraic derivations have been left out of the text and inserted in the form of problems. Many of these problems involve the use of actual experimental data. Many instructors will wish to supplement these problems with their own selection of exercises.

This book is not meant to be a comprehensive discussion of all the topics of quantum mechanics, spectroscopy, and electronic structure. It is the author's prejudice that undergraduate students should get used to the idea that all the necessary material for understanding a particular subject will not be found in a single text. For this reason, many subjects which are well covered in other books have not been repeated in this one. Rather, references to many points about which students are likely to want more information are given in the body of the text. Students using this book are encouraged to spend considerable time in the library reading other works. To facilitate this process, a rather substantial annotated bibliography has been given at the end of the book. Three general texts will be used many times as references, and the student should certainly become familiar with the material contained in them. These texts are: H. Margenau and G. M. Murphy, *The Mathematics of Physics and Chemistry* (New York: Van Nostrand, 1943); H. Eyring, J. Walter, and G. E. Kimball, *Quantum Chemistry* (New York: John Wiley, 1944); and Walter Kauzmann, *Quantum Chemistry* (New York: Academic Press, 1957). These will be referred to in the text as I, II, and III, respectively. They are also designated this way in the bibliography.

Much of the credit for this book should go to my instructors in quantum chemistry. It was the courses and informal discussions with Professors Norman Davidson, J. de Heer, William Lipscomb, and Harden McConnell that contributed most to my knowledge and interest in the fields covered by this book. I owe a special debt of gratitude to Professor Walter Kauzmann for reading the entire final manuscript and making numerous suggestions that made the presentation more rigorous and understandable. My students in the second semester of physical chemistry also deserve thanks. It was their interest that stimulated me to write the book, and their penetrating questions added much to its final form. Thanks are also due to Mrs. Gretchen Bales for her painstaking work on the manuscript.

MELVIN W. HANNA

Boulder, Colorado
May 1965

Contents

Chapter 1

MATHEMATICAL

PRELIMINARIES

PHYSICAL CHEMISTRY is a science requiring the application of mathematics and mathematical reasoning to chemical problems. Emphasis on the use of mathematics is especially pronounced in the branch of physical chemistry called quantum mechanics and molecular structure. The purpose of this chapter is to outline briefly some of the mathematics which the student should be familiar with in order to understand what follows. Other mathematical procedures will be introduced later as needed. The student interested in advanced work in physical chemistry should make his mathematical background as extensive as possible, and it is recommended that such students supplement the material in this chapter with additional study from Reference **I** in the Bibliography.

1-1   Coordinate systems[1]

The purpose of a coordinate system is to make it convenient to describe a point or the motion of a point in space. There are many different kinds of coordinate systems, and four will be used

[1] For a more complete discussion of coordinate systems, see **I**, Chapter 5.

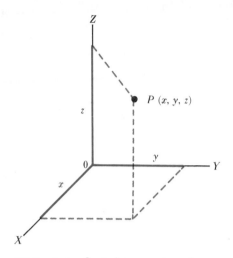

FIG. 1-1 *Cartesian or rectangular coordinates. A point $P(x, y, z)$ is defined by three distances along three mutually perpendicular axes.*

in this text: (1) rectangular or Cartesian coordinates, (2) spherical polar coordinates, (3) cylindrical coordinates, and (4) confocal ellipsoidal coordinates. The choice of what kind of coordinates to use depends on the problem one is trying to solve. The coordinate system is always chosen to make the mathematical equations that describe the problem as simple as possible. Of course, any numerical result which one calculates must be independent of the choice of a coordinate system.

Cartesian coordinates are the most familiar. A point P in "Cartesian space" is represented by distances along three mutually perpendicular axes called X, Y, and Z (Figure 1-1). A rectangular coordinate system should always make use of the "right-hand rule." This rule states that, when the fingers of the *right* hand are curled so that they point from the X to the Y axis, the thumb points along Z.

The other kinds of coordinates are most conveniently expressed in terms of Cartesian coordinates. In spherical polar coordinates (Figure 1-2), a point $P(r, \theta, \phi)$ is represented by one distance r and two angles θ and ϕ. The coordinate r is the length of the line OP drawn from the origin to point P. The angle θ is called the

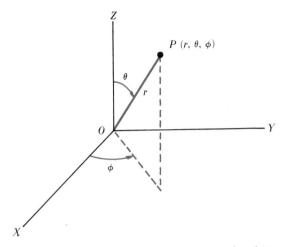

FIG. 1-2 *Spherical polar coordinates. A point P(r, θ, φ) is defined by two angles and one distance.*

polar angle, and is the angle between the Z axis and line OP. The angle ϕ is called the azimuthal angle and is the angle between the X axis and the projection of line OP in the XY plane. It is left for the student to show that the Cartesian coordinates of point P are related to the spherical polar coordinates by the relations

$$
\begin{aligned}
x &= r \sin \theta \cos \phi \\
y &= r \sin \theta \sin \phi \\
z &= r \cos \theta
\end{aligned}
\tag{1-1}
$$

EXERCISE 1-1 Express the quantity $(x^2 + y^2 + z^2)$ in spherical polar coordinates.

Cylindrical coordinates are shown in Figure 1-3. The location of point P is given by two distances and one angle. The two distances are z and the length of the projection of line OP in the XY plane, ρ. The angle ϕ is the same as in spherical polar coordinates. The student may easily verify the relations

$$
\begin{aligned}
x &= \rho \cos \phi \\
y &= \rho \sin \phi \\
z &= z
\end{aligned}
\tag{1-2}
$$

Confocal ellipsoidal coordinates, sometimes just called elliptical coordinates, are shown in Figure 1-4. These coordinates are used

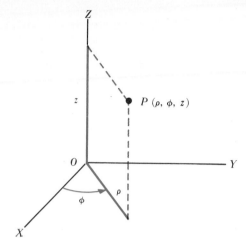

FIG. 1-3 *Cylindrical coordinates. A point $P(\rho, \phi, z)$ is defined by two distances and one angle.*

for problems involving two centers, A and B, a fixed distance R apart. A point P can be described by specifying the distances r_A and r_B and the angle ϕ which the projection of line OP in the XY plane makes with the X axis. Elliptical coordinates μ and ν are then defined as

$$\mu = \frac{r_A + r_B}{R} \quad \text{and} \quad \nu = \frac{r_A - r_B}{R} \tag{1-3}$$

The third coordinate is the angle ϕ described above. With a little thought, the student may verify that surfaces of constant μ are ellipsoids of revolution with the points A and B as foci. Surfaces of constant ν are hyperboloids of revolution about the bond axis. These surfaces are shown in Figure 1-4.

In problems of quantum mechanics, one will often be required to evaluate integrals over all space. To do this, the differential volume element, called $d\tau$, must be known for each kind of coordinate system. These volume elements for the various coordinate systems, and the limits of integration that include all space are [2]:

---

[2] For a discussion of the derivation of these volume elements see, **I**, page 168; **II**, page 363 ff.

Cartesian
$$d\tau = dx\,dy\,dz$$

$$-\infty \leq x \leq +\infty$$
$$-\infty \leq y \leq +\infty$$
$$-\infty \leq z \leq +\infty$$

Spherical polar
$$d\tau = r^2 \sin\theta\,dr\,d\theta\,d\phi$$

$$0 \leq r \leq +\infty$$
$$0 \leq \theta \leq \pi$$
$$0 \leq \phi \leq 2\pi$$

Cylindrical
$$d\tau = \rho\,d\rho\,d\phi\,dz$$

$$0 \leq \rho \leq \infty$$
$$0 \leq \phi \leq 2\pi$$
$$-\infty \leq z \leq +\infty$$

Elliptical
$$d\tau = \frac{R^2}{8}(\mu^2 - \nu^2)\,d\mu\,d\nu\,d\phi$$

$$0 \leq \mu \leq \infty$$
$$-1 \leq \nu \leq +1$$
$$0 \leq \phi \leq 2\pi$$

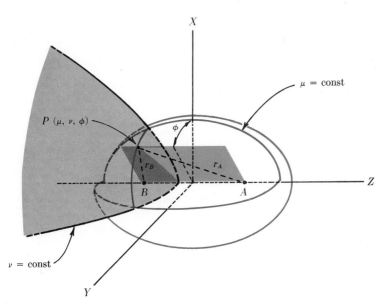

FIG. 1-4   *Confocal ellipsoidal coordinates.   Surfaces of constant* μ *are ellipsoids of revolution about the Z axis.   Surfaces of constant* ν *are paraboloids of revolution.   The intersection of these two surfaces defines a circle.   The final coordinate* ϕ *specifies a point* $P(\mu, \nu, \phi)$ *on the circle.*

1-2   *Determinants*

A determinant is an arrangement of quantities or elements, A_{ij}, in rows and columns in which the number of rows is equal to the number of columns.   The order of a determinant is the number of rows or columns.   Thus, the Quantities 1-4a and 1-4b

$$\begin{vmatrix} x - E & B \\ B & 2x - E \end{vmatrix} \tag{1-4a}$$

$$\begin{vmatrix} 8 & 5 & 3 \\ 3 & 5 & 8 \\ 5 & 3 & 8 \end{vmatrix} \tag{1-4b}$$

are determinants, the first of order 2 and the second of order 3. The most convenient way to evaluate a determinant is to make use of the method of *signed minors* or *cofactors*.   The minor of an element A_{ij} is the determinant left when both the row i and column j of the original determinant are struck out.   To form the cofactor, the minor is given a sign according to the position of the element A_{ij} in the original determinant.   This sign is $(-1)^{i+j}$.   A determinant can be evaluated by taking the algebraic sum of the product of each element of one row or column and its cofactor.   Example: Evaluate the determinant 1-4b by the method of cofactors.

$$\begin{vmatrix} 8 & 5 & 3 \\ 3 & 5 & 8 \\ 5 & 3 & 8 \end{vmatrix} = 8 \begin{vmatrix} 5 & 8 \\ 3 & 8 \end{vmatrix} - 5 \begin{vmatrix} 3 & 8 \\ 5 & 8 \end{vmatrix} + 3 \begin{vmatrix} 3 & 5 \\ 5 & 3 \end{vmatrix}$$

$$= 8(40 - 24) - 5(24 - 40) + 3(9 - 25)$$

$$= 128 + 80 - 48 = 160$$

Two useful properties of determinants that will be used in this text are:

1. The value of a determinant changes sign when two rows or two columns are interchanged.

2. If two rows are equal, or if two columns are equal, the determinant is zero.

EXERCISE 1-2   Evaluate the determinant

$$\begin{vmatrix} 4 & 1 & 2 & 3 \\ 1 & 2 & 3 & 4 \\ 2 & 3 & 4 & 1 \\ 3 & 4 & 1 & 2 \end{vmatrix}$$

by the method of cofactors.

1-3 Vectors

Most numerical and algebraic quantities that the student is familiar with have been scalar quantities. These are quantities such as 106 and $(x^2 + 3x + 2)$ which have magnitude only. A vector is a symbol used to represent a physical quantity which has *both* magnitude and direction. Quantities such as force, an electric field, or an acceleration are all vector quantities. A vector will be represented in this book by **boldface type.** It can also be represented by a symbol with an arrow above or below it, i.e., $\vec{r}$ or $\underset{\rightarrow}{E}$. The length of a vector is called its magnitude and is a scalar quantity. A vector that has a length of one unit is called a unit vector. A vector often used is the radius vector **r.** In Figure 1-2, this is the vector whose length or magnitude is r and whose direction is from the origin to the point P.

It is usually most convenient to work with vectors in terms of their components. To do this, three mutually perpendicular unit vectors called **i, j,** and **k** are defined that point along the X, Y, and Z axes, respectively. Any vector can then be written in terms of its components (projections) along these three axes. The radius vector becomes simply

$$\mathbf{r} = x\mathbf{i} + y\mathbf{j} + z\mathbf{k} \tag{1-5}$$

Just as multiplication and division of numbers follow certain rules, so there are rules which define the combination of vectors. These rules will now be summarized:

1. *Addition:* Addition of vectors can either be done graphically or analytically. Consider the vector sum

$$\mathbf{A} + \mathbf{B} = \mathbf{C} \tag{1-6}$$

In the graphical method, the tail of **B** is placed at the head of **A.** The sum **C** is the vector which starts at the tail of **A** and ends at the head of **B** (Figure 1-5a). Note that it is permissible to translate a vector through space as long as its magnitude or direction is not changed.

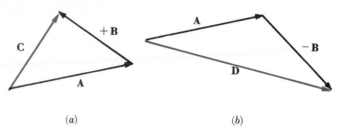

FIG. 1-5 *Illustration of the graphical addition (a) and subtraction (b) of two vectors* **A** *and* **B**.

If the vectors **A** and **B** can be written in terms of their components, then the addition can be done analytically. Thus, if

$$\mathbf{A} = A_x\mathbf{i} + A_y\mathbf{j} + A_z\mathbf{k} \qquad (1\text{-}7a)$$

and

$$\mathbf{B} = B_x\mathbf{i} + B_y\mathbf{j} + B_z\mathbf{k} \qquad (1\text{-}7b)$$

then

$$\mathbf{C} = (A_x + B_x)\mathbf{i} + (A_y + B_y)\mathbf{j} + (A_z + B_z)\mathbf{k} \qquad (1\text{-}7c)$$

2. *Subtraction:* Vectors are subtracted by adding the negative of the appropriate vector. Thus, $\mathbf{A} - \mathbf{B} = \mathbf{D}$ is illustrated in Figure 1-5b. Analytically

$$\mathbf{D} = (A_x - B_x)\mathbf{i} + (A_y - B_y)\mathbf{j} + (A_z - B_z)\mathbf{k} \qquad (1\text{-}8)$$

3. *Magnitude:* Frequently one needs to express the magnitude of a vector in terms of its components. By elementary trigonometry, the student may verify that the length of the radius vector **r** in Figure 1-3 is

$$r = (x^2 + y^2 + z^2)^{\frac{1}{2}} \qquad (1\text{-}9)$$

Similarly, the magnitude of any vector $\mathbf{A} = A_x\mathbf{i} + A_y\mathbf{j} + A_z\mathbf{k}$ is $|A| = (A_x{}^2 + A_y{}^2 + A_z{}^2)^{\frac{1}{2}}$.

4. *Multiplication:* Two different kinds of vector multiplication have been defined. The first kind, symbolized $\mathbf{A} \cdot \mathbf{B}$, is called the dot or scalar product and results in a number. The second kind, symbolized $\mathbf{A} \times \mathbf{B}$, is called the vector or cross product and results in a vector.

The scalar product $\mathbf{A} \cdot \mathbf{B}$ is defined as

$$\mathbf{A} \cdot \mathbf{B} \equiv AB \cos \theta \qquad (1\text{-}10)$$

where A and B are the magnitudes of **A** and **B**, respectively, and where θ is the angle between **A** and **B**. The student should note that there is a simple geometrical interpretation to the dot product. It is equal to the length **A** times the length of the projection of **B** on **A** *or vice versa*. If two vectors are perpendicular

$$\cos \theta = \cos 90° = 0 \tag{1-11}$$

and $\mathbf{A} \cdot \mathbf{B} = 0$. Conversely, it is also true that if $\mathbf{A} \cdot \mathbf{B} = 0$, then **A** and **B** are perpendicular. When this is the case, the two vectors are said to be *orthogonal*. For two vectors written in terms of their components, one can show that

$$\mathbf{A} \cdot \mathbf{B} = A_x B_x + A_y B_y + A_z B_z \tag{1-12}$$

EXERCISE 1-3 Prove Equation 1-12 making use of the definitions of $\mathbf{A} \cdot \mathbf{B}$ and of the unit vectors **i**, **j**, and **k**.

The cross product $\mathbf{A} \times \mathbf{B}$ is defined as

$$\mathbf{A} \times \mathbf{B} = \mathbf{n} A B \sin \theta \tag{1-13}$$

where A, B, and θ have the same meaning as above. The vector **n** is a unit vector perpendicular to *both* **A** and **B**. If **A** and **B** are parallel, $\sin \theta = 0$ and $\mathbf{A} \times \mathbf{B} = 0$. Conversely, if $\mathbf{A} \times \mathbf{B} = 0$, the two vectors are parallel.

The "right-hand rule" must be used in evaluating the cross product. To use this rule, one places the bottom edge of the right palm along **A** and curls the fingers toward **B**. The thumb will then point in the direction of **n** as shown in Figure 1-6. As a result of this rule, it should be clear that

$$\mathbf{A} \times \mathbf{B} \neq \mathbf{B} \times \mathbf{A}$$

In fact

$$\mathbf{A} \times \mathbf{B} = -\mathbf{B} \times \mathbf{A} \tag{1-14}$$

When an equation such as Equation 1-14 is true, it is said that the quantities $\mathbf{A} \times \mathbf{B}$ and $\mathbf{B} \times \mathbf{A}$ do not *commute*, or that they are not commutative.

The geometrical interpretation of the cross product $\mathbf{A} \times \mathbf{B}$ is that of a vector perpendicular to both **A** and **B** whose length is equal to the area of the parallelogram defined by **A** and **B**. A consideration of Figure 1-7 may help clarify this point. In terms

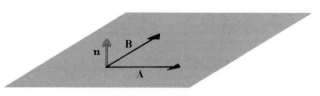

FIG. 1-6   *The use of the right-hand rule to determine the direction of the vector* **A** ✕ **B**.   *In using the right-hand rule, the angle between* **A** *and* **B** *is always chosen to be less than 180°.*

FIG. 1-7   *The geometrical significance of* **A** ✕ **B**. *The quantity AB sin θ is the area of the parallelogram. The vector* **n** *is one unit in length.*

of components, **A** ✕ **B** is most conveniently written in the form of a determinant.   Thus,

$$\mathbf{A} \times \mathbf{B} = \begin{vmatrix} \mathbf{i} & \mathbf{j} & \mathbf{k} \\ A_x & A_y & A_z \\ B_x & B_y & B_z \end{vmatrix} \tag{1-15}$$

$$= \mathbf{i}(A_y B_z - A_z B_y) - \mathbf{j}(A_x B_z - B_x A_z) + \mathbf{k}(A_x B_y - B_x A_y)$$

For proof of Equation 1-15, the reader is referred to one of the many standard works on vector analysis.[3]

EXERCISE 1-4 Let $A = 4i + j + 3k$, $B = i - 3j - k$. Evaluate $A + B$, $A - B$, $A \cdot B$, and $A \times B$.

5. *Division* of vectors is not defined.

6. *Differentiation of vectors:* A vector is differentiated simply by differentiating its components. Thus,

$$
\begin{aligned}
\mathbf{r} &= x\mathbf{i} + y\mathbf{j} + z\mathbf{k} \\
\frac{d\mathbf{r}}{dt} &= \frac{dx}{dt}\mathbf{i} + \frac{dy}{dt}\mathbf{j} + \frac{dz}{dt}\mathbf{k} \\
&= v_x\mathbf{i} + v_y\mathbf{j} + v_z\mathbf{k} \\
&= \mathbf{v}
\end{aligned}
\tag{1-16}
$$

where $\mathbf{v}$ is the velocity vector.

7. *Vector equations:* It should be noted that a vector equation is actually a summary of three scalar equations because, for two vectors to be equal, the appropriate components on both sides of the equal sign must be equal.

EXERCISE 1-5 In physics, the angular momentum L is defined as

$$L = r \times p$$

when p is the linear momentum at a point r. Write the equation for each component of angular momentum L_x, L_y, and L_z in terms of x, y, and z and the components of linear momentum p_x, p_y, and p_z.

1-4 Complex numbers

A complex number is one which contains the $\sqrt{-1}$ or i as it is usually symbolized. Thus, $A + iB$ is a complex number. We speak of the real (A) and the imaginary (B) part of a complex number. If

$$C = A + iB \tag{1-17}$$

then the complex conjugate of C, called C^*, is formed by replacing

[3] See, for example, **I**, page 137 ff.

i wherever it appears by $-i$. Thus

$$C^* = A - iB \qquad (1\text{-}18)$$

The magnitude or absolute value of a complex number is defined as

$$|C| \equiv (CC^*)^{\frac{1}{2}} = (A^2 + B^2)^{\frac{1}{2}} \qquad (1\text{-}19)$$

Note that the magnitude of a complex number is always real. Two complex numbers are equal only if *both* their real and imaginary parts are equal. Addition and subtraction follow the same rules as for vectors. That is, the real and imaginary parts are added independently. Thus, if $z_1 = x_1 + iy_1$, and $z_2 = x_2 + iy_2$, then $z_1 + z_2 = (x_1 + x_2) + i(y_1 + y_2)$.

An equation which will often be used in dealing with complex numbers is Euler's formula

$$e^{i\alpha} = \cos \alpha + i \sin \alpha \qquad (1\text{-}20)$$

Euler's formula can be derived by expanding each of the quantities $e^{i\alpha}$, $\cos \alpha$ and $\sin \alpha$ in a Maclaurins series. By equating the power series expansions, it can easily be shown that Equation 1-20 leads to an identity.

1-5   Operators

In a study of quantum mechanics, it is necessary to think in terms of mathematical *operators*. An operator is nothing more than a symbol that tells one to do something to what follows the symbol. Thus, in the expression $\sqrt{2}$, the $\sqrt{}$ is an operator telling one to take the square root of what follows, in this case 2. Likewise, in the expression

$$\frac{d}{dx} (x^2 + 5x + 1) \qquad (1\text{-}21)$$

$\dfrac{d}{dx}$ is an operator telling one to take the derivative with respect to x of what follows, i.e. $(x^2 + 5x + 1)$. General operators will be indicated by a symbol with a tent over it, i.e., $\hat{P}$ or $\hat{Q}$.

The algebra of operators follows definite mathematical procedures which the student is familiar with. Thus, if

$$\hat{P} = \left(\frac{\partial}{\partial x}\right)_{yz} \quad \text{and} \quad \hat{Q} = \left(\frac{\partial}{\partial y}\right)_{xz} \quad \text{then}$$

$$\hat{P}\hat{Q} = \left[\frac{\partial}{\partial x}\left(\frac{\partial}{\partial y}\right)_{xz}\right]_{yz} = \frac{\partial^2}{\partial x\, \partial y}$$

(1-22)

When dealing with operators one must be careful of the order of operations because operations are not necessarily commutative. By convention, one always begins with the operator on the right and works toward the left. In Equation 1-22, it turns out that $\hat{P}$ and $\hat{Q}$ do commute. That is

$$\hat{P}\hat{Q} = \hat{Q}\hat{P} \quad \text{since} \quad \frac{\partial^2}{\partial x\, \partial y} = \frac{\partial^2}{\partial y\, \partial x}$$

(1-23)

but this, in general, will not be the case (see Exercise 1-6).

EXERCISE 1-6 Let $\hat{P} = \dfrac{d}{dx}$, $\hat{Q} = x$ (multiply by x) and $f(x) = x^2 + 2x + 1$. Show that $\hat{Q}\hat{P}f(x) \neq \hat{P}\hat{Q}f(x)$. For these two operators, can you derive a general expression for $\hat{P}\hat{Q} - \hat{Q}\hat{P}$?

The quantity $(\hat{P}\hat{Q} - \hat{Q}\hat{P})$ is called the commutator of $\hat{P}$ and $\hat{Q}$, and is often symbolized $[\hat{P}, \hat{Q}]$. If $\hat{P}$ and $\hat{Q}$ commute, then the value of the commutator is zero. Conversely, if the value of the commutator is zero, the operators $\hat{P}$ and $\hat{Q}$ commute.

An operator can be a vector or a complex quantity. If an operator is a vector, one usually works with it in terms of its components. An example of a vector operator is "del."

$$\nabla = \frac{\partial}{\partial x}\mathbf{i} + \frac{\partial}{\partial y}\mathbf{j} + \frac{\partial}{\partial z}\mathbf{k}$$

(1-24)

The quantity ∇f, where f is some scalar function, is called the gradient of f. For example, suppose $f = x^2 + y^2 + z^2$, then the gradient of f is the vector

$$\nabla f = 2x\mathbf{i} + 2y\mathbf{j} + 2z\mathbf{k}$$

(1-25)

The gradient will be used in the next chapter in the discussion of classical mechanics.

If an operator $\hat{P}$ is complex, the complex conjugate $\hat{P}*$ is formed by replacing i by $-i$ wherever it occurs. Thus, if $\hat{P} = i\dfrac{d}{dx}$, $\hat{P}* = -i\dfrac{d}{dx}$.

In quantum mechanics, only linear operators are used. An operator is linear if it is true that

$$\hat{P}(f + g) = \hat{P}f + \hat{P}g$$

or

$$\hat{P}af = a\hat{P}f \text{ where } a \text{ is a number} \tag{1-26}$$

The student may easily verify that $\dfrac{d}{dx}$ is a linear operator whereas $\sqrt{}$ is not.

EXERCISE 1-7 It is true in algebra that

$$(P + Q)(P - Q) = P^2 - Q^2$$

What is the value of $(P + Q)(P - Q)$ if P and Q are operators? Under what conditions will the first relation be true for operators?

An operator which will be used often in quantum mechanics is the operator $\nabla^2 \equiv \nabla \cdot \nabla$. From Equations 1-12 and 1-24,

$$\nabla^2 = \frac{\partial^2}{\partial x^2} + \frac{\partial^2}{\partial y^2} + \frac{\partial^2}{\partial z^2} \tag{1-27}$$

1-6   *Eigenvalue equations*

An equation of the type

$$\hat{P}\Psi = p\Psi \tag{1-28}$$

where $\hat{P}$ is an operator and p is a number is called an *eigenvalue equation*. When such an equation holds, Ψ is called an eigenfunction of the operator $\hat{P}$, and p is called the eigenvalue.

Eigenvalue equations play a major role in the mathematical formalism of quantum mechanics. In quantum mechanics $\hat{P}$ is usually a differential operator and, therefore, the eigenvalue equation is a differential equation. The principal mathematical problem of quantum mechanics is to find the solutions Ψ and the eigenvalues p to these eigenvalue equations. The student must keep in mind that the mathematics of these equations were known long before quantum mechanics was developed. The mathematical properties of these equations, which are true by *definition*, should not be confused with the physical interpretation to be placed upon them in the later discussion of quantum mechanics.

EXERCISE 1-8 Show that the function $Ae^{-\alpha x}$ is an eigenfunction of the operator $\dfrac{d^2}{dx^2}$. What is the eigenvalue?

EXERCISE 1-9 Show that the function $\cos ax \cos by \cos cz$ is an eigenfunction of the operator ∇^2. What is the eigenvalue?

EXERCISE 1-10 Under what conditions is the function e^{-aq^2} an eigenfunction of the operator

$$\frac{d^2}{dq^2} - kq^2$$

where k is a constant. What is the eigenvalue under these conditions?

1-7 *Summary*

1. Some of the properties of coordinate systems, determinants, vectors, and complex numbers were reviewed.

2. Mathematical operators were introduced and some of their properties were discussed.

3. Several terms were introduced which will be important throughout the book. The student should be especially familiar with the meaning of the terms orthogonal, commute and commutator, complex conjugate, eigenvalue and eigenfunction.

Chapter 2

CLASSICAL MECHANICS

THE FUNDAMENTAL problem of classical mechanics is to describe the motion of systems of particles under various kinds of forces and initial conditions. More practically, the problem is to solve the differential equations resulting from Newton's law

$$\mathbf{F}_i = m\mathbf{a}_i \tag{2-1}$$

where $\mathbf{F}_i$ is the force acting on the i'th particle in the system, and $\mathbf{a}_i$ is its acceleration.

2-1 Conservative systems

Before going into more detail concerning the solutions to Equation 2-1, it is necessary to distinguish between two types of systems—conservative and nonconservative. For our purposes, it will be sufficient to define a conservative system as one in which the sum of the kinetic and potential energy of the system remains constant with time. A conservative system is, therefore, an isolated system and is not acted upon by external forces. Also, it cannot have any internal dissipative forces such as friction.

An equivalent definition of a conservative system is that it is a system in which the forces can be represented as the negative gradient (see Section 1-5) of some potential function V. That is,

$$\mathbf{F}_i = -\nabla_i V \tag{2-2}$$

To show that these two definitions are equivalent, consider the case of a single particle constrained to move in one dimension, say the x direction. Newton's law for this case is

$$F_x = m \frac{d^2 x}{dt^2} \tag{2-3}$$

and, if Equation 2-2 holds,

$$F_x = -\frac{dV(x)}{dx} \tag{2-4}$$

Substituting Equation 2-4 into Equation 2-3, performing several straightforward algebraic manipulations, and integrating, one obtains

$$-\frac{dV(x)}{dx} = m\ddot{x} = \frac{m\,d\dot{x}}{dt}$$

$$-\int \frac{dV(x)}{dx}\,dx = -\int dV = m\int \frac{d\dot{x}}{dt}\dot{x}\,dt = m\int \dot{x}\,d\dot{x}$$

$$-V(x) + C = \frac{1}{2} m\dot{x}^2$$

$$\frac{1}{2} m\dot{x}^2 + V(x) = C \tag{2-5}$$

where C is an arbitrary constant of integration. Thus, if Equation 2-2 is assumed, the sum of the potential and kinetic energies of the particle is independent of the time t, and the two definitions of a conservative system are equivalent.

The plausibility of Equation 2-2 can also be seen from the properties of a particle constrained to move in one dimension. The work done in moving a particle from x_1 to x_2 is $\int_{x_1}^{x_2} F_x\,dx$ so that V in Equation 2-4 will have units of work. The change in potential energy when the particle is moved from x_1 to x_2 is then equal to minus the work done.

Any property of a mechanical system independent of time is called a constant of motion of the system.   In this particular case, the constant of motion is just the total energy of the particle E. In what follows, the symbol T will be used for kinetic energy. Equation 2-5 then becomes $C = T + V$, and it becomes clear that the constant of integration in Equation 2-5 is the total energy of the system.

2-2   *The Lagrangian and Hamiltonian forms of the equations of motion*

Newtonian mechanics was later expanded and generalized by two mathematicians, Joseph Lagrange and William Hamilton.   In classical mechanics, there are two functions, called the Lagrangian and Hamiltonian functions, which can be written in such a way that the equations of motion derived from these functions remain the same regardless of the coordinate system used in a specific problem.   Hamilton's function is especially important because it is directly used in the transformation from classical to quantum mechanics.

Before discussing these two forms of the equations of motion, it is necessary to introduce the idea of generalized coordinates, velocities, and momenta.

Suppose a conservative system containing three particles is considered.   In order to specify completely the state of the system at a given time t, one would have to specify the positions and velocities of the three particles.   To do this, one would have to specify 9 coordinates, i.e. $(x_1, y_1, z_1, \ldots x_3, y_3, z_3)$ and nine velocities, i.e. $(\dot{x}_1, \dot{y}_1, \dot{z}_1, \ldots \dot{x}_3, \dot{y}_3, \dot{z}_3)$.   In general, for a system containing N particles, one would have to specify $3N$ coordinates and $3N$ velocities.   Such a system would have $6N$ degrees of freedom.[1]   It may not always be convenient to use rectangular coordinates, however.   In problems involving central forces, for example, it is much more convenient to use spherical polar coordi-

---

[1] This statement is true only if there are no constraints inherent in the system which make some of the $6N$ variables dependent.   For instance, if the three particles were required to move on the spherical surface $x^2 + y^2 + z^2 = R^2$, then only six degrees of freedom would exist rather than nine.   We will always assume that the coordinates have been chosen so that the restraints have already been accounted for.

nates. It would be highly advantageous if the laws of classical mechanics could be formulated so that they were independent of the particular coordinate system chosen for any specific problem. In order to accomplish this formulation, we introduce generalized coordinates, q_i, and generalized velocities, $\dot{q}_i = \dfrac{dq_i}{dt}$. We will then derive the Lagrangian and Hamiltonian forms of the equations of motion in terms of these generalized coordinates and velocities. When working problems, these generalized quantities are given a specific form.

The Lagrangian function $L(\dot{q}, q)$ is defined as

$$L(\dot{q}, q, t) = T(\dot{q}, q) - V(q, t) \tag{2-6}$$

where T is the kinetic energy expressed as a function of the generalized velocities and coordinates, and V is the potential energy expressed as a function of the generalized coordinates and the time t. For conservative systems, the Lagrangian function, L, and the potential energy, V, will not depend explicitly on the time. For these systems, L is a function only of the $6N$ q_i and $\dot{q}_i$. Going through considerable algebra, one can show that the equations of motion in Lagrangian form are [2]

$$\frac{d}{dt}\left(\frac{\partial L}{\partial \dot{q}_i}\right)_{q_j, \dot{q}_j \neq i} = \left(\frac{\partial L}{\partial q_i}\right)_{q_j \neq i, \dot{q}_j} \tag{2-7}$$

These equations, since they are in generalized coordinates, hold for any system of coordinates. It should be pointed out that in the partial derivatives in Equation 2-7, the other $6N - 1$ variables are held constant. From this point on, the constancy of these variables will be understood and the subscripts will not be used.

The student can see that the Lagrangian equations of motion are a set of $3N$ second-order differential equations. To derive the equations of motion in Hamiltonian form, we transform these to a set of $6N$ first-order equations. To do this, we first define

---

[2] There are several ways to do this. See, for example, N. Davidson, *Statistical Mechanics*, McGraw-Hill Book Company, Inc., New York (1962) page 7 ff. or R. C. Tolman, *The Principles of Statistical Mechanics*, Oxford University Press, London (1930) page 23 ff.

the generalized momenta p_k as

$$p_k = \left(\frac{\partial L}{\partial \dot{q}_k}\right) \tag{2-8}$$

Using Cartesian coordinates for a system containing a single particle of mass m, these momenta are just the ordinary components of momentum $m\dot{x}$, $m\dot{y}$, and $m\dot{z}$ for the particle.

We next define a new function $\mathcal{H}$ by the equation

$$\mathcal{H} = \sum_{i=1}^{3N} p_i \dot{q}_i - L \tag{2-9}$$

Again, after considerable algebra, one can show that for a conservative system[3]

$$\frac{\partial \mathcal{H}}{\partial p_i} = \dot{q}_i$$
$$\frac{\partial \mathcal{H}}{\partial q_i} = -\frac{\partial L}{\partial q_i} = \dot{p}_i \tag{2-10}$$

These are the equations of motion in Hamiltonian form. When $\mathcal{H}$ is expressed as a function of the coordinates and the *momenta*, it is called the Hamiltonian function for the system. The Hamiltonian function for a conservative system has the property that it is equivalent to the total energy of the system. To show this, we substitute Equation 2-6 into Equation 2-9 to obtain

$$\mathcal{H} = \sum_i \dot{q}_i \frac{\partial L}{\partial \dot{q}_i} - T + V \tag{2-11a}$$

$$= \sum_i \dot{q}_i \frac{\partial T}{\partial \dot{q}_i} - T + V \tag{2-11b}$$

Equation 2-11b follows from Equation 2-11a because, for conservative systems, all of the dependence of L on $\dot{q}_i$ is in the T term. The

[3] R. C. Tolman, *loc. cit.*, page 26 ff.

first term in Equation 2-11, however, is equal to $2T$. To show this, consider the example of a system in which one particle is constrained to move in one dimension. The kinetic energy for Cartesian coordinates is

$$T = \frac{1}{2} m \dot{q}_i^2$$

It is easily seen, then, that

$$\frac{\partial T}{\partial \dot{q}_i} = m \dot{q}_i$$

and

$$\dot{q}_i \frac{\partial T}{\partial \dot{q}_i} = m \dot{q}_i^2 = 2T$$

For the many particle, many dimension system, using Cartesian coordinates $T = \frac{1}{2} \Sigma m_i \dot{q}_i$ and, following an argument similar to the above, it can be shown that

$$\sum_i \dot{q}_i \frac{\partial T}{\partial \dot{q}_i} = 2T \tag{2-12}$$

Using this result in Equation 2-11b, it follows that

$$\mathcal{K} = 2T - T + V = T + V \tag{2-13}$$

Thus, we see that Hamilton's function is identical with the total energy.

EXERCISE 2-1 Consider the case of a particle of mass m moving in a gravitational field. Write the laws of motion starting with Newton's laws.

EXERCISE 2-2 Write the Lagrangian function for the particle of mass m moving in a gravitational field. Derive the equations of motion from Equation 2-7. Show that the equations obtained by this method are the same as those obtained from Newton's laws.

A simple prescription for writing down Hamilton's function is as follows:

1. Write $x_i = x_i(q_1, q_2, \ldots)$

2. Write $\dot{x}_i = \sum_j \left(\dfrac{\partial x_i}{\partial q_j}\right) \dot{q}_j$

3. Write $T = \dfrac{1}{2} \sum_i m_i \dot{x}_i^2$

4. Replace the $\dot{x}_i$ in step 3 with the equations in step 2 to obtain

$$T(q_i, \dot{q}_i) = \frac{1}{2} \sum_i m_i \left[\sum_j \left(\frac{\partial x_i}{\partial q_j}\right) \dot{q}_j \right]^2 \text{ and write } V(q_i).$$

5. Write $L = T - V$.

6. Calculate the appropriate momenta p_i as a function of q_i and $\dot{q}_i$ using Equation 2-8.

7. Rewrite T as a function of p_i and q_i.

8. Use the T derived in step 4 to write $\mathcal{3C} = T + V$.

EXERCISE 2-3   Write Hamilton's function for the case of a particle of mass m in a gravitational field. Write the equations of motion and show that they are identical with Newton's equations.

EXERCISE 2-4   A particle is constrained to move in the XY plane under the potential $V = \frac{1}{2}k(x^2 + y^2)$.

1. Using Cartesian coordinates, write the equations of motion in Newtonian form.

2. Write the Lagrangian function L in Cartesian and polar coordinates.

3. Write the equations of motion in polar coordinates using the Lagrangian form.

4. Find the momenta p_r and p_ϕ.

5. Write the Hamiltonian function in both systems of coordinates.

6. What famous conservation law is obvious from the results of 3?

2-3   Internal coordinates and the motion of the center of mass

A specific problem that will be of great importance in quantum mechanics is that of two interacting particles of masses m_1 and m_2, where the potential is only a function of their distance apart.[4]

[4] The following treatment is essentially that of N. Davidson, *Statistical Mechanics*, McGraw-Hill Book Company, Inc., New York (1962) page 15.

If the Cartesian coordinates of the particles are x_1, y_1, z_1, and x_2, y_2, z_2, respectively, the square of their distances apart is

$$r_{12}{}^2 = (x_2 - x_1)^2 + (y_2 - y_1)^2 + (z_2 - z_1)^2 \qquad (2\text{-}14)$$

The problem discussed above can be greatly simplified by transforming to new coordinates which involve the coordinates of the center of mass X, Y, Z and the "internal" or relative coordinates x, y, z. Thus, we define

$$X = \frac{m_1 x_1 + m_2 x_2}{m_1 + m_2}, \quad Y = \frac{m_1 y_1 + m_2 y_2}{m_1 + m_2}, \quad Z = \frac{m_1 z_1 + m_2 z_2}{m_1 + m_2} \qquad (2\text{-}15)$$

$$x = x_2 - x_1, \qquad y = y_2 - y_1, \qquad z = z_2 - z_1$$

EXERCISE 2-5   Write an expression for the kinetic energy of a system containing two particles of masses m_1 and m_2 moving in only two dimensions. Let the coordinates be x_1, y_1, x_2, y_2. Transform this expression to the new coordinate system X, Y, x, y making use of the relations 2-15. Show that the final expression is

$$T = \frac{1}{2}(m_1 + m_2)(\dot{X}^2 + \dot{Y}^2) + \frac{1}{2}\frac{m_1 m_2}{m_1 + m_2}(\dot{x}^2 + \dot{y}^2)$$

Write the corresponding equation for a system of two particles moving in three dimensions.

Making use of the results of Exercise 2-5, we can write

$$L = \frac{1}{2}(m_1 + m_2)(\dot{X}^2 + \dot{Y}^2 + \dot{Z}^2)$$

$$+ \frac{\mu}{2}(\dot{x}^2 + \dot{y}^2 + \dot{z}^2) - V(x, y, z) \qquad (2\text{-}16)$$

where $\mu = \dfrac{m_1 m_2}{m_1 + m_2}$ and is called the reduced mass, and where V is a function only of x, y, z since, by hypothesis, the potential energy only depends on the internal or relative coordinates.

From the Lagrangian function in Equation 2-16, the equations of motion for the six coordinates can be calculated using Equation 2-7. These six equations of motion are:

$$(m_1 + m_2)\ddot{X} = (m_1 + m_2)\ddot{Y} = (m_1 + m_2)\ddot{Z} = 0 \qquad (2\text{-}17)$$

$$\mu\ddot{x} = -\frac{\partial V}{\partial x}, \; \mu\ddot{y} = -\frac{\partial V}{\partial y}, \; \mu\ddot{z} = -\frac{\partial V}{\partial z} \qquad (2\text{-}18)$$

Equations 2-17 are identical to the equations of motion that are obtained if the problem of the motion of a free particle (i.e., one subject to no forces) of mass M is solved. Thus, the motion of the center of mass of our two particle system is just the same as the motion of a free particle with mass equal to the total mass of the system. Equations 2-17 can be integrated to give

$$M\dot{q}_i = C \qquad\qquad\qquad\qquad\qquad (2\text{-}19)$$

where $M = (m_1 + m_2)$, $\dot{q}_i$ can be $\dot{X}$, $\dot{Y}$, or $\dot{Z}$, and C is a constant. Equation 2-19 shows that the three components of the velocity of the center of mass are constants. The kinetic energy due to the motion of the center of mass must also be a constant, therefore.

Equations 2-18 are identical to those that are obtained in solving the problem of the motion of a particle with mass μ subject to the potential function $V(x, y, z)$. The total energy of the system is the sum of the energies due to the motion of the center of mass and to the internal motion of the system. Since the translational energy of the center of mass adds only a constant to the total energy, it is usual to neglect its contribution and solve only the problem of the internal motion of the system. This example points up the power of expressing the laws of motion in generalized coordinates. In this case, we let $q_1 = X$, $q_2 = Y \cdots q_6 = z$, etc., and we can immediately write down the equations of motion from the Lagrangian function.

The above example is an extremely important one that should be thoroughly understood. In general terms, its significance is that, as long as the potential energy depends only on the internal coordinates of the system, *the motion of the center of mass can always be separated from the internal motion of the system*, and the two problems can be solved independently.

2-4 *The basic assumptions of classical mechanics*

At this point, it is good to think about the semiphilosophical implications inherent in classical mechanics. First, it is implied that an experimentalist can precisely measure the positions and velocities of all of the particles in a system at some time t in order to describe the state of the system. Secondly, once this initial state is specified, the laws of mechanics and a knowledge of the forces acting on the system enable the system to be characterized at any later time. In principle, then, an experimentalist could measure the position, velocity, energy, momentum, etc. of any particle at any time and compare it with the theoretical prediction. The following three statements summarize the assumptions inherent in this view.

1. There is no limit to the accuracy with which one or more of the dynamical variables of a classical system can be measured *except* the limit imposed by the precision of the measuring instruments.

2. There is no restriction on the number of dynamical variables that can be accurately measured simultaneously.

3. Since the expressions for velocity are continuously varying functions of time, the velocity and, hence, the kinetic energy can vary continuously. That is, there are no restrictions on the values that a dynamical variable can have.

We shall see that when very small particles are involved, all three of these assumptions must be abandoned. For these systems, classical mechanics fails completely to describe their behavior. The new mechanics that was developed for these systems is called quantum mechanics.

2-5 *Summary*

1. A conservative system was defined as a system in which the sum of the kinetic and potential energies remains constant with time.

2. The Lagrangian and Hamiltonian forms of the equations of motion were introduced and instructions were given for writing down Hamilton's function for any problem. Generalized coordinates were introduced.

3. For systems containing many particles, the motion of the center of mass was shown to be separable from the internal motion of the system as long as the potential energy depended only on the relative coordinates of the particles.

4. The basic assumptions of classical mechanics were discussed.

5. Terms which the student should understand are conservative system, Lagrangian function, Hamiltonian function, internal coordinates, and reduced mass.

Chapter 3

QUANTUM MECHANICS

AT THE end of the nineteenth century three types of observations
made it apparent that classical mechanics could not give correct
results when it was applied to molecular and atomic phenomena.
These observations involved studies of atomic spectra, blackbody
radiation, and the photoelectric effect. In the section that follows, each of these experiments will be discussed, and it will be
shown how the basic assumptions of classical mechanics had to
be abandoned. Following this, quantum mechanics will be introduced by a series of postulates, and these postulates will then be
applied to calculations on some simple systems.

3-1 Atomic spectra, blackbody radiation, and the photoelectric effect

The discipline of spectroscopy began in the early part of the nineteenth century with the observation of the sunlight spectrum by
Josef Fraunhofer. The study of the spectra of atoms was begun
in 1861 by Kirchoff and Bunsen, who extensively studied the
spectrum of the alkali metals. In 1885, Balmer discovered the
series of lines in the spectrum of atomic hydrogen that now bears

his name, and found that he could write an empirical relationship
that gave the positions of all the lines.   This relationship was

$$\frac{1}{\lambda} = R\left(\frac{1}{2^2} - \frac{1}{n_1{}^2}\right) \qquad n_1 = 3, 4, 5 \qquad (3\text{-}1)$$

where λ is the wavelength of the observed line and R is a constant
called the Rydberg constant.   This constant is one of the most
accurately known physical constants and has the value 109,677.581
cm^{-1}.

There were several striking features about atomic spectra.   The
first was the sharpness of the spectral lines.   Apparently, energy
was not emitted or absorbed by atoms in bands, or in a continuous
fashion, but only at certain very precise frequencies.   It was this
sharpness of spectral lines that enabled the constant R to be determined with such accuracy.   The second striking feature was the
fact that the spectrum of each kind of atom was highly characteristic.   In fact, the best proof for the presence of a particular
element in a sample was the existence of its characteristic spectrum.   It is clear that any theory of the structure of atoms would
have to explain these two features of atomic spectra.   In addition,
for the hydrogen atom, the characteristic frequencies would have
to be those predicted by Equation 3-1.   We will see later how
classical mechanics was at a loss to account for these facts if the
Rutherford model of the atom was accepted.

The observation which gave one of the clearest demonstrations
of the failure of classical mechanics is one of the most difficult
as far as mathematics is concerned.   This is the problem of the
spectral distribution of blackbody radiation.

Blackbody radiation is a familiar phenomenon even though the
name may seem mysterious.   When the heating element of an
electric stove is turned on, it emits infrared radiation.   This
radiation can be detected by placing one's hand at some distance
above the heating element.   If the stove element is further
heated, the wavelength distribution of the radiation emitted is
shifted to shorter values, and the heating element is seen to glow
red.

In the laboratory, blackbody radiation is studied by constructing
a cavity that is insulated so that the only energy that can be
absorbed is energy added in the form of heat to raise the temperature of the cavity.   The cavity is evacuated, and there is a

small hole in one side of the apparatus through which radiation can pass. The approximation is made that the radiation coming from the hole in the cavity is a good sample of the equilibrium radiation inside the cavity. The intensity of the radiation emitted from the hole is then studied as a function of wavelength at several different cavity temperatures. When this is done, data like that plotted in Figure 3-1 is obtained.

This problem was treated classically by Rayleigh and Jeans, who derived a perfectly exact equation (given the assumptions of classical mechanics) for this spectral distribution by assuming that a blackbody is made up of a lot of tiny oscillators. The Rayleigh-Jeans formula is

$$\rho(\nu, T) \, d\nu = \frac{8\pi\nu^2 kT}{c^2} \, d\nu \tag{3-2}$$

where $\rho(\nu, T) \, d\nu$ is the density of radiation at absolute temperature T between frequencies ν and $\nu + d\nu$. The student will notice that this equation predicts the density of radiation to increase continuously as the square of the frequency. This is contrary to the experimental results shown in Figure 3-1. Furthermore, the integral of Equation 3-2 from zero to infinity is infinite, a result that is obviously incorrect.[1] Equation 3-2 did fit the experimental data in the longer wavelength regions, however. The inability of classical mechanics to explain the falloff of radiation density in the ultraviolet region of the spectrum has been dubbed the "ultraviolet catastrophe."

A physicist, Max Planck, next attacked this problem. He found that he could derive a relationship that fit the experimental data if he assumed that the vibrating constituents of a hot body could only emit energy in discrete amounts called quanta. Planck hypothesized that these fundamental quanta had an energy equivalent to $h\nu$, where ν was the fundamental frequency of the oscillator and where h is the now famous Planck's constant. At the time, this assumption had no precedent and was justified only in that it gave the right answer. In this assumption, the idea of the existence of discrete energy states in matter was born.

---

[1] Rayleigh and Jeans realized that this result was incorrect, but they didn't know how to remedy the situation using the assumptions of classical mechanics.

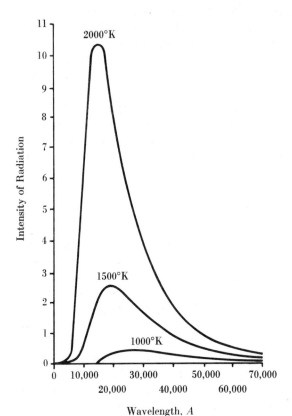

Wavelength, *A*

FIG. 3-1   *Typical data for the intensity*
of blackbody radiation plotted as a func-
tion of wavelength.   The student should
note the rapid falloff of intensity in the
ultraviolet region of the spectrum as well as
the "blue shift" of the maximum as the
temperature increases.   (Reproduced by
permission from F. Daniels and R. A.
Alberty, Physical Chemistry, John Wiley
& Sons, Inc., New York (1961) p. 452.)

It was not long before Planck's quantity, $h\nu$, had another application.   In 1905, in order to explain the photoelectric effect, Albert Einstein postulated that light energy also had to be quantized.   Planck originally thought that only the oscillators in a blackbody were quantized.

The photoelectric effect can best be illustrated by the description of an actual experiment.   A schematic diagram of the apparatus is shown in Figure 3-2.   The apparatus consists of a special cell, C, which contains a screen or grid and a receiving element constructed of a piece of metal which has been plated with a thin film of the metal to be studied.   When the switch in Figure 3-2 is at position A, the screen is connected to the receiver element through a battery and a sensitive galvanometer, G.   The special cell is highly evacuated.   Also included is a device, R, for chang-

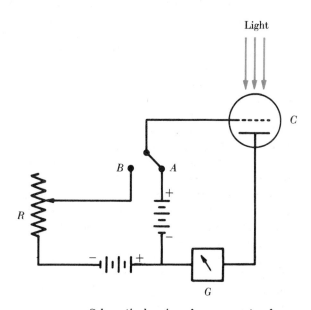

FIG. 3-2 *Schematic drawing of an apparatus for studying the photoelectric effect. The apparatus consists of a special cell, C, a galvanometer, G, a variable resistor, R, and a switch to connect the screen of the cell to either A or B. Note that when the switch is at B the screen is negative with respect to the plate.*

ing the potential of the screen with respect to the receiving element. When light strikes the surface of the receiving element, electrons are ejected from the surface of the metal and are attracted to the positively charged screen. This causes current to flow in the galvonometer. The current registered by the galvanometer is proportional to the number of electrons striking the screen. When the switch is at B, a negative potential can be applied to the screen. When this negative potential energy just balances the kinetic energy of the emitted electrons, the current is reduced to zero. The voltage necessary to do this can then be recorded. Experimental observations in a typical experiment are:

A. No electrons are emitted until the frequency of the light becomes larger than a certain value. This minimum frequency is called the threshold frequency.

B. At light frequencies higher than the threshold frequency, the electrons are ejected with excess kinetic energy. This extra kinetic energy of the electrons is independent of the intensity of the incident light, but is directly proportional to its frequency.

C. When the frequency of the light is higher than the threshold frequency the current flowing in the apparatus is dependent only on the intensity of the incident light. Below the threshold frequency no current flows.

These results can most easily be explained by the hypothesis that, when light is absorbed by metal, it acts as though it were a stream of particles each of which has an energy proportional to its frequency. These light "particles," or quanta, are called photons, and the energy of a light quantum is $h\nu$. When a photon is absorbed by a metal, its total energy is given to one of the electrons in the conduction band of the metal. If the light quantum has enough energy, the electron can overcome the potential energy barrier at the surface of the metal and be attracted to the positively charged screen. The potential energy barrier of a metal is called its work function. The excess kinetic energy which an ejected electron has is then

$$\frac{1}{2} mv^2 = h\nu - h\nu_0 = h\nu - W \qquad (3\text{-}3)$$

where ν_0 is the threshold frequency and W is the work function of the metal. When a potential is applied to the screen so as to stop the electron flow, the kinetic energy is just balanced by the potential energy of an electron in an electric field. Thus,

$$\frac{1}{2} mv^2 = h\nu - h\nu_0 = \mathcal{E}e \tag{3-4}$$

where e is the electronic charge and $\mathcal{E}$ is the potential difference between screen and receiver element. One can see that, by plotting ν versus $\mathcal{E}e$, one should get a straight line of slope h and intercept W. This is one of the ways in which Planck's constant can be determined.

EXERCISE 3-1 An experiment was done on the emission of photoelectrons from a sodium surface by light of different wavelengths. The following values for the potentials at which the photoelectric current was reduced to zero were obtained. Plot the voltage against frequency

$\lambda, \AA$	E, volts
3125	− 0.382
3650	− 0.915
4047	− 1.295
4339	− 1.485
5461	− 2.043

and calculate (a) the threshold frequency and (b) Planck's constant. Data from R. A. Millikan, *Phys. Rev.*, **7**, 355 (1916).

We have seen how it was impossible to explain certain observations connected with the behavior of incandescent solids and of light striking a metal surface by a consistent application of classical mechanics. The final obstacle, which eventually led to the abandonment of classical mechanics to describe microscopic phenomena, was its failure to accommodate the structure of atoms.

We have already pointed out that in atomic spectra the lines are unusually sharp and occur at definite frequencies characteristic of each atom. These results led to a peculiar paradox.

In 1911, Rutherford had enunciated the nuclear model of the atom. In this model, the positive charge and most of the mass is concentrated in the center of the atom, called the nucleus. The electrons were postulated to revolve around it like planets around the sun. It is a simple consequence of Newton's laws that, for an electron subject to the attractive force from the nucleus to move in a stable orbit, it must be accelerated. Further, according to classical electrodynamics, an accelerated charge must constantly lose energy by radiating. The paradox in this view of the structure of atoms is that an atom should not be stable. That is, as the electron radiates, it will lose energy and spiral inward, eventually colliding with the nucleus. Experimentally, it is known that atoms are stable indefinitely (unless they react to form molecules). Further, instead of continually radiating as the above picture predicts, atoms only radiate when excited by some means, and then only at a definite frequency. It is clear that the picture of the atom arising from classical physics had some gross inadequacies.

In 1913, Niels Bohr proposed a hypothesis to try to explain these discrepancies between classical theory and experiment. Bohr's hypothesis was that the lines in an atomic spectrum come from a transition of an electron between two discrete states in an atom. He assumed that [2]

1. The Planck-Einstein relation, which relates an energy difference to the quantity $h\nu$, held for the emission and absorption of radiation from an atom. Thus, if the energies of the two discrete states of the electron in an atom are E_1 and E_2, respectively, the frequency of a spectral line due to a transition of an electron from state 1 to state 2 is

$$h\nu = E_2 - E_1$$

2. In the discrete states, the angular momentum of the electron can only have the values

$$\text{angular momentum} = n\left(\frac{h}{2\pi}\right) = n\hbar$$

where n is an integer and $\hbar$ is used for the quantity $h/2\pi$.

3. The behavior of an electron during a transition cannot be visualized or explained classically.

To calculate the allowed orbits predicted by Bohr's theory for the hydrogen atom, we begin with Newton's law

$$f = m\mathbf{a} \tag{3-5}$$

[2] This statement of Bohr's postulates is an abbreviated form of that in W. Moore, *Physical Chemistry*, 3rd ed., Prentice-Hall, Inc., Englewood Cliffs, New Jersey (1962) page 473.

The force is just the coulombic force between the positively charged nucleus and the electron,

$$f = -\frac{(Ze)e}{r^2} \tag{3-6}$$

where Z is the nuclear charge. The acceleration is the centripetal acceleration $\dfrac{mv^2}{r}$, and is opposed to the force. Equation 3-5 then becomes

$$\frac{Ze^2}{r^2} = \frac{mv^2}{r} \tag{3-7a}$$

$$mv^2 r = Ze^2 \tag{3-7b}$$

But, applying assumption 2 above, we have

$$p \equiv mvr = \frac{nh}{2\pi} = n\hbar \tag{3-8}$$

Rearranging and combining (3-8) with (3-7b) one obtains

$$v^2 = \frac{n^2\hbar^2}{r^2 m^2} \tag{3-9a}$$

$$mr\,\frac{n^2\hbar^2}{m^2 r^2} = Ze^2 \tag{3-9b}$$

$$r = \frac{n^2\hbar^2}{me^2 Z} \tag{3-9c}$$

The student should notice that, because of assumption 2, the value of r is now restricted to certain orbits, i.e., $\dfrac{\hbar^2}{me^2 Z}$, $\dfrac{4\hbar^2}{me^2 Z}$, . . . etc. For the smallest allowed orbit in the hydrogen atom, $Z = 1$, $n = 1$, and

$$r_0{}^H \equiv a_0 = \frac{\hbar^2}{me^2} = 0.529 \text{ Å} \tag{3-10}$$

where a_0 is a symbol universally used for the radius of the first Bohr orbit.

The total energy of the atom is

$$E = T + V \tag{3-11a}$$

where

$$T = \frac{1}{2} mv^2 = \frac{1}{2} \frac{Ze^2}{r} \tag{3-11b}$$

and, since the system is conservative,

$$f = - \frac{\partial V}{\partial r}$$

and

$$V = - \int_{\infty}^{r} f \, dr = + \int_{\infty}^{r} \frac{Ze^2}{r^2} = - \frac{Ze^2}{r} \tag{3-11c}$$

Therefore,

$$E = \frac{1}{2} \frac{Ze^2}{r} - \frac{Ze^2}{r} = - \frac{1}{2} \frac{Ze^2}{r} \tag{3-12}$$

Substituting 3-9c into 3-12, we obtain

$$E = - (mZ^2 e^4)/(2n^2 \hbar^2) \tag{3-13}$$

It should be noticed that in Equation 3-13, only discrete energy levels appear because of the integer n^2 in the denominator.

It is of interest at this point to calculate the wavelength of the transitions in the hydrogen atom making use of assumption 1 above. For an absorption spectrum, one obtains

$$h\nu = E_2 - E_1 = \frac{me^4}{2\hbar^2} \left(\frac{1}{n_1^2} - \frac{1}{n_2^2} \right) \tag{3-14a}$$

or, since $\nu = \dfrac{c}{\lambda}$,

$$\frac{1}{\lambda} = \omega = \frac{2\pi^2 me^4}{h^3 c} \left(\frac{1}{n_1^2} - \frac{1}{n_2^2} \right) \tag{3-14b}$$

where ω is a commonly used spectroscopic unit called the wave number. Notice that ω has units of cm^{-1}, is proportional to the energy, and is the reciprocal of the wavelength of a spectral line.

If one works out all of the constants in 3-14b, one obtains the value 109,737 cm^{-1} which is in excellent agreement with the observed Rydberg constant. Setting $n_1 = 2$, the formula derived by Balmer for the lines in the Balmer series is obtained (Equation 3-1). Other series of lines for atomic hydrogen were also found, and they were equally well correlated by Equation 3-14b by setting $n_1 = 1, 3, 4$, and 5. These series are called the Lyman, Paschen, Brackett, and Pfund series, respectively, after their discoverers.

EXERCISE 3-2 Calculate the wavelength, frequency, and wave number for the first five lines in the Balmer series for atomic hydrogen. Sketch the spectrum on a piece of graph paper. What is the wave number of the series limit? What is the physical significance of the series limit?

It can be seen that the Bohr theory for the hydrogen atom worked very well indeed. Unfortunately, along with other difficulties, the theory *failed* to account for the spectrum of any atom having more than one electron. It was still necessary, therefore, to look for a more general form of mechanics for the treatment of atomic and molecular behavior.

The next step in the historical development of quantum mechanics was the suggestion in 1924 by the physicist Louis de Broglie [3] that if light, although usually regarded as a wave, sometimes could act like a particle, electrons, although usually regarded as particles, sometimes could act like waves. De Broglie suggested that the bridge between the particle and wave descriptions of the electron was given by

$$\lambda = \frac{h}{p} = \frac{h}{mv} \tag{3-15}$$

where λ is the wavelength of the "electron wave" and m and v are its mass and velocity, respectively. De Broglie's suggestion received dramatic confirmation in the electron diffraction experiments of G. P. Thomson and of Davisson and Germer in 1927. [4] Diffraction is a property that is only associated with wave motion, and the wavelength of the electrons involved was just that predicted by Equation 3-15.

EXERCISE 3-3 Calculate (a) the wavelength of a beam of electrons accelerated by a voltage increment of 110 volts and (b) the kinetic energy of an electron having a de Broglie wavelength of 1.5×10^{-13} cm.

[3] L. de Broglie, *Phil. Mag.*, **47**, 446 (1924).
[4] Davisson and Germer, *Nature*, **119**, 558 (1927).

Shortly after de Broglie's suggestion, quantum mechanics was
founded practically simultaneously by Erwin Schrödinger and
Werner Heisenberg.

3-2 *The formulations of quantum mechanics*

In its beginnings, quantum mechanics was approached in two
completely different ways. Schrödinger, reasoning that electronic
motions could be treated as waves, developed wave mechanics.
In this treatment, he took over the great body of information
from classical physics about wave motion and applied it to electronic and molecular motions. The stationary states that an
electron or a molecule might have were analogous to standing
waves (such as occur in a violin string) set up by applying appropriate boundary conditions. Later on, a mathematical
formalism became associated with the Schrödinger method that
related observable quantities to certain mathematical operations.
Werner Heisenberg, independently and slightly earlier, had used
the properties of matrices to get the same results as Schrödinger.
This approach to quantum mechanics looked very different, but a
little later M. Born and P. Jordon showed that they were equivalent. Later still, in the more general treatments of quantum
mechanics by Dirac and von Neumann, the Schrödinger and
Heisenberg approaches were shown to be specific cases of a more
general theory.

In chemistry texts, one finds many variations of these approaches. Usually, the time-independent Schrödinger equation
(see below) is given in an *ad hoc* manner with the statement that
the solutions to all atomic and molecular problems are the solutions to this second-order differential equation. This approach
leaves something to be desired, because the student usually wants
to know *where* the Schrödinger equation came from and *why* its
solutions give the answer to the allowed energy levels in atoms and
molecules. A more rigorous mathematical approach is to press
the analogy between the allowed states in atoms and molecules and
standing and traveling waves. Difficulties arise in this approach
because the average chemistry student has had little, if any,
background in the physics and mathematics of wave motion. In
the absence of a long introduction to wave mechanics, this approach becomes identical with the first in leaving something to be
desired.

There is a formulation of quantum mechanics within the Schrödinger method that can be used in a consistent way in an introductory course. This approach treats quantum mechanics as a new subject with its own set of postulates analogous to the way that Euclid's geometry is formulated. The basic ideas of quantum mechanics are introduced as postulates and these postulates are justified entirely by the fact that the results that one gets by using them agree with the results of experiment. With this formalism as a background, the student is free to go as far as he likes in either the wave or matrix mechanics formulation of quantum mechanics and is in a position to read the modern scientific literature in these fields much earlier than would normally be the case. Furthermore, with this basis, it is possible to give a much more rigorous, and hopefully more satisfying, treatment of molecular spectra and magnetic resonance phenomena.

3-3   *The postulates of quantum mechanics*

The postulates of any theory are a set of fundamental statements that the student is asked to take on faith. The ease with which a postulate may be made to appear reasonable depends on how readily it may be related to everyday experience. In quantum mechanics, the postulates are about atomic and molecular properties, and these are, in general, quite far from everyday experience. Consequently, the postulates may in this sense be "difficult to understand." The main point to keep in mind is that *the postulates are justified only by their ability to predict and correlate experimental facts and by their general applicability.*

Before going to the postulates themselves, it is necessary to understand the meaning of the terms dynamical variable and observable. Any property of a system of interest is called a dynamical variable. Thus, the position x, the energy E, the x-component of linear momentum p_x, etc. are all dynamical variables even though some of them may be constants. An observable is any property of a system that may be experimentally observed. It might appear at first thought that all dynamical variables would be observables, but such is not the case. For example, in Chapter 6, it is shown that only one component of the spin angular momentum vector of an electron can be measured. This component, usually taken to be the z-component, defines the angle θ between the spin angular momentum vector and the z-axis. The angle

ϕ, even though it is a dynamical variable, cannot be determined and, consequently, the angle ϕ is not an observable.

The first postulate is sometimes given as a definition rather than a postulate. It amounts to the same thing.

POSTULATE I

(a) *Any state of a dynamical system of N particles is described as fully as possible by a function $\Psi(q_1, q_2 \cdots q_{3N}, t)$*

(b) *If an experimentalist knows that a system is described by Ψ, then the quantity $\Psi^*\Psi \, d\tau$ gives the probability of finding q_1 between q_1 and $(q_1 + dq_1)$, q_2 between q_2 and $(q_2 + dq_2) \cdots q_{3N}$ between q_{3N} and $(q_{3N} + dq_{3N})$ at a specific time t.*

What this postulate says (in less succinct form) is that all the information about the properties of a system is contained in a Ψ function (usually called a wave function) which is a function only of the coordinates of the N particles and the time t. If the wave function includes the time explicitly, it is called a time-dependent wave function. If the observable properties of a system do not change with time, the system is said to be in a *stationary* state. A Ψ function describing such a state is called a stationary state wave function, and the time dependence of such a wave function can be separated out. The second part of the postulate gives a physical interpretation of the Ψ function. This interpretation is easiest to visualize for a system containing a single particle constrained to move in one dimension. The quantity $\Psi^*\Psi \, dx$ is then just the probability of finding the particle between x and $x + dx$ at a given time t.

In order for these functions to be in accord with physical reality, they are subject to certain restrictions. These restrictions are that the function should be everywhere finite, should be single valued, and should have integrable squares. These restrictions all arise from the postulate that $\Psi^*\Psi \, d\tau$ represents a probability. The restriction of integrable squares is simply the requirement that the probability of finding the system in all space must be finite. A special case of this requirement is when the integral

$$\int_{\text{all space}} \Psi^*\Psi \, d\tau = 1 \tag{3-16}$$

When this is true, the function Ψ is said to be normalized. The physical meaning of this for a single-particle system is just that the probability of finding the particle in some region in space must be 1. We will always work with normalized functions. It should be noted that Ψ functions may be complex. Hence, by square, we mean the square of the magnitude of Ψ. Usually, though, the functions encountered in this course will be real.

POSTULATE II *For every observable property of a system, there exists a linear Hermitian operator, and the physical properties of the observable can be inferred from the mathematical properties of its associated operator.*

The idea of a linear operator should be familiar to the student from Section 1-5 in Chapter 1. The only new property of operators in Postulate II is their Hermitian property. This property ensures that one always obtains real answers in the calculation of observables. A Hermitian operator is defined by the relation

$$\int_{\text{all space}} \Psi^* \hat{\alpha} \Phi \, d\tau = \int_{\text{all space}} \Phi \hat{\alpha}^* \Psi^* \, d\tau \tag{3-17}$$

where Ψ^* and Φ are any two functions which satisfy the conditions for acceptability stated above, and where $\hat{\alpha}$ is the operator of interest.

EXERCISE 3-4 Making use of the expression for integrating by parts

$$\int u \, dv = uv - \int v \, du$$

show that the operator d/dx is not Hermitian whereas the operator $i\dfrac{d}{dx}$ is.

This definition of a Hermitian operator is sometimes confusing to students. For this text, it is only necessary for the student to know that there is such a class of operators, and these are the operators for which Equation 3-17 is true.

At this point it is convenient to introduce a new notation for integrals of the type used in Equation 3-17. This notation represents the integration over all space by parentheses or brackets. Thus,

$$\int_{\text{all space}} \Psi^* \hat{\alpha} \Phi \, d\tau \equiv (\Psi^* | \hat{\alpha} | \Phi) \quad \text{or} \quad \langle \Psi^* | \hat{\alpha} | \Phi \rangle$$

and $\tag{3-18}$

$$\int \Psi^* \Psi \, d\tau \equiv (\Psi^* | \Psi) \quad \text{or} \quad \langle \Psi | \Psi^* \rangle$$

Equation 3-17, in this notation, becomes

$$(\Psi^*|\hat{\alpha}|\Phi) = (\Phi|\hat{\alpha}^*|\Psi^*)$$

To illustrate the use of Equation 3-17, it will be used to prove the theorem that eigenvalues of a Hermitian operator must be real.

Suppose we have a set of eigenfunctions Ψ_i of some Hermitian operator $\hat{\alpha}$. That is

$$\hat{\alpha}\Psi_i = a_i\Psi_i \tag{A}$$

The complex conjugate of this equation is

$$\hat{\alpha}^*\Psi_i^* = a_i^*\Psi_i^* \tag{B}$$

We now multiply Equation A by Ψ_i^* and Equation B by Ψ_i and integrate to obtain

$$(\Psi_i^*|\hat{\alpha}|\Psi_i) = (\Psi_i^*|a_i|\Psi_i) = a_i(\Psi_i^*|\Psi_i) \tag{C}$$

and

$$(\Psi_i|\hat{\alpha}^*|\Psi_i^*) = (\Psi_i|a_i^*|\Psi_i^*) = a_i^*(\Psi_i|\Psi_i^*) \tag{D}$$

Terms a_i and a_i^* can be brought outside the integral because they are constants. Since $\hat{\alpha}$ was postulated to be Hermitian, the left-hand sides of Equations C and D must be equal. Therefore,

$$a_i(\Psi_i^*|\Psi) = a_i^*(\Psi_i|\Psi_i^*)$$

Since Ψ_i^* and Ψ_i are functions (not operators), the order of multiplication is immaterial, and $(\Psi_i^*|\Psi_i) = (\Psi_i|\Psi_i^*)$. Therefore,

$$a_i = a_i^*$$

and the eigenvalue must be real because only real numbers equal their complex conjugates (Section 1-4). The Hermitian property of operators will also be used to prove additional theorems in Chapter 6.

The question naturally arises as to how one gets the operators for a given observable. A fairly rigorous way to do this is to relate the commutator of two operators to a classical quantity called a Poisson bracket, but in this text we will follow the following prescription. First, the classical expression for the observable of interest is written down in terms of coordinates, momenta, and the time. Next, the following replacements are made:

1. The time and all coordinates are left just as they are.

2. The momenta p_q are placed by the differential operator $-i\hbar \dfrac{\partial}{\partial q}$.

As an example of this prescription, let us construct the quantum mechanical operator for the kinetic energy, T. The classical expression for the kinetic energy of a particle in Cartesian coordinates is

$$T = \frac{1}{2m} \left(p_x{}^2 + p_y{}^2 + p_z{}^2 \right) \tag{3-19}$$

Using step 2 in the above prescription, and being careful of the order of operations, this becomes

$$T = \frac{1}{2m}\left[\left(-i\hbar \frac{\partial}{\partial x} \right)\left(-i\hbar \frac{\partial}{\partial x} \right) + \left(-i\hbar \frac{\partial}{\partial y} \right)\left(-i\hbar \frac{\partial}{\partial y} \right) \right.$$
$$\left. + \left(-i\hbar \frac{\partial}{\partial z} \right)\left(-i\hbar \frac{\partial}{\partial z} \right) \right] \tag{3-20}$$

or

$$T = -\frac{\hbar^2}{2m}\left(\frac{\partial^2}{\partial x^2} + \frac{\partial^2}{\partial y^2} + \frac{\partial^2}{\partial z^2} \right) = -\frac{\hbar^2}{2m}\nabla^2 \tag{3-21}$$

Perhaps the most important operator that will concern us is the operator connected with the total energy of a system E. The classical expression for the total energy is Hamilton's function, and the corresponding operator is called the Hamiltonian. The expression for the Hamiltonian for a single-particle system is

$$\hat{\mathcal{H}} = \hat{T} + \hat{V}$$

But $\hat{T}$ is given by Equation 3-21, and $\hat{V}$ is only a function of the coordinates q that, according to our prescription, remain the same. Therefore,

$$\hat{\mathcal{H}} = -\frac{\hbar^2}{2m}\nabla^2 + V(q) \tag{3-22}$$

EXERCISE 3-5   Derive the quantum mechanical operators for the three components of angular momentum. For the classical expression see Exercise 1-5.

POSTULATE III   *Suppose that $\hat{\alpha}$ is an operator corresponding to an observable and that there is a set of identical systems known to be in* *state* Ψ_s. *Suppose further that* Ψ_s *is an eigenfunction of* $\hat{\alpha}$. *That is,* $\hat{\alpha}\Psi_s = a_s\Psi_s$ *where* a_s *is a number. Then, if an experimentalist makes a series of measurements of the quantity corresponding to* $\hat{\alpha}$, *he will always get the result* a_s. *It is only under this condition that an experiment will give precise results.*

This is one of the postulates that bridges the gap between the mathematical formalism of quantum mechanics and experimental measurements in the laboratory. For example, suppose one is interested in calculating the allowed energies in a molecular or atomic system and comparing them with the result of experiment. Postulate III states that, for an energy measurement on a series of identical systems to be exactly reproducible (i.e., precise), the state of the system must be described by a function Ψ which is an eigenfunction of the operator corresponding to the total energy, the Hamiltonian. The problem of computing the allowed energies then is reduced to finding the Ψ_n and E_n that satisfy the eigenvalue equation

$$\hat{\mathcal{H}}\Psi_n = E_n\Psi_n \tag{3-23a}$$

Substituting Equation 3-22 into Equation 3-23a, one obtains for a single-particle system

$$-\frac{\hbar^2}{2m}\nabla^2\Psi + V\Psi = E\Psi \tag{3-23b}$$

or

$$+\frac{\hbar^2}{2m}\nabla^2\Psi + (E - V)\Psi = 0 \tag{3-23c}$$

Equation 3-23c is Shrödinger's wave equation for a single particle in a stationary state.

If one is interested in calculating other properties of the system, such as the value of the angular momentum about the z-axis, the procedure is the same, but the appropriate operator must be used in deriving the eigenvalue equation.

Many times we will wish to know the behavior of a property for a system not characterized by an eigenfunction appropriate to the operator corresponding to that property. This is the purpose of Postulate IV.

POSTULATE IV *Given an operator $\hat{\alpha}$ and a set of identical systems characterized by a function Φ_s that is not an eigenfunction of $\hat{\alpha}$, a series of measurements of the property corresponding to $\hat{\alpha}$ will not give the same result. Rather, a distribution of results will be obtained, the average of which will be*

$$\langle \hat{\alpha} \rangle = \frac{(\Phi_s | \hat{\alpha} | \Phi_s)}{(\Phi_s | \Phi_s)} \tag{3-24}$$

This is the so-called "mean value" theorem that tells what the experimental result will be when a system is not described by an eigenfunction of the operator involved. The symbol $\langle \hat{\alpha} \rangle$ is called the *average* or *expectation* value of the quantity associated with $\hat{\alpha}$. The "average value" in quantum mechanics should not be confused with a time average in classical mechanics. Rather, it is the number average of a large number of measurements of the property corresponding to $\hat{\alpha}$. Obviously, if Φ_s is an eigenfunction of $\hat{\alpha}$, the average value will be the same as the eigenvalue.

3-4 *Applications of the postulates to simple systems*

As an application of the above postulates, we will now discuss a simple problem—that of a particle constrained to move in a one-dimensional box. This problem is an excellent one because it illustrates a number of quantum mechanical principles, and at the same time shows how discrete energy levels inevitably arise whenever a small particle is confined to a region in space. Consider the situation shown in Figure 3-3. The particle is constrained to move in a one-dimensional box of length a. The potential energy inside the box can be taken as zero, and everywhere outside the box as infinite. The observable that we are interested in is the energy of a particle; therefore, the quantum mechanical operator that will be appropriate to the problem is the Hamiltonian $\hat{\mathcal{H}}$. According to Postulate III, if a definite result is to be obtained when a measurement of the energy of the system is made, the system must be described by an eigenfunction of $\hat{\mathcal{H}}$. Therefore, to find the allowed energies and wave functions for this particle, the eigenvalue equation $\hat{\mathcal{H}}\Psi_n = E_n \Psi_n$ must be solved. The solution is most conveniently divided into two parts corresponding to the regions outside

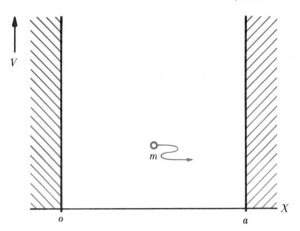

FIG. 3-3 *Quantities characterizing the problem of
a particle moving in a one-dimensional box.   The
potential energy is zero between $x = 0$ and $x = a$,
and is infinity everywhere else.   This is not the only
choice of coordinates for this problem.   Solutions
with the origin at the middle of the box are discussed
in Exercise 3-12.*

and inside the box.   Outside the box, T is just the first term in
Equation 3-22, and $V = \infty$.   Equation 3-23a then becomes

$$\frac{\hbar^2}{2m}\frac{d^2\Psi}{dx^2} + (E - \infty)\Psi = 0$$

or

$$\frac{d^2\Psi}{dx^2} = \infty\,\Psi \tag{3-25}$$

since E is small compared with infinity, and $\dfrac{2m}{\hbar^2}\,\infty$ is still infinity.

A little thought should convince the student that there is no function subject to the restrictions discussed under Postulate I that,
when differentiated twice, will give infinity times itself.   Therefore, the only solution outside the box is $\Psi = 0$.   This means,
according to part b of Postulate I, that the probability of finding
the particle somewhere outside the box is zero, which is the result
we would expect.

Inside the box, the eigenvalue equation is (since $V = 0$)

$$\frac{\hbar^2}{2m}\frac{d^2\Psi}{dx^2} + E\Psi = 0 \qquad (3\text{-}26a)$$

or, by rearranging

$$\frac{d^2\Psi}{dx^2} = -\frac{2mE}{\hbar^2}\Psi \qquad (3\text{-}26b)$$

This is a second-order differential equation whose solutions are functions that, when differentiated twice, will give the same function back multiplied by a constant. In spite of all the powerful methods of modern mathematics, one of the best ways to solve differential equations of this type is to guess a solution and try it to see if it works. Thus, we must inquire about which functions give the same function back when they are differentiated twice. Exponentials, sine and cosine functions have this property, so our first guess might be to try a function of the type [5]

$$\Psi = A \sin \alpha x \qquad (3\text{-}27)$$

Differentiating Equation 3-27 twice, one obtains

$$\frac{d\Psi}{dx} = \alpha A \cos \alpha x$$

$$\frac{d^2\Psi}{dx^2} = -\alpha^2 A \sin \alpha x = -\alpha^2\Psi \qquad (3\text{-}28)$$

which is identical to 3-26 if we identify the constant α^2 with $\frac{2mE}{\hbar^2}$. Thus, 3-27 is a solution to 3-26. So far in the solution there is nothing which restricts the values which E can have.

We now apply the boundary conditions. The requirement that Ψ must be single valued means that it must become zero at the edges of the box. That is,

$$\Psi(0) = \Psi(a) = 0 \qquad (3\text{-}29)$$

---

[5] A second order differential equation will, in general, contain two arbitrary constants. These constants can be determined in the integrated form from the appropriate boundary conditions and the normalization requirement. Equation 3-27 only has one arbitrary constant, A, and is not the most general solution. For the most general solution see Exercise 3-12.

The quantity $\Psi(0)$ is clearly equal to zero, but $\Psi(a) = A \sin \alpha a$. Equation 3-29 requires that

$$\Psi(a) = A \sin \alpha a = 0$$

and this is true only if $\alpha a = n\pi$, where n is any integer. We thus have the requirement that

$$\alpha = \frac{n\pi}{a}, \qquad n = 1, 2, 3 \cdots$$

or that

$$\alpha^2 = \frac{2mE}{\hbar^2} = \frac{n^2\pi^2}{a^2} \tag{3-30}$$

Thus, the energies which the particle can have become

$$E = \frac{\hbar^2 n^2 \pi^2}{2ma^2} = n^2 \left(\frac{h^2}{8ma^2}\right), \quad n = 1, 2, 3 \cdots \tag{3-31}$$

where the imposition of the boundary conditions has restricted the energy to discrete values.

To complete the calculation of the wave functions, they must be normalized. This requires that

$$\int_0^a \left(A \sin \frac{n\pi x}{a}\right)^2 dx = 1 \tag{3-32}$$

Equation 3-32, when the integral is evaluated, requires that A must have the value

$$A = \left(\frac{2}{a}\right)^{\frac{1}{2}} \tag{3-33}$$

To summarize, the allowed wave functions and energies for the particle in a box are

$$\Psi_n = \left(\frac{2}{a}\right)^{\frac{1}{2}} \sin \frac{n\pi x}{a} \qquad E_n = \frac{n^2 h^2}{8ma^2}$$

These results are represented diagrammatically in Figure 3-4. In this figure, each wave function is plotted at a height proportional

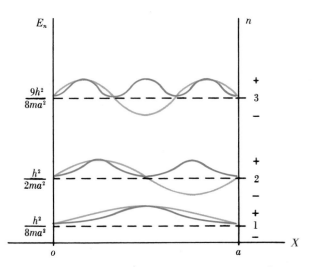

FIG. 3-4 *Schematic drawing of E_n, Ψ_n, and $\Psi_n{}^2$ for the case of a particle moving in a one-dimensional box. The plot of Ψ_n as a function of x is a solid line; the colored line is a plot of $\Psi_n{}^2$. Note that Ψ_n changes sign at each node while $\Psi_n{}^2$ always remains positive. Also note that the energy spacing between levels diverges as n increases.*

to its energy.   The solid line is a plot of Ψ_n as a function of x, the colored line is a plot of $\Psi_n{}^2$ as a function of x.

There are several instructive features of this example.   For the same value of the quantum number n, the energy is inversely proportional to the mass of the particle and the length of the box. Thus, as the particle becomes heavier and the box larger, the energy levels become more closely spaced.   It is only when the quantity ma^2 is of the same order as h^2 that quantized energy levels become important in experimental measurements.   When dealing with dimensions of 1 g and 1 cm, the energy levels become so closely spaced that they seem to us to be continuous.   The quantum mechanical formula, therefore, gives the classical result for systems with dimensions such that $ma^2 \gg h^2$.   This is an illustration of the "correspondence principle" that states that the quantum mechanical result must become identical with the classical one in the limit where the quantum numbers describing the system become very large. These statements are illustrated by Exercises 3-6 and 3-7.

E X E R C I S E 3 - 6   Calculate the energy in cm^{-1} of the first two energy levels of a particle in a box, and the energy difference $\Delta E_{2-1} = E_2 - E_1$ for (a) An electron in a box 2 Å in length and (b) a ball bearing of mass 1 g in a box 10 cm long.

E X E R C I S E 3 - 7   Calculate the value of n necessary to give an energy equal to kT at room temperature for a 1 g ball bearing in a 10 cm long box. k is Boltzmann's constant and T is the absolute temperature.

The second feature of the solutions to the particle in a box problem that should be pointed out is the relationship between the energy of a state and the number of nodes in the wave function. A node is a point where the wave function becomes zero. Neglecting the nodes at the end of the box, in the state $n = 2$ there is one node, in $n = 3$, two nodes, and state n, $n - 1$ nodes. It is a general property of wave functions that the greater the number of nodes in a wave function, the higher the energy of the corresponding state. This is shown in Figure 3-4, and is reasonable when considered along with the de Broglie relationship, Equation 3-15. The greater the number of nodes in the length of the box, the shorter the wavelength must be. According to Equation 3-15, if the wavelength becomes shorter, the momentum and, hence, the kinetic energy of the particle must become greater.

We next inquire about some other properties of the particle in a box. Suppose one is interested in measuring the component of momentum in the x direction for a set of identical systems in which the particle is known to be in the lowest energy state. The appropriate operator to use in the calculation of the expected result is $- i\hbar \dfrac{d}{dx}$, and one obtains

$$\hat{p}_x \Psi_1 = - i\hbar \frac{d}{dx} \left(A \sin \frac{\pi x}{a} \right) = - i\hbar \, A \frac{\pi}{a} \cos \frac{\pi x}{a} \qquad (3\text{-}34)$$

It is clear that Ψ_1 is not an eigenfunction of $\hat{p}_x$; therefore, according to Postulate IV, a series of measurements of $\hat{p}_x$ will not yield precise results. One must use the average value theorem to calculate the expectation value of $\hat{p}_x$. This gives

$$\langle \hat{p}_x \rangle = \frac{\displaystyle\int_0^a \Psi_1 \hat{p}_x \Psi_1 \, dx}{\displaystyle\int_0^a \Psi_1{}^2} = \frac{\dfrac{2}{a} \displaystyle\int_0^a \sin \dfrac{\pi x}{a} \left(-i\hbar \dfrac{\pi}{a} \right) \cos \dfrac{\pi x}{a} \, dx}{1} = 0$$

$$(3\text{-}35)$$

Accordingly the average of a large number of measurements of $\hat{p}_x$ on the set of identical systems is zero.

Suppose one now considers the square of the momentum in the x direction. The appropriate operator is $-\hbar^2 \dfrac{d^2}{dx^2}$ and, applying this operator to Ψ_1, one obtains

$$-\hbar^2 \frac{d^2}{dx^2} A \sin \frac{\pi x}{a} = +\hbar^2 \frac{\pi^2}{a^2} A \sin \frac{\pi x}{a} \qquad (3\text{-}36)$$

Ψ_1 is thus an eigenfunction of $p_x{}^2$, and a series of measurements of $p_x{}^2$ on a set of identical systems will always give a precise result, namely the eigenvalue

$$p_x{}^2(\text{state } 1) = \hbar^2 \frac{\pi^2}{a^2} = 2mE_1$$

Taking the square root, one obtains

$$p_x{}^{(1)} = \pm \sqrt{2mE_1} \qquad (3\text{-}37)$$

The results calculated in Equations 3-35 and 3-37 present an interesting dilemma. The results of Equation 3-35 indicate that the average value of $p_x(1)$ is zero. The results of Equation 3-37 indicate that $p_x(1)$ must be either $\pm (2mE_1)^{\frac{1}{2}}$. The apparent contradiction is resolved by considering the meaning of Postulates III and IV. Since a measurement of $p_x{}^2$ always gives the result $2mE$, the momentum p_x must always be $\pm (2mE)^{\frac{1}{2}}$. A single measurement of p_x will give either of these values. What the mean postulate states is that, if one makes a large number of measurements of p_x, one will end up with $p_x(1) = - (2mE)^{\frac{1}{2}}$ as often as $+ (2mE)^{\frac{1}{2}}$, and the average value of p_x will be zero. One never knows in advance whether an experimental result will give $\pm (2mE)^{\frac{1}{2}}$. It can, therefore, be said that an uncertainty exists in one's knowledge of the momentum, and the magnitude of this uncertainty is equal to $2(2mE)^{\frac{1}{2}}$.

In a similar manner, we can argue that if we know that the particle is in state Ψ_n, the maximum uncertainty about the position of the particle is that it is somewhere in the box. That is, our uncertainty in the x coordinate of the particle is a. It is of interest to calculate the product of our uncertainties in the position and the momentum of a particle in a box. This is

$$\Delta x \, \Delta p_x \geqq a \cdot 2 \sqrt{2mE_n} \geqq 2a \cdot \frac{n\pi\hbar}{a} \tag{3-38}$$
$$\geqq nh$$

This will have its smallest value when $n = 1$, and thus one obtains the result that

$$\Delta x \, \Delta p_x \approx h \tag{3-39}$$

This, of course, is a form of the Heisenberg uncertainty principle which states that the simultaneous measurement of both position and momentum cannot be made to an accuracy greater than Planck's constant, h. Planck's constant is a very small number, however, and it is clear why the uncertainty principle is of no consequence in measurements on systems of large dimensions and/ or containing particles with large masses.

EXERCISE 3-8   Calculate the uncertainty in momentum and velocity of an electron in a 1 Å box, a hydrogen atom in a 10 Å box, and a 1 g ball bearing in a 10 cm box.

It should be emphasized that Equation 3-39 is much more general than our derivation from the properties of a particle in a box would indicate. In fact, it is possible to start with the uncertainty principle and, from it, derive the allowed energies for a particle in a box. Further, Equation 3-39 is a fundamental property of nature and is not just a statement of the fact that engineers need to devise better measuring instruments.[6]

EXERCISE 3-9   Calculate the expectation value of the x position of a particle known to be in the state $n = 2$ of a one-dimensional box. What is the probability of finding an electron in a small unit of length dx at this position? Can you rationalize these results?

[6] For a contrary opinion see "The Evolution of the Physicist's Picture of Nature" by P. A. M. Dirac, *Sci. Amer.*, **208**, 45 (1963).

EXERCISE 3-10 Given a particle in the state $n = 1$ of a one-dimensional box, what is the probability of finding it somewhere in the region between 0 and $\frac{1}{4}a$?

EXERCISE 3-11 Evaluate for a particle in a one-dimensional box (a) the integral $(\Psi_1|\Psi_2)$ and (b) the integral $(\Psi_1|x - a/2|\Psi_2)$.

One additional feature of the solutions to the particle in a box is illustrated in Exercise 3-11. In this problem, it is shown that the value of the integral $(\Psi_1|\Psi_2)$ is zero. In fact, it can be shown that, for all of the wave functions characterizing the motion of a particle in a box, the integral

$$(\Psi_i|\Psi_j) = 0 \tag{3-40}$$

for $i \neq j$. When a relation such as Equation 3-40 holds, the functions Ψ_i and Ψ_j are said to be orthogonal.[7] The orthogonality of functions is a very important property in quantum mechanics, and some of the conditions for orthogonality will be discussed in Chapter 6.

There are, of course, other solutions to Equation 3-26. The most general are

$$\Psi = A \sin \alpha x + B \cos \alpha x \tag{3-41a}$$

and

$$= Ae^{-i\alpha x} + Be^{+i\alpha x} \tag{3-41b}$$

The use and interpretation of these solutions are illustrated in Exercises 3-12 and 3-13.

EXERCISE 3-12 Show that Equation 3-41a is a solution to Equation 3-26, with the same value for α. Use the appropriate boundary conditions to evaluate the constants A and B. Suppose, instead of the coordi-

---

[7] The value of integrals over pairs of functions for the particle in a box can be summarized by the relation

$$(\Psi_i|\Psi_j) = \delta_{ij}$$

where δ_{ij} is called the Kronecker delta. This latter quantity has the property that

$$\delta_{ij} = 1 \text{ for } i = j$$
$$\delta_{ij} = 0 \text{ for } i \neq j$$

The integral relation above means that each function is normalized, and that all pairs of functions are orthogonal. Whenever such a relationship holds, the set of functions is called an *orthonormal* set.

nates of Figure 3-3, one were to let the box go from $x = -\dfrac{a}{2}$ to $x = +\dfrac{a}{2}$.
That is, put the origin in the middle of the box. What values will the constants A and B in Equation 3-41a have then?

EXERCISE 3-13 Show that Equation 3-41b is a solution of Equation 3-26. Evaluate the constants A and B (see Equation 1-20). Re-evaluate A and B, placing the origin at the middle of the box. What happens when p_x operates on either half of Equation 3-41b? What does a solution in the form of Equation 3-41b imply about measurements of p_x?

It is instructive also to consider the problem of a particle in a three-dimensional box because it illustrates a particular technique which will be useful in solving other quantum mechanical problems. The eigenvalue equation for inside the box becomes

$$-\frac{\hbar^2}{2m}\nabla^2\Psi = E\Psi$$

or

$$\frac{\partial^2\Psi}{\partial x^2} + \frac{\partial^2\Psi}{\partial y^2} + \frac{\partial^2\Psi}{\partial z^2} = -\frac{2mE}{\hbar^2}\Psi \tag{3-42}$$

To solve Equation 3-42, the technique of separation of variables is used. To separate the variables in a differential equation, one tries to find a solution of the form

$$\Psi = X(x)\,Y(y)Z(z) \tag{3-43}$$

where $X(x)$, $Y(y)$, $Z(z)$ are functions of only x, y, or z, respectively. Substituting Equation 3-43 into Equation 3-42, and performing the indicated partial differentiations, one obtains

$$YZ\frac{\partial^2 X}{\partial x^2} + XZ\frac{\partial^2 Y}{\partial y^2} + XY\frac{\partial^2 Z}{\partial z^2} = -\frac{2mE}{\hbar^2}XYZ \tag{3-44}$$

Dividing both sides of Equation 3-44 by Equation 3-43 and rearranging, one obtains

$$\frac{1}{X}\frac{\partial^2 X}{\partial x^2} + \frac{1}{Y}\frac{\partial^2 Y}{\partial y^2} + \frac{2mE}{\hbar^2} = -\frac{1}{Z}\frac{\partial^2 Z}{\partial z^2} \tag{3-45}$$

Equation 3-45 must hold for all values of x, y, and z. The only way that this can be true is if both sides of the equation are equal to a constant. We arbitrarily (at this point) call this constant $\frac{2mE_z}{\hbar^2}$. Equation 3-45 then becomes two equations

$$-\frac{1}{Z}\frac{\partial^2 Z}{\partial z^2} = \frac{2mE_z}{\hbar^2} \tag{3-46}$$

and

$$\frac{1}{X}\frac{\partial^2 X}{\partial x^2} + \frac{1}{Y}\frac{\partial^2 Y}{\partial y^2} + \frac{2mE}{\hbar^2} = \frac{2mE_z}{\hbar^2} \tag{3-47}$$

But Equation 3-47 can be rearranged to give

$$\frac{1}{X}\frac{\partial^2 X}{\partial x^2} + \frac{2m}{\hbar^2}(E - E_z) = -\frac{1}{Y}\frac{\partial^2 Y}{\partial y^2} \tag{3-48}$$

and, applying the same argument as above, both sides of this equation must equal a constant, which we call $\frac{2m}{\hbar^2}E_y$. We are then left with

$$-\frac{1}{Y}\frac{\partial^2 Y}{\partial y^2} = \frac{2mE_y}{\hbar^2} \tag{3-49}$$

and

$$\frac{1}{X}\frac{\partial^2 X}{\partial x^2} = -\frac{2m}{\hbar^2}(E - E_z - E_y) = -\frac{2m}{\hbar^2}E_x \tag{3-50}$$

Equations 3-46, 3-49, and 3-50 are exactly the same as the equation for a particle in a one-dimensional box except that Ψ has been replaced by X, Y, and Z, and E has been replaced by E_x, E_y, and E_z. The one-dimensional problem has already been solved, though, and we can write down the answer immediately. If a, b, and c are the lengths of the box in the x, y, and z directions, respectively, then

$$\begin{aligned}
X &= \left(\frac{2}{a}\right)^{\frac{1}{2}}\sin\frac{n_x\pi x}{a} \qquad & E_x &= \frac{n_x{}^2 h^2}{8ma^2} \\
Y &= \left(\frac{2}{b}\right)^{\frac{1}{2}}\sin\frac{n_y\pi y}{b} \qquad & E_y &= \frac{n_y{}^2 h^2}{8mb^2} \\
Z &= \left(\frac{2}{c}\right)^{\frac{1}{2}}\sin\frac{n_z\pi z}{c} \qquad & E_z &= \frac{n_z{}^2 h^2}{8mc^2}
\end{aligned} \tag{3-51}$$

and

$$\Psi = XYZ = \left(\frac{8}{abc}\right)^{\frac{1}{2}} \sin\frac{n_x\pi x}{a} \sin\frac{n_y\pi y}{b} \sin\frac{n_z\pi z}{c} \qquad (3\text{-}52)$$

$$E = E_x + E_y + E_z$$

$$= \frac{h^2}{8m}\left(\frac{n_x{}^2}{a^2} + \frac{n_y{}^2}{b^2} + \frac{n_z{}^2}{c^2}\right) \qquad (3\text{-}53)$$

It is important to realize what has been done. Separation of variables reduced the three-dimensional problem to three one-dimensional problems that could readily be solved. There is a general rule about when such a separation can be made. When the Hamiltonian operator $\hat{\mathfrak{K}}$ can be written as a sum of terms, each of which is a function of only one variable, then it is always possible to find a solution to Equation 3-23 of the form in which Ψ is a product of single coordinate functions. In more mathematical terms, when

$$\hat{\mathfrak{K}} = \sum_i \hat{h}_i$$

where each $\hat{h}_i$ can be expressed as a function of a single coordinate and derivatives with respect to that coordinate, then Ψ can always be written in the form

$$\Psi = \prod_i \phi(q_i)$$

where $\phi(q_i)$ depends only on the single coordinate q_i. It will be true, furthermore, that the total energy E can be expressed as a sum of single orbital energies ϵ_i where each orbital energy arises from the motion with respect to one coordinate q_i. Thus,

$$E = \sum_i \epsilon_i$$

where the index i goes over all of the coordinates of all of the particles.

The separation of variables is used widely in "many electron" problems in quantum mechanics. In these problems, the assumption is often made that the total Hamiltonian $\hat{\mathfrak{K}}$ can be written as a sum of single particle or "one-electron" operators, that is, operators that depend only on the coordinates of a single electron or particle. If this is true, then the total wave function of the system can be written as a product of single electron functions, and the energy is just the sum of the single electron energies. This assumption about many electron systems is called the independent particle model. It is usually a poor assumption because all of the interparticle interaction terms must be left out of the Hamiltonian. This point will be discussed at some length in a later chapter. The general theory of the separation of variables will be used many times in the material that follows; it is important that the student have a good understanding of this procedure.

One further point of interest arises from the problem of a particle in a three-dimensional box if all three sides have equal lengths. Then $a = b = c$ and Equation 3-53 becomes

$$E = \frac{h^2}{8ma^2} (n_x{}^2 + n_y{}^2 + n_z{}^2) \qquad (3\text{-}54)$$

Suppose we consider the state with next to lowest energy. This state arises when one of the quantum numbers is 2 and the other two are 1 and $E = \frac{3}{4} \frac{h^2}{ma^2}$. There are three different combinations of quantum numbers which will give this energy, however. If the values of three quantum numbers n_x, n_y, and n_z are listed in parentheses after the energy, we can express this as

$$E(2, 1, 1) = E(1, 2, 1) = E(1, 1, 2) = \frac{3}{4} \frac{h^2}{ma^2} \qquad (3\text{-}55)$$

When more than one state has the same energy, the states are said to be *degenerate*. The number of states with the same energy is the degree of degeneracy. Thus, the second state for a particle in a cubical box is *threefold degenerate*.

3-5 Summary

1. The historical development of quantum mechanics was traced, and a discussion of three significant experiments in this development was given. These three experiments involved the study of blackbody radiation, the photoelectric effect, and atomic spectra.

2. Bohr's theory of the energy levels of the hydrogen atom was presented.

3. Quantum mechanics was introduced with four postulates that relate a mathematical formalism used in the theory to experimental measurements performed in the laboratory.

4. The problem of a particle in a one-dimensional box was discussed. It was shown that quantized energy levels arise when the boundary conditions were applied to the solutions of the appropriate eigenvalue equation. The various postulates were illustrated with this simple problem.

5. The Heisenberg uncertainty principle was introduced using the particle in a box solutions as an example.

6. The separation of variables method for solving differential equations was illustrated for the problem of the energy levels in a three-dimensional box.

7. Many new terms were introduced. The student should study the meanings of Hermitian operator, normalized function, orthogonal function, stationary state, degenerate orbitals, Kronecker delta and correspondence principle.

Chapter 4

SPECTROSCOPY AND
SPECTROSCOPIC
MEASUREMENTS

BEFORE INDIVIDUAL types of spectroscopy are studied in detail, some features common to spectroscopic measurements in general will be discussed. All types of spectroscopy depend on the absorption or emission of electromagnetic radiation by the sample being studied. A spectroscopic experiment usually involves measuring two experimental parameters: the energy of the electromagnetic radiation absorbed or emitted by the sample and the intensity of the absorption or emission. The discussion that follows will be limited to absorption spectra, but most of the material holds true for emission spectra as well. The first section of this chapter summarizes the different units used to specify the energy of the radiation absorbed or emitted by the sample; the second section discusses factors related to the intensity of an absorption spectrum; the final section briefly surveys the various types of spectroscopy.[1]

[1] The student interested in experimental techniques in spectroscopy should see *Chemical Applications of Spectroscopy*, edited by W. West, vol. 9 of *Techniques of Organic Chemistry*, edited by A. Weisburger, Interscience Publishers, Inc., New York, 1963.

4-1   Units

The energy of the electromagnetic radiation absorbed by an atomic or molecular system is always equal to an energy *difference* between two allowed states of the system.   Any quantity related to this energy difference can be used as a unit.   Units used in spectroscopy can be divided into two classes depending on whether they are directly or inversely proportional to the energy.

The cgs unit of energy is the erg, but because of its size the erg is not usually used as a spectroscopic unit.   The commonly used energy units are the electron volt, wave number, calorie, and kilocalorie.   In addition, a consideration of the Planck relation $h\nu = \Delta E$ indicates that the frequency of electromagnetic radiation is proportional to the energy; hence, frequency units such as cycles per second (cps), megacycles per second (mc), etc. can be used as energy units.

The Planck relation also allows the energy of absorbed radiation to be expressed in wavelength units.   Since the frequency of electromagnetic radiation is related to the wavelength by the relation $\nu\lambda = c$ where c is the speed of light, the wavelength of absorbed radiation is *inversely* proportional to the energy of the transition. The most common wavelength units are angstroms (Å), millimicrons (mμ), and microns (μ) which are 10^{-8}, 10^{-7}, and 10^{-4} cm, respectively.

The reciprocal of the wavelength $1/\lambda$ is directly proportional to the energy and is the wave number unit referred to above.   It has dimensions of cm^{-1}.   The student should verify that an expression for the energy in ergs can be converted to an expression in wave numbers by dividing the energy in ergs by the quantity hc. Some conversion factors between these units are given in Table 4-1.

EXERCISE 4-1   A blue dye has an absorption band in the visible region of the spectrum at 7000 Å.   Calculate the energy of the transition in cps, cm^{-1}, eV, kcal mole^{-1}, and ergs molecule^{-1}.

4-2   Some facts about absorption strengths

The absorption strength of a spectral band or line can be described in a number of ways.   Experimentally, absorption strengths are measured using the Lambert-Beer law.   To derive the Lambert-

TABLE 4-1 CONVERSION FACTORS FOR USE IN CHANGING ENERGY UNITS—TO OBTAIN THE WAVELENGTH EQUIVALENT OF ANY ENERGY DIFFERENCE, THE ENERGY SHOULD BE EXPRESSED IN WAVE NUMBERS AND THE RECIPROCAL TAKEN

To convert from energy in	To an energy in				
	$ergs\ molecule^{-1}$	ev	cm^{-1}	$kcal\ mole^{-1}$	mc
	multiply by				
$ergs\ molecule^{-1}$	—	6.242×10^{11}	5.035×10^{15}	1.440×10^{13}	1.509×10^{20}
ev	1.602×10^{-12}	—	$8,067$	23.05	2.418×10^{8}
cm^{-1}	1.986×10^{-16}	1.240×10^{-4}	—	2.859×10^{-3}	2.998×10^{4}
$kcal\ mole^{-1}$	6.944×10^{-14}	4.337×10^{-2}	349.9	—	1.048×10^{7}
mc	6.6256×10^{-21}	4.136×10^{-9}	3.336×10^{-5}	9.541×10^{-8}	—

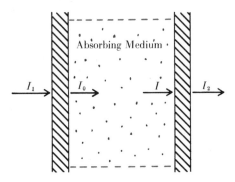

FIG. 4-1 *Intensities of a light beam at different points in an absorbing system. (Reprinted by permission from J. Waser, Quantitative Chemistry, W. A. Benjamin, Inc., New York, New York, 1962.)*

Beer law, consider the situation shown in Figure 4-1.[2] In this figure, I_1 is the intensity of an incident beam of monochromatic radiation, I_0 is the intensity of the beam after it has passed through one cell wall, I is the intensity after it has passed through the absorbing medium, and I_2 is the intensity after the beam has traversed the last cell wall. The transmittance T is defined as

$$T = \frac{I_2}{I_1} \qquad (4\text{-}1)$$

and is the quantity that is usually measured in spectrophotometers. The quantity of interest to the physical chemist is the internal transmittance of the system

$$T_i = \frac{I_0}{I} \qquad (4\text{-}2)$$

Usually T and T_i are not very different because cells are constructed of materials that do not absorb or scatter much light. Even this difference can be eliminated by using matched cells, one containing the sample of interest and one containing a suitable reference material (usually air or solvent). If T is set at 100%

[2] This derivation is essentially that of J. Waser, *Quantitative Chemistry*, W. A. Benjamin, Inc., New York (1962) pp. 155 ff. For a more rigorous treatment see D. F. Swinehart, *J. Chem. Ed.*, **39**, 333 (1962).

for the reference cell, than a measurement of T of the sample gives T_i.

The quantity I/I_0 is related to the length of the absorbing medium (Bouguer-Lambert law) and to the concentration of absorbing medium (Beer's law). The Bouguer-Lambert law states that, for a thin layer of absorbing material, the decrease in intensity of a monochromatic light beam in an absorbing material is directly proportional to the incident intensity and the length of the layer. In differential form, this law becomes

$$- dI = kI \, dx \tag{4-3}$$

where k is called the absorption coefficient. Separating variables and integrating, one obtains

$$- \ln I \Big|_{I(x=0)}^{I(x)} = kx \Big|_{x=0}^{x} \tag{4-4}$$
$$- \ln I/I_0 = kx$$

since, by definition, $I = I_0$ at $x = 0$. Since it is easier to use base 10 than natural logarithms, Equation 4-4 is usually written

$$- \log I/I_0 = (k/2.303)x = ax \tag{4-5}$$

where a is called the absorbancy index of the medium. Experimentally, the sample is usually contained in a cell of fixed length l and Equation 4-5 becomes

$$- \log I/I_0 = al$$
or $$\tag{4-6}$$
$$I = I_0 10^{-al}$$

In 1852, Beer reasoned that, for a solution in which the solvent was transparent ($a = 0$), the exponent a could be written as

$$al = a_m Cl \tag{4-7}$$

where C is the concentration of solute in moles per liter and a_m is a property of the absorbing molecule called the *molar absorbancy index*.[3] Combining Equations 4-7 and 4-5, one obtains the Lambert-Beer law

$$- \log I/I_0 = a_m Cl \tag{4-8}$$

[3] In much of the early literature, the molar absorbancy index is designated by the symbol ϵ and is called the molar extinction coefficient.

Sometimes spectrophotometers are calibrated in units of $\log I_0/I$. This quantity is called the absorbancy or optical density of the medium.

When more than one absorbing species is present, the molar absorbancy index is given by the sum

$$Ca_m = \sum_j C_j a_{mj} \tag{4-9}$$

where $C = \Sigma C_j$ is the total concentration, and C_j and a_{mj} are the concentration and molar absorbancy indices of the substance j, respectively. This additivity law is of great importance in that it permits spectroscopic analysis of solutions containing several components.

EXERCISE 4-2 Benzene and toluene both absorb light at 255 mμ and 269 mμ. For benzene, the molar absorbancy index at these two wavelengths is 234 and 12.5 l mole^{-1} cm^{-1}; for toluene, the molar absorbancy indices are 210 and 267 l mole^{-1} cm^{-1}. When a spectrum of the mixture of benzene and toluene was run, the optical density at 255 mμ was 0.800 and the optical density at 269 mμ was 0.267. Calculate the concentrations of benzene and toluene in the mixture.

The molar absorbancy index in Equation 4-8 is a property characteristic of the absorbing species, and it is a measure of that species' ability to absorb light of a given frequency. It should be related to the theoretical absorption strength of a spectral line and this strength should, at least in principle, be calculable by the methods of quantum mechanics if the wave functions characterizing the two energy states involved in a transition are known. Some of the factors involved in a calculation of absorption strengths will now be considered.

All spectroscopic measurements depend on the presence of some type of interaction between the particle, atom, or molecule being studied and an electromagnetic wave. The absorption strength of a spectral line will depend on two factors:

1. The magnitude of the interaction with the light wave
2. The difference in population between the initial and final states of the transition

An electromagnetic wave can be regarded as oscillating electric and magnetic field vectors propagating through space, as in Figure

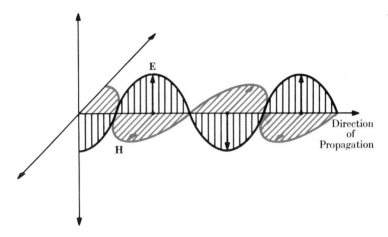

FIG. 4-2 *Oscillating electric* (**E**) *and magnetic* (**H**) *field vectors in a plane polarized electromagnetic wave. The interaction of the oscillating electric field with a changing dipole moment of an atom or molecule causes a transition between allowed energy states.*

4-2. For simplicity, a light wave that is plane polarized is shown. For an unpolarized wave, the electric field (or magnetic field) vector is not confined to a single plane. Before a particle or molecule can absorb energy from such a wave, there must be some means by which it can interact with either the electric or magnetic field. In most types of spectroscopy, the interaction of interest is with the electric field of the electromagnetic wave. For the various kinds of magnetic resonance spectroscopy (see below and Chapter 9) the system being studied interacts with the magnetic field. In order to interact with the electric field of the electromagnetic wave, the system being studied must have a charge distribution which *changes* when the system makes the transition from the initial to the final state. The transitions of interest in the remainder of this book will arise from the interaction of a changing dipole moment [4] in the atom or molecule with the electric or magnetic field of the light wave. These transitions are called electric or magnetic dipole transitions.

[4] Students unfamiliar with the concept of a dipole moment should consult one of the references B1 to B4 in the bibliography.

The magnitude of the interaction between the electromagnetic wave and the changing dipole moment of the sample for a given transition is given by a quantity called the transition moment, $\mathbf{R}^{kn}$. The transition moment is a vector quantity defined by the relation

$$\mathbf{R}^{kn} = (\Psi_k{}^* |\hat{\mathbf{u}}| \Psi_n) \tag{4-10}$$

where $\hat{\mathbf{u}}$ is the dipole moment operator appropriate for the system being studied, $\Psi_k{}^*$ is the wave function for the initial state in the transition and Ψ_n is the wave function for the final state. Only when the transition moment is not zero will the system absorb energy from the electromagnetic wave.

Let P_{kn} be the probability that in one second of exposure of a system to electromagnetic radiation of frequency ν_{kn} the system will absorb energy $h\nu_{kn}$ and be excited from state Ψ_k to state Ψ_n. If $\rho(\nu_{kn})$ is the energy density of the radiation, then it seems reasonable to expect that

$$P_{kn} = B_{kn}\rho(\nu_{kn}) \tag{4-11}$$

where B_{kn} is a property of the transition known as *Einstein's coefficient of induced absorption*. The quantum mechanical theory shows that the Einstein coefficient is related to the transition moment in the following way [5]

$$B_{kn} = \frac{8\pi^3}{3h^2} |\mathbf{R}^{kn}|^2 \tag{4-12}$$

We wish now to relate the probability of absorption in unit time, P_{kn}, to the observed molar absorbancy index.[6] The Lambert-Beer law can be written in the differential form

$$-dI = 2.303 a_m(\nu) I C\, dx \tag{4-13}$$

The radiation density $\rho(\nu)$ is related to the radiation intensity I by

---

[5] The relation between the transition moment and the probability of a transition occurring can be derived using time dependent perturbation theory. The derivation is not discussed in this book, but interested students can find derivations in **II**, Chapter 8, and G. Barrow, *An Introduction to Molecular Spectroscopy*, McGraw-Hill Book Company, Inc., New York, 1962, Chapter 4.

[6] The treatment that follows is essentially that of S. J. Strickler and R. A. Berg, *J. Chem. Phys.*, **37**, 814 (1962).

the relationship

$$I = \frac{c}{n} \rho(\nu) \tag{4-14}$$

where c is the speed of light and n is the refractive index of the medium. Equation 4-14 is reasonable when it is recalled that the intensity of light is defined as the energy flowing through a 1 cm^2 cross-sectional area in one second. The energy density ρ is the energy in 1 cm^3, and c/n is the speed of light in the absorbing medium. Since the intensity of the incident light varies with both the frequency of the light and with the location, x, in the cell, the energy density must be a function of both ν and x, so we shall write it as $\rho(\nu, x)$. Making use of Equation 4-14, the differential form of the Lambert-Beer law may be written

$$- d\rho(\nu, x) = 2.303 a_m(\nu)\rho(\nu, x)C \, dx \tag{4-15}$$

where $- d\rho(\nu, x)$ is the decrease in energy density when the light moves a distance dx through the medium. If N' is the number of absorbing molecules per cubic centimeter, then the number of molecules in an element of volume one cm^2 in cross section and dx in width is $N' \, dx$, so that

$$C \, dx = 1000N' \, dx/N_0 \tag{4-16}$$

where N_0 is Avogadro's number. In addition, if P_{kn} is the transition probability for a single molecule in one second, then $P_{kn}N' \, dx$ is the number of molecules excited in the layer in one second, with an energy absorption of $h\nu_{kn}$ for each molecule. Therefore, the loss of intensity in the light beam in passing through the layer is

$$- dI = P_{kn}N' \, dx \, h\nu_{kn} \tag{4-17}$$

The corresponding decrease in radiation density will be given by

$$- \frac{c}{n} \, d\rho = P_{kn}N' \, dx \, h\nu_{kn} \tag{4-18}$$

which on making use of Equations 4-15 and 4-16 gives

$$P_{kn} = \frac{2303 c a_m(\nu_{kn})}{n N_0 h\nu_{kn}} \rho(\nu_{kn}, x) \tag{4-19}$$

Electronic transitions in molecules do not, however, occur at a single frequency, but over a range of frequencies, so that Equation 4-19 must be integrated over the band to get the total probability of absorption from state Ψ_k to state Ψ_n. In doing this the energy density $\rho(\nu)$ at a single frequency must be replaced by the energy density $\rho'(\nu)\, d\nu$ in the frequency range between ν and $\nu + d\nu$. We then obtain for the total probability that a molecule will be excited when exposed to radiation covering the entire absorption band

$$P'_{kn} = \int_{\text{band}} P_{kn}\, d\nu = \frac{2303c}{hnN_0} \int_{\text{band}} a_m(\nu)\rho'(\nu)d \ln \nu \qquad (4\text{-}20a)$$

If the radiation density $\rho'(\nu)$ is constant throughout the band (this is usually a safe assumption), and if we write this constant as ρ, then Equation (4-20) can be written as

$$P_{kn}' = \left[\frac{2303c}{hnN_0} \int_{\text{band}} a_m(\nu)d \ln \nu \right] \rho \qquad (4\text{-}20b)$$

If equations 4-20b and 4-11 are compared, it is seen that

$$B_{kn} = \frac{2303c}{hnN_0} \int_{\text{band}} a_m(\nu)d \ln \nu \qquad (4\text{-}21)$$

This equation is the desired link between the theoretically computed absorption intensities (using Equation 4-12) and experimental absorption measurements. For narrow absorption bands, it is a good approximation to take the center frequency of the band out of the integral in Equation 4-21 giving

$$B_{kn} = \frac{2303c}{h\nu_{kn}nN_0} \int_{\text{band}} a_m(\nu)\, d\nu \qquad (4\text{-}22)$$

Equation 4-22 is the formula used in most elementary texts and involves the integrated absorption intensity $\int a_m(\nu)\, d\nu$.

The second factor involved in absorption strengths arises from the difference in population of states Ψ_k and Ψ_n. Obviously, before molecules can be excited from state Ψ_k, this state must be populated. In addition, a treatment similar to that discussed above shows that the probability of induced *emission* (i.e., a transition from state Ψ_n to state Ψ_k) is equal to the probability of induced absorption. The net absorption of energy from the sample will depend, therefore, on the difference in population of the two states involved in the transition. If the populations of the two states are equal, no absorption will be observed. Experimental conditions that equalize the populations in two states involved in a transition occur quite often in magnetic resonance spectroscopy, and this gives rise to the phenomenon of *saturation*. Under certain conditions, it is possible to make the population of an excited state temporarily larger than that of the ground state. If light of the appropriate energy then strikes the crystal, the number of ions that can emit radiation exceeds the number that can absorb, and an emission is obtained which is more intense than the exciting light. Under these conditions, the sample acts as an optical amplifier or *laser*.

To calculate the population differences between various states of a system, use is made of the Boltzmann distribution law.[7] For our purposes, this law can be taken in the form

$$N_j = q^{-1} g_j e^{-\epsilon_j / kT} \tag{4-23}$$

where

N_j = number of systems in state j

q = the partition function of the system—a constant for our purposes

g_j = degeneracy of state j

ϵ_j = energy of state j

k = Boltzmann's constant = 1.3804×10^{-16} erg deg^{-1} (molecule)$^{-1}$

T = Absolute temperature

If the lowest state of the system is arbitrarily assigned a population of 1.00, Equation 4-23 can be used to calculate the relative populations of the higher states. Such a calculation is illustrated in Exercise 4-3.

EXERCISE 4-3 For a set of identical systems each containing a helium atom in a one-dimensional box of length 5 Å, calculate the relative populations of the states $n = 2$ and $n = 1$ at 300°K.

[7] For a simple derivation of this law, see W. J. Moore, *Physical Chemistry*, 3rd ed., Prentice-Hall, Inc., Englewood Cliffs, New Jersey, 1962, pp. 619 ff.

EXERCISE 4-4   Calculate kT at 300°K (approximately room temperature) in ergs molecule^{-1}, cm^{-1}, ev and kcal mole^{-1}.

4-3   Survey of types of spectroscopy

In this section, the various types of spectroscopy will be listed in the order of increasing size of the quantum of radiation used.   A brief description will be given of each type.

1. *Nuclear magnetic and nuclear quadrupole resonance spectroscopy.*   This type of spectroscopy utilizes a portion of the radio-frequency region of the electromagnetic spectrum, usually 5–100 Mc.   Nuclear magnetic resonance spectroscopy detects transitions between nuclear spin states in an applied magnetic field and is discussed in more detail in Chapter 9.   Quadrupole resonance spectroscopy detects the splitting in the nuclear spin levels arising from the interaction of an unsymmetrical charge distribution in certain nuclei with an electric field gradient.   For more details, the student should consult **III**, pp. 484 ff., after studying Chapter 9.   The quantum size in this region of the spectrum is very small.   A frequency of 100 Mc corresponds to an energy of only 0.0033 cm^{-1} and a wavelength of 300 cm or 3 m.   This energy is much less than kT at room temperature (see Exercise 4-4) and all of the nuclear spin states are almost equally populated.   Detection of resonance signals is quite difficult and requires fairly large and/or highly concentrated samples.

2. *Electron Spin Resonance Spectroscopy.*   If a sample containing unpaired electrons—e.g., organic free radicals or certain transition metal ions—is placed in an applied magnetic field, transitions between different *electron spin* states can be induced by radiation in the microwave range.   Microwaves are characterized by the fact that they are generated by klystrons and magnetons instead of LC circuits.   Usually, they are conducted by waveguides (hollow pieces of metal tubing with either a circular or rectangular cross section) instead of wires.   Experiments are usually performed at 9,500 Mc (X-band) or 12,000 Mc (K-band) but, in general, any frequency in the range of 2,000 Mc to 36,000 Mc can be used.   A frequency of 10,000 Mc corresponds to a wavelength of 3 cm and an energy of 0.3 cm^{-1}, still considerably less than kT at room temperature.   The different electron spin states are still almost equally populated, but there is a larger excess population in the lowest

electron spin state than there is in the corresponding nuclear spin state.   Consequently, saturation effects, when the populations of the lowest and excited states become equal, are not as pronounced as with nuclear magnetic resonance.   Electron spin resonance spectroscopy is discussed in Chapter 9.

3. *Pure Rotational Spectroscopy.*   In this type of spectroscopy, transitions are observed between different rotational states of a molecule.   Most of these transitions also occur in the microwave region except those for light molecules (HCl, HF, etc.) which take place in the far infrared.   The remarks made about quantum size and populations under ESR spectroscopy also apply here.   Pure rotational spectroscopy is discussed in Chapter 5.

4. *Vibrational (Infrared) and Vibration-Rotation Spectroscopy.* Transitions between vibrational states in molecules absorb energy in the infrared region of the electromagnetic spectrum.   Conventional infrared spectrometers usually scan the range of 200 cm^{-1} to 4000 cm^{-1}.   These energies correspond to a wavelength range of 50 μ to 2.5 μ.   Radiation in this region is produced by a hot glowing wire and is an example of a practical use of "blackbody" radiation.   The optics of infrared spectrometers are constructed from large single crystals of sodium chloride, lithium chloride, or potassium bromide.   The quantum size in this region, except at the low energy end of the range, is greater than kT at room temperature and, as a result of this, only the lowest vibrational state has appreciable population.

Overtones of high energy vibrational transitions are found in the near infrared region which extends from 2.5 μ to 800 mμ (8000 Å). Some low energy electronic transitions are also found in the high energy part of this region.   Vibrational spectroscopy is also discussed in Chapter 5.

5. *Raman Spectroscopy.*   Raman spectroscopy measures vibrational transition energies, but does so by observing the frequency of scattered light rather than that of absorbed light.   An intense beam of monochromatic light, usually in the visible region of the spectrum, is allowed to strike a sample, and the intensity of scattered light is observed at right angles to the incident beam.   Most of the scattered light will have the same frequency as the incident beam, but a small amount of light will have frequencies different from that of the incident beam.   The energy differences between these weak lines and between the weak lines and the main line

TABLE 4-2 **WAVELENGTH RANGES DEFINING THE VISI-BLE, ULTRAVIOLET, AND VACUUM ULTRAVIOLET RE-GIONS OF THE SPECTRUM—THE CORRESPONDING ENERGY RANGES IN CM^{-1} AND EV ARE GIVEN IN THE THIRD AND FOURTH COLUMNS**

Regions	Wavelength limits	cm^{-1}	ev
Visible	8000 Å–4000 Å	12,500–25,000	1.55–3.10
Ultraviolet	4000 Å–1800 Å	25,000–66,500	3.10–8.25
Vacuum Ultraviolet	1800 Å–50 Å	66,500–2 × 10^6	8.25–248

correspond to vibrational and/or rotational transitions in the system being studied.

6. *Electronic Spectroscopy.* In electronic spectroscopy, transitions between allowed electronic states of atoms and molecules are observed. It is electronic transitions that give rise to atomic line spectra discussed in Chapter 3. These transitions occur over a wide range of energies encompassing the visible, ultraviolet, and vacuum ultraviolet regions. These ranges are summarized in Table 4-2.

7. *Gamma Ray or Mössbauer Spectroscopy.* This type of spectroscopy measures the transition energy between allowed states of certain nuclei. Chemical applications of Mössbauer spectroscopy [8] have mainly used compounds containing Fe^{57} or Sn^{119}. Gamma ray emissions from these isotopes are characterized by being extremely narrow. This narrowness can be used to construct an extremely sensitive time measuring device, and such a device has recently been used to test the general theory of relativity. Energies in the gamma ray regions are extremely large, ranging from 8×10^3 to 1×10^5 ev.

4-4 Summary

1. Any unit related to an energy difference can be used as a spectroscopic unit. Some common units used in spectroscopic measurements are cm^{-1}, ev, kcal mole^{-1}, μ, mμ, Å, and mc.

---

[8] For a recent review, see *Science*, **144**, 253 (1964).

2. The Bouger-Lambert-Beer law was derived. This law relates the absorbance of the sample to its length and to the concentration and the molar absorbancy index of the absorbing species.

3. Factors affecting the intensity of a transition were discussed. Intensities are determined by the magnitude of the interaction between the sample being studied and the light wave and by the relative populations of the states involved in the transitions.

4. The Boltzmann distribution law was introduced to make it possible to calculate relative populations.

5. Various types of spectroscopy were surveyed briefly.

6. The student should be familiar with the terms: molar absorbancy index, transition moment, population of a state, integrated absorption intensity, dipole moment, and Einstein's coefficient of induced absorption.

Chapter 5

ROTATION AND VIBRATION
SPECTROSCOPY

IN THIS chapter, we will use the methods discussed in Chapter 3 to calculate the allowed rotational and vibrational energy levels of a diatomic molecule. The calculation will be started by assuming that the rotational motion is similar to that of a rigid rotor, and that the vibrational motion is like that of a harmonic oscillator. Following this treatment, the energy levels will be corrected to take into account the fact that real molecules do not behave quite like rigid rotors and harmonic oscillators. Finally, a brief discussion of the vibrational motion of polyatomic molecules will be given.

5-1 The rigid rotor approximation

We have shown in Chapter 2 that, in problems where the potential energy is only a function of the internal coordinates, the motion of the center of mass can be separated from the internal motion of the molecule. In the rigid rotor approximation, we assume that a diatomic molecule can be regarded as a dumbell with atoms of masses m_A and m_B at the ends held together by a massless bar of

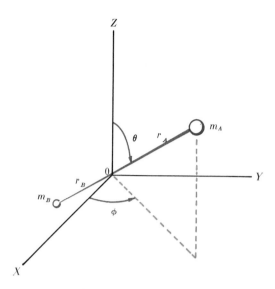

FIG. 5-1 *Quantities used in the description of the rotational motion of a diatomic molecule. The origin is taken at the center of mass.*

length r_e, the equilibrium bond length.   Since there is no potential energy in rotational motion (in the absence of electric and magnetic fields), the separation of the motion of the center of mass can be made, and the internal motion of the molecule can be treated as a separate problem.

The problem of rotational motion is most conveniently solved using spherical polar coordinates.   The appropriate quantities are shown in Figure 5-1, where the origin has been placed at the center of mass of the system.   From the definition of the center of mass, we can write

$$m_B r_B = m_A r_A \qquad r_B = (m_A/m_B)r_A \qquad (5\text{-}1)$$

Using the fact that the equilibrium distance $r_e = r_A + r_B$, the student can easily show that

$$r_A = \frac{m_B}{m_A + m_B} r_e \qquad (5\text{-}2)$$

$$r_B = \frac{m_A}{m_A + m_B} r_e$$

The moment of inertia I about an axis is defined as

$$I = \sum_i m_i r_i^2 \tag{5-3}$$

where m_i is the mass of the i'th particle and where r_i is the distance of the i'th particle from the axis. For a diatomic rotor, the moment of inertia about an axis through the center of mass and perpendicular to the molecular axis is

$$I = m_A r_A^2 + m_B r_B^2 \tag{5-4}$$

After a little algebra, the student can show that Equation 5-4 becomes

$$I = \left(\frac{m_A m_B}{m_A + m_B}\right) r_e^2 = \mu r_e^2 \tag{5-5}$$

where μ is the reduced mass of the system.

The next problem is to write an expression for the kinetic energy of the rigid rotor. It can be written immediately that

$$T = \frac{1}{2} m_A v_A^2 + \frac{1}{2} m_B v_B^2 \tag{5-6}$$

Transforming to spherical polar coordinates, it can be shown that Equation 5-6 becomes

$$T = \frac{1}{2} I(\dot{\theta}^2 + \sin^2 \theta \dot{\phi}^2) \tag{5-7}$$

EXERCISE 5-1   Beginning with Equation 5-6 and the relations in Section 1-2, derive Equation 5-7. Hint: remember that $v^2 = \dot{x}_A^2 + \dot{y}_A^2 + \dot{z}_A^2$.

The general method for solving quantum mechanical problems is now followed. This includes

1. Writing down the classical Hamiltonian.
2. Transforming to the corresponding quantum mechanical operator.
3. Finding the solutions to the eigenvalue equation $\mathcal{H}\psi_i = E_i\psi_i$.

The first task of finding the classical Hamiltonian requires that Equation 5-7 be written in terms of the appropriate momenta, p_θ

and p_ϕ. Using Equation 2-8, these quantities are

$$p_\theta = \left(\frac{\partial T}{\partial \dot\theta}\right) = I\dot\theta$$
$$p_\phi = \left(\frac{\partial T}{\partial \dot\phi}\right) = I\sin^2\theta\dot\phi \tag{5-8}$$

By solving Equations 5-8 for $\dot\theta$ and $\dot\phi$, and substituting into Equation 5-7, one obtains

$$T = \frac{1}{2I}\left(p_\theta{}^2 + \frac{p_\phi{}^2}{\sin^2\theta}\right) \tag{5-9}$$

We next transform to the corresponding quantum mechanical operator by letting p_q become $-i\hbar\dfrac{\partial}{\partial q}$. Unfortunately, one encounters a minor difficulty in that the resulting operator does not satisfy the requirement in postulate II that an operator corresponding to an observable be Hermitian. The operator derived from Equation 5-9 can be made Hermitian by multiplying the first term by $\sin\theta/\sin\theta$ and writing it as

$$T = \frac{1}{2I}\left[\frac{1}{\sin\theta}p_\theta(\sin\theta)p_\theta + \frac{p_\phi{}^2}{\sin^2\theta}\right] \tag{5-10}$$

before substituting $p_q = -i\hbar\dfrac{\partial}{\partial q}$. The corresponding operator is then

$$\hat{\mathfrak{K}} = \frac{-\hbar^2}{2I}\left[\frac{1}{\sin\theta}\frac{\partial}{\partial\theta}\left(\sin\theta\frac{\partial}{\partial\theta}\right) + \frac{1}{\sin^2\theta}\frac{\partial^2}{\partial\phi^2}\right] \tag{5-11}$$

The final step necessary to find the allowed rotational energy levels is to find the functions and energies that make the equation

$$\hat{\mathfrak{K}}\psi_i = E_i\psi_i \tag{5-12}$$

true for the $\hat{\mathfrak{K}}$ given in Equation 5-11.

This approach is similar to that of the problem of the particle in a three-dimensional box. That is, we will try to reduce the two-dimensional problem to two one-dimensional problems.[1] To

---

[1] The student should note that this problem in spherical coordinates is only a two-dimensional problem. This is obscured in Cartesian coordinates where three variables are apparently involved.

do this, we try to separate the variables θ and ϕ by trying solutions
of the form

$$\Psi = T(\theta)U(\phi) \tag{5-13}$$

where T is a function of θ only and U is a function of ϕ only. Substituting Equations 5-13 and 5-11 into Equation 5-12, and performing some straightforward algebra, one obtains

$$\frac{\sin^2 \theta}{T}\left[\frac{1}{\sin \theta}\frac{\partial}{\partial \theta}\left(\sin \theta \frac{\partial T}{\partial \theta}\right) + \frac{2IET}{\hbar^2}\right] + \frac{1}{U}\frac{\partial^2 U}{\partial \phi^2} = 0$$

Since T and U are functions of θ and ϕ only, the partial derivatives
can be replaced by total derivatives. Rearranging, one then
obtains

$$\frac{\sin^2 \theta}{T}\left[\frac{1}{\sin \theta}\frac{d}{d\theta}\left(\sin \theta \frac{dT}{d\theta}\right) + \frac{2IET}{\hbar^2}\right] = \frac{1}{U}\frac{d^2 U}{d\phi^2} \tag{5-14}$$

Once again the familiar argument of Chapter 3 is applied. If
Equation 5-14 is to hold for all values of θ and ϕ, it must be true
that both sides are equal to a constant. Calling this constant β,
Equation 5-14 becomes the two equations

$$-\frac{1}{U}\frac{d^2 U}{d\phi^2} = \beta \tag{5-15a}$$

$$\frac{\sin^2 \theta}{T}\left[\frac{1}{\sin \theta}\frac{d}{d\theta}\left(\sin \theta \frac{dT}{d\theta}\right) + \frac{2IET}{\hbar^2}\right] = \beta \tag{5-15b}$$

Equation 5-15a is by now a familiar one, and the solutions can be
immediately written down. For reasons illustrated in Exercises
5-2 and 5-3, we will choose the solutions in the form

$$U = Ae^{im\phi} \tag{5-16}$$

By differentiating twice, the constant β is shown to be equal to m^2
and by applying the "single valuedness" condition, m is restricted
to the values $0, \pm 1, \pm 2 \cdots$.

EXERCISE 5-2 Find the allowed energies and wave functions for a
particle constrained to move on a circle. The potential energy may be
taken to be zero on the circle and infinity everywhere off the circle. For
a boundary condition, the restriction that acceptable wave functions
must be single valued is used.

EXERCISE 5-3 Show that in spherical coordinates the operator for the z component of angular momentum becomes

$$\hat{L}_z = i\hbar \frac{\partial}{\partial \phi}$$

Show that the functions 5-16 are eigenfunctions of $\hat{L}_z$ while the functions $U = A \sin m\phi$, or $U = A \cos m\phi$ are not.

EXERCISE 5-4 Evaluate the normalization constant A in Equation 5-16.

If Equation 5-15b is expanded, and if the substitution $x = \cos \theta$ is made, one obtains

$$(1 - x^2) \frac{d^2 T}{dx^2} - 2x \frac{dT}{dx} + \left(\frac{2IE}{\hbar^2} - \frac{\beta}{(1 - x^2)} \right) T = 0 \qquad (5\text{-}17)$$

EXERCISE 5-5 Starting with Equation 5-15b, derive Equation 5-17.

Equation 5-17 is an equation of the form

$$(1 - x^2)z'' - 2xz' + \left[l(l + 1) - \frac{m^2}{1 - x^2} \right] z = 0 \qquad (5\text{-}18)$$

This equation is a well-known equation of physics called the associated Legendre equation. Functions z that are finite, have integrable squares, and are single valued, exist only for the conditions that l is a positive integer or zero, and that $|m| \leq l$. The solutions to Equation 5-17 are called the associated Legendre polynomials. The solutions for $l = 0$ to $l = 2$ are given in Table 5-1.[2]

TABLE 5-1 THE NORMALIZED ASSOCIATED LEGENDRE POLYNOMIALS T(l, m)

l	m	$T(l, m)$
0	0	$1/\sqrt{2}$
1	0	$(\frac{3}{2})^{\frac{1}{2}} \cos \theta$
1	± 1	$(\frac{3}{4})^{\frac{1}{2}} \sin \theta$
2	0	$(\frac{5}{8})^{\frac{1}{2}} (3 \cos^2 \theta - 1)$
2	± 1	$(\frac{15}{4})^{\frac{1}{2}} \sin \theta \cos \theta$
2	± 2	$(\frac{15}{16})^{\frac{1}{2}} \sin^2 \theta$

[2] For the mathematical details leading to these solutions, the student is referred to I, pages 61 ff. or II, pages 52 ff.

EXERCISE 5-6 By direct substitution, show that the functions $T(1, 0)$, $T(1, 1)$, and $T(2, 0)$ are solutions of Equation 5-17.

Comparing Equations 5-17 with 5-18, one obtains the result that solutions to Equation 5-17 exist only if

$$\frac{2IE}{\hbar^2} = l(l + 1) \tag{5-19}$$

Thus, the allowed energies for the rigid rotor are

$$E = J(J + 1) \frac{\hbar^2}{2I} \tag{5-20}$$

where $J = 0, 1, 2, 3 \ldots$ The symbol J has been substituted for l in Equation 5-20 because l is reserved for the quantum number of electronic angular momentum (see Chapter 6).

The allowed wave functions are those given by Equation 5-13 and depend on two quantum numbers, J and m. Thus,

$$\Psi(J, m) = T(J, m) U(m)$$

It should be noted that, for every value of J, there will be $2J + 1$ values of m. Thus, if $J = 2$, m can have the five values ± 2, ± 1, 0. Because the energy depends only on J, each energy level will be $(2J + 1)$ fold degenerate. In the presence of an electric or magnetic field, this degeneracy is removed if the molecule contains an electric or magnetic dipole moment, and the energy of the state will depend on m also.

5-2 Pure rotational spectroscopy

In pure rotational spectroscopy, allowed transitions between rotational states are observed. As was pointed out in Chapter 4, these transitions occur in the far infrared or microwave region of the electromagnetic spectrum. By convention, spectroscopists designate quantities referring to the upper and lower states in a transition by single and double primes, respectively. The energy of the transition $\Psi(J'', m'') \rightarrow \Psi(J', m')$ is then

$$E' - E'' = \frac{\hbar^2}{2I} [J'(J' + 1) - J''(J'' + 1)] \tag{5-21}$$

It will be shown below that only transitions for which $\Delta J = \pm 1$ are allowed. If this selection rule is used in Equation 5-21, the expression for the energy of a rotational transition becomes

$$E' - E'' = \frac{\hbar^2}{2I} 2(J'' + 1)$$

Spectroscopists usually use wave number units. Hence, the energies of the allowed rotational transitions can be written

$$\omega_R(cm^{-1}) = \frac{E' - E''}{hc} = \frac{h}{8\pi^2 cI} 2(J'' + 1) = 2B(J'' + 1)$$

$$(5-22)$$

where the constant $B = h/8\pi^2 cI$ is called the rotational constant of the molecule. At this level of approximation, the pure rotational spectrum of a diatomic molecule consists of a series of equally spaced lines with spacing $2B$.

A study of rotational spectra is one of the powerful methods that the experimentalist has available to obtain information about molecular structure. The value of B obtained from the pure rotational spectrum can be used to calculate the moment of inertia I, and this quantity in turn gives the internuclear distance r. In this respect, pure rotational spectroscopy supplements X-ray crystallography because it can be used to study the structure of gases whereas X-ray crystallography is limited to studies of crystalline materials.

EXERCISE 5-7 Calculate the moment of inertia of

(a) HCl^{35} (b) HCl^{37} (c) DCl^{35}

all of which have an equilibrium bond length of 1.275 Å. Calculate the positions of the first three rotational transitions for HCl^{35} and DCl^{35}. Plot these lines on a frequency abscissa.

EXERCISE 5-8 Carbon monoxide absorbs energy in the microwave region of the spectrum at 1.153×10^5 Mc. This absorption can be attributed to the $J = 0$ to $J = 1$ transition. Calculate the internuclear distance and the moment of inertia of CO.

5-3 *Intensities and selection rules*

It was pointed out in Chapter 4 that the intensity of a spectral line depended on the magnitude of the transition moment and on the relative populations of the two states involved in a transition. Many times it can be shown that, for some classes of transitions,

$\mathbf{R}^{kn} = 0$. This means that the transition is not allowed—that is, it will have zero intensity. This result, coupled with a statement of the restrictions on the transitions to which it applies, constitutes a "selection rule." Thus, in the case of rotational spectra of most diatomic molecules, $\mathbf{R}^{kn} = 0$ unless $\Delta J \equiv (J_n - J_k) = \pm 1$ and $\Delta m \equiv (m_n - m_k) = 0, \pm 1$. Specific examples of calculations of $\mathbf{R}^{kn}$ are given in Exercises 5-9 and 5-10.

EXERCISE 5-9 An electron moves in a one-dimensional box of length a, with a unit positive charge at $a/2$. Show that the transition $\Psi_1 \rightarrow \Psi_2$ is allowed, but the transition $\Psi_1 \rightarrow \Psi_3$ is not. Can you derive a general selection rule for a particle in a one-dimensional box? See Exercise 3-11 when starting to evaluate integrals.

EXERCISE 5-10 Show that the transition $J = 0$ to $J = 2$ is not allowed for rotational transitions in a diatomic molecule with wave functions as in Table 5-1. Remember the dipole moment is a vector $\mathbf{\mu} = \mu_x\mathbf{i} + \mu_y\mathbf{j} + \mu_z\mathbf{k}$. Transform μ_x, μ_y, and μ_z to polar coordinates and evaluate each component separately. Remember that $\mu_x = \sum_i e_i x_i$.

Among the allowed transitions just discussed, the relative intensities of the lines in a pure rotational spectrum will depend on the relative populations of the initial state for each transition. These relative populations can be calculated from the Boltzmann distribution law given in Chapter 4. Applied to the rotational states of a diatomic molecule, Equation 4-20 becomes

$$\frac{N_J}{N_{J=0}} = (2J + 1)e^{BJ(J+1)/kT} \qquad J = 1, 2, 3 \cdots \quad (5\text{-}23)$$

Since Equation 5-23 contains the degeneracy factor $(2J + 1)$, the population of rotational states will not continually decrease as their energy increases. Instead, there will be a maximum in a plot of relative population versus quantum number J.

EXERCISE 5-11 For HCl^{35} the equilibrium bond length is 1.275 Å. Use the Boltzmann distribution law to calculate the relative populations at room temperature of the states $J = 1, 2, 3, 4, 6,$ and 10 at 25°C. Give the state with $J = 0$ a weight of 1.0. Plot the relative populations *vs.* J value. How should a similar diagram look if the calculations were carried out at 500°C?

An example of the relative populations of rotational states in HCl is given in Exercise 5-11. If the transition moments were equal for all J (and they are almost independent of J),[3] the intensities of the lines in the pure rotational spectrum of HCl^{35} would vary in a similar manner as the population graph calculated in Exercise 5-11.

5-4   *The harmonic oscillator and vibrational spectroscopy*

As a first approximation to the vibrational motion of a diatomic molecule, the molecule will be regarded as a pair of mass points connected by an ideal spring with force constant k.   This is called the harmonic oscillator approximation.   Before solving the quantum mechanical equation, some of the classical results will be reviewed. Because an ideal spring is one in which the force is proportional to the displacement, and because the potential energy is only a function of the relative distance apart, the Lagrangian function for the internal motion of this system is

$$L = \frac{1}{2} \mu \dot{q}^2 - kq^2 \tag{5-24}$$

where $q = r - r_e$ is the displacement from the equilibrium internuclear distance.   The equation of motion for this one-dimensional harmonic oscillator is

$$\frac{d}{dt} (\mu \dot{q}) = - kq$$

$$\ddot{q} = - \frac{k}{\mu} q \tag{5-25}$$

This is the differential equation for simple harmonic motion which has solutions

$$q = A \cos \left(\frac{k}{\mu}\right)^{\frac{1}{2}} t \tag{5-26}$$

The period of the oscillator τ is the time required for one oscillation and is equal to the reciprocal of the oscillator frequency.   If we increase t from some initial value t_0 to the value $t_0 + \tau$, then q must be unchanged.   This is true only if the argument of the cosine is

[3] G. Herzberg, *Spectra of Diatomic Molecules*, D. Van Nostrand, Inc., Princeton, New Jersey (1950) page 125 ff.

increased by 2π. Thus, we have

$$q_0 = q_\tau = A \cos\left(\frac{k}{\mu}\right)^{\frac{1}{2}} t_0 = A \cos\left(\frac{k}{\mu}\right)^{\frac{1}{2}} (t_0 + \tau)$$

and

$$2\pi = \tau \left(\frac{k}{\mu}\right)^{\frac{1}{2}}$$

therefore,

$$\nu = \frac{1}{\tau} = \frac{1}{2\pi}\left(\frac{k}{\mu}\right)^{\frac{1}{2}} \tag{5-27}$$

Thus, the frequency of an oscillator is proportional to the square root of the force constant and the reciprocal of the square root of the reduced mass.

To solve the quantum mechanical problem, we first write Hamilton's function, and then transform to the appropriate quantum mechanical operator. Thus,

$$p_q = \frac{\partial L}{\partial \dot{q}} = \mu\dot{q} \tag{5-28}$$

$$\mathcal{H} = \frac{1}{2\mu} p_q{}^2 + \frac{1}{2} kq^2 \tag{5-29}$$

and

$$\hat{\mathcal{H}} = -\frac{\hbar^2}{2\mu}\frac{d^2}{dq^2} + \frac{1}{2} kq^2 \tag{5-30}$$

To find the allowed energies and wave functions, one must solve the eigenvalue equation

$$-\frac{\hbar^2}{2\mu}\frac{d^2\Psi}{dq^2} + \frac{1}{2} kq^2\Psi = E\Psi \tag{5-31}$$

If Equation 5-31 is rearranged, it can be written in the form

$$\frac{d^2\Psi}{dq^2} + (\alpha - \beta^2 q^2) = 0 \tag{5-32}$$

where $\alpha = \dfrac{2\mu E}{\hbar^2}$, and $\beta^2 = \dfrac{\mu k}{\hbar^2}$. To solve Equation 5-32, the substitution $\xi = \sqrt{\beta}\, q$ is first made. Then $\dfrac{d^2}{dx^2} = \beta \dfrac{d^2}{d\xi^2}$ and Equation

5-32 becomes

$$\frac{d^2\Psi}{d\xi^2} + \left(\frac{\alpha}{\beta} - \xi^2\right)\Psi = 0. \tag{5-33}$$

If Equation 5-33 is investigated for large values of ξ to see what form $\Psi(\xi)$ takes under these conditions, one obtains the equation

$$\frac{d^2\Psi}{d\xi^2} = \xi^2\Psi \tag{5-34}$$

since $\xi^2 \gg \dfrac{\alpha}{\beta}$ for large ξ. The solutions to Equation 5-34 are approximately

$$\Psi' = Ae^{\pm \xi^2/2} \tag{5-35}$$

since a factor of ± 1 can be neglected with respect to ξ^2. The solution with the plus sign can be discarded because Ψ would not have an integrable square under these conditions. This behavior of Ψ at large ξ suggests that a solution to Equation 5-33 of the form

$$\Psi = u(\xi)e^{-\xi^2/2} \tag{5-36}$$

be tried. If Equation 5-36 is substituted into Equation 5-33, it is seen that, if there is to be a solution in the form of Equation 5-36, then $u(\xi)$ must satisfy the differential equation

$$\frac{d^2u}{d\xi^2} - 2\xi\frac{du}{d\xi} + \left(\frac{\alpha}{\beta} - 1\right)u = 0 \tag{5-37}$$

EXERCISE 5-12   Derive Equation 5-37 as outlined above.

Once again, however, Equation 5-37 is a well-known equation of physics called the Hermite equation, providing that the quantity $\left(\dfrac{\alpha}{\beta} - 1\right) = 2v$ where v is an integer. The solutions $u(\xi)$ are called the Hermite polynomials of degree v, and form an orthogonal set of functions.[4] The first few Hermite polynomials are given in Table 5-2.

---

[4] For an outline of the solutions to Hermite's equations, see I, pages 177 ff. or II, pages 60 ff.

TABLE 5-2 HERMITE POLYNOMIALS FOR $v = 0$ TO $v = 4$

v	$H_v(\xi)$
0	1
1	2ξ
2	$4\xi^2 - 2$
3	$8\xi^3 - 12\xi$
4	$16\xi^4 - 48\xi^2 + 12$

EXERCISE 5-13   By substitution, verify that H_1 and H_3 are solutions of Equation 5-37.

The corresponding normalized wave functions for the one-dimensional harmonic oscillator are

$$\Psi_v(\xi) = \left(\frac{\sqrt{\beta/\pi}}{2^v v!}\right)^{\frac{1}{2}} H_v(\xi) e^{-\xi^2/2} \qquad \xi = \sqrt{\beta}\, q \tag{5-38}$$

From the restriction that $\left(\dfrac{\alpha}{\beta} - 1\right) = 2v$, it is straightforward to show that

$$E_v = \frac{h}{2\pi} \sqrt{k/\mu} \left(v + \frac{1}{2}\right) = \left(v + \frac{1}{2}\right) h\nu \tag{5-39}$$

where the energy of the system is restricted to the discrete set of values $\frac{1}{2}, \frac{3}{2}, \frac{5}{2} \cdots$ times the energy $h\nu$ associated with the classical frequency of oscillation. It should be noticed that even in its lowest state ($v = 0$), a quantum mechanical oscillator still has energy $\frac{1}{2}h\nu$. This is called the vibrational zero point energy. It is the zero point energy difference between hydrogen-carbon and deuterium-carbon bonds that gives rise to the isotope effects used in the kinetic study of the mechanism of chemical reactions.

EXERCISE 5-14   Calculate the ratio of zero point energies of a C—H and a C—D bond vibration. You may assume that these bond vibrations follow Equation 5-39, and that the force constants for the C—H and C—D vibrations are the same.

In vibrational or infrared spectroscopy, transitions between allowed vibrational states are observed. Within the context of the harmonic oscillator approximation, the selection rule for vibrational transitions is $\Delta v = \pm 1$. The allowed transitions are then given in wave number units by

$$\omega_v = \frac{E_{v+1} - E_v}{hc} \tag{5-40}$$

where $\omega_v = \nu/c$ is the fundamental vibration frequency in wave number units. It should be noted that only *one* transition is observed in the vibrational spectrum of a diatomic molecule because all of the vibrational levels are equally spaced.[5] Since the energy spacing between vibrational levels is much greater than the spacing between rotational transitions, only the lowest state has an appreciable population at room temperature.

EXERCISE 5-15 HCl^{35} absorbs radiation at 2885.9 cm^{-1}. Using the Boltzmann distribution law, calculate the relative populations of the ground and first excited vibrational states at 25°C. You may give the ground state an arbitrary population of 1.000.

We next consider the selection rules for vibrational spectroscopy. The dipole moment of a vibrating diatomic molecule will obviously be a function of the equilibrium internuclear distance. For small displacements, this dipole moment can be expanded in a power series as a function of the displacement coordinate

$$\mu = \mu_0 + \left(\frac{d\mu}{dq}\right)_{q=0} q + \cdots \tag{5-41}$$

The first term in Equation 5-41 is the permanent dipole moment. The second term involves the change in the dipole moment upon displacement, and higher terms in the expansion are neglected.

The transition moment for a transition $\Psi_0 \rightarrow \Psi_k$ is then

$$R_v{}^0 = \int_{\text{all space}} \Psi_0 \left[\mu_0 + \left(\frac{d\mu}{dq}\right)_{q+0} q \right] \Psi_k \, dq$$

$$= \int \Psi_0 \mu_0 \Psi_k \, dq + \int \Psi_0 \left(\frac{d\mu}{dq}\right)_{q=0} q \Psi_k \, dq \tag{5-42}$$

The first integral in Equation 5-42 vanishes because μ_0 is a constant, and Ψ_0 and Ψ_k are orthogonal. In order to obtain a non-

[5] It will be shown below how this statement must be modified for real oscillators.

vanishing transition moment, the second integral must be nonzero. This means that the quantity $\left(\dfrac{d\mu}{dq}\right)_{q=0}$ must be nonzero. The important point to realize is that, for a vibrational transition to be infrared allowed, there must be a change in the dipole moment during a vibrational cycle. Thus, homonuclear diatomic molecules will have no infrared spectrum. By using the second integral in Equation 5-41 and the recursion relations for Hermite polynomials,[6] the general selection rule can be derived.

5-5   *Vibration-rotation spectroscopy*

In any real molecule, vibration and rotation are taking place at the same time. The first two vibrational energy levels and the rotational sublevels can be represented schematically as in Figure 5-2. A transition will start at a rotational sublevel of the $v = 0$ vibrational state and end at a rotational sublevel of the $v = 1$ state. The selection rules for these transitions for most diatomic molecules are a combination of those from rotational and vibrational spectroscopy. Thus, for absorption

$$\Delta v = +1 \qquad \Delta J = \pm 1$$

It is convenient to discuss these transitions in two groups. For $\Delta v = 1$, $\Delta J = +1$, and, taking $v = 0$ as the lowest state, one obtains

$$\omega_{v,R} = \frac{3}{2}\omega_v + B(J'' + 1)(J'' + 2) - \frac{1}{2}\omega_v$$
$$- BJ''(J'' + 1) \quad (5\text{-}43a)$$
$$= \omega_v + 2B(J'' + 1) \qquad J'' = 0, 1, 2, 3$$

where, as before, J'' is the quantum number of the lowest rotational state. This group of transitions is called the R branch of the spectrum. The lines of the R branch are labeled by the rotational quantum number of the lowest state. This labeling is illustrated in the idealized vibration-rotation spectrum in Figure 5-2*b*.

---

[6] **II**, page 62.

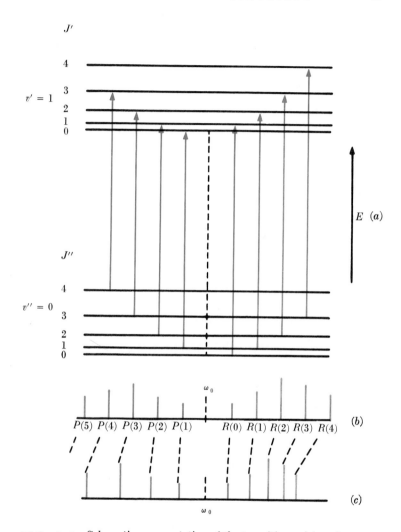

FIG. 5-2   *Schematic representation of the transitions giving rise to
the vibration-rotation spectrum of a diatomic molecule: a, energy level
diagram showing the first few P and R branch transitions; b, idealized
vibration-rotation spectrum; c, vibration-rotation spectrum that takes
vibration-rotation coupling into account.   The heights of the lines in b and
c are to give a general idea of the intensity distribution in rotation-
vibration spectra.*

Similarly, for the case $\Delta v = 1$, $\Delta J = -1$, it can be shown that

$$\omega_{v,R} = \omega - 2BJ'' \qquad J = 1, 2, 3 \tag{5-43b}$$

This group of lines is called the P branch. The P branch lines and their labeling are shown on the left-hand side of the idealized vibration rotation spectrum in Figure 5-2b. Thus, within the context of the rigid rotor-harmonic oscillator approximation, the vibration-rotation spectrum is made up of two sets of equally spaced lines with spacing $2B$ with a gap between sets, the center of which is the fundamental vibration frequency ω.

In a few molecules, transitions corresponding to $\Delta J = 0$ are also allowed, and this group of lines, when present, is called the Q branch. In real molecules, the appearance of the spectrum is modified by vibration rotation coupling (see Section 5-6) and looks like the bottom spectrum in Figure 5-2c.

5-6   *More exact theory of vibration-rotation spectroscopy*

It is important at this point to inquire about the validity of the rigid rotor and harmonic oscillator approximations. From physical intuition, it can be argued that there are three ways that the above picture of the vibration-rotation motion of a diatomic molecule should be modified for real molecules. These three modifications are:

1. Correction of the rotational motion for the effects of *centrifugal stretching*.

2. Correction of the vibrational motion for the *anharmonicity* of the vibration.

3. Correction of the rotational constant for changes in the moment of inertia for different vibrational states. This correction is called *vibration-rotation coupling*.

The physical argument for centrifugal stretching is easily visualized for a diatomic molecule. As the molecule rotates faster—that is, is excited to higher rotational states—it will stretch due to the centrifugal force on the end atoms. This will increase the moment of inertia, and consequently decrease the rotational constant B. For an actual molecule, then, the spacing between rotational lines should decrease as the quantum number J increases.

The anharmonicity correction is most easily visualized by a consideration of Figure 5-3. The potential energy function for a harmonic oscillator is a parabola (colored line in Figure 5-3). This is immediately seen to be unsatisfactory, for it is known that, given enough vibrational energy, a molecule will dissociate. A parabolic potential energy curve predicts no dissociation. An actual potential energy curve for a diatomic molecule [7] (solid line in Figure 5-3) does predict dissociation. The deviation of the actual potential energy curve from the parabolic curve is a measure of the anharmonicity of the vibration. It is clear from Figure 5-3 that anharmonicity effects will become more important the higher the vibrational quantum number v.

Vibration-rotation coupling arises from the fact that the average internuclear distance in an excited vibrational state will be larger than in the ground state. This effect is also due mainly to vibrational anharmonicity. The rotational constant B should, therefore, be a function of the vibrational quantum number v.

These three effects can be treated quantitatively by using an approximation method for solving eigenvalue equations called perturbation theory. The mathematical details are beyond the scope of this text, but an outline of the reasoning and the important results will be given.

For centrifugal stretching, the stretching effect as the molecule is excited to higher rotational states will be opposed by the force constant of the bond. The force constant is, in turn, related to the vibrational frequency ω. Furthermore, one would expect this effect to become more important the higher the value of J. The energy levels for a real rotor, then, should include a correction term to the rigid-rotor energy, and this correction term would be expected to involve ω, and become more important as J increases. Applying perturbation theory,[8] one obtains

$$E_J = BJ(J + 1) - \frac{4B^3}{\omega_v^2} J^2(J + 1)^2 \qquad (5\text{-}44a)$$

$$= BJ(J + 1) - DJ^2(J + 1)^2 \qquad (5\text{-}44b)$$

---

[7] The origin of these potential energy curves will be discussed in Chapter 7.

[8] For more details, see G. M. Barrow, *Introduction to Molecular Spectroscopy*, McGraw-Hill Book Company, Inc., New York (1962) pages 57 ff.

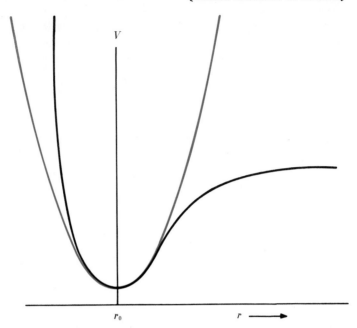

FIG. 5-3 *Comparison of the harmonic oscillator potential function with the actual potential function of a diatomic molecule.*

where D is called the centrifugal stretching constant. It should be noted that, since $B \ll \omega_v$, D is very small. The second term becomes relatively more important for large J since it depends on higher powers of J.

Inclusion of the centrifugal stretching correction will have the effect that the lines in a pure rotational spectrum will no longer be evenly spaced. For transitions at higher J, the spacing between observed lines will become progressively smaller. Consideration of Equation 5-44a shows that accurate measurements of the rotational spectrum of a diatomic molecule can also give an estimate of the fundamental vibrational frequency.

To take into account the anharmonicity of vibration, we expand the potential function for a diatomic molecule as a power series; thus,

$$V = \frac{1}{2}\left(\frac{\partial^2 V}{\partial q^2}\right)_{q=0} q^2 + \frac{1}{3!}\left(\frac{\partial^3 V}{\partial q^3}\right)_{q=0} q^3 + \cdots \qquad (5\text{-}45)$$

where q is the displacement coordinate $(r - r_e)$. The derivative $\dfrac{\partial^2 V}{\partial q^2}$ is the force constant k, and we call $\left(\dfrac{\partial^3 V}{\partial q^3}\right)$ the anharmonicity constant $\omega_e x_e$. Again, applying an approximation procedure known as perturbation theory, we find that the energy of the n'th vibrational state is

$$E_n = \left(v + \frac{1}{2}\right)\omega_e - \omega_e x_e \left(v + \frac{1}{2}\right)^2 \qquad (5\text{-}46)$$

In Equation 5-47, ω_e is the vibrational energy that the molecule would have in the absence of any anharmonicity. In most molecules, anharmonicity affects even the lowest vibrational levels so that the observed fundamental frequency ω_v will be slightly different from ω_e. Also, it is seen that the correction term to the vibrational energy involves the square of the vibrational quantum number. This means, of course, that the correction term will become more important at higher v values. This is the expected result.

Anharmonicity has two important effects on the vibrational spectrum of a diatomic molecule. First of all, it modifies the energy levels so that they are no longer evenly spaced. This means that the transition frequency ω_v that one observes will be a function of the quantum number v for the lowest state involved in that transition. Secondly, anharmonicity modifies the vibrational wave functions, and this results in modified selection rules. For a real diatomic molecule, $\Delta v = \pm\, 2, 3, \ldots$ transitions can be observed, although they are weak. These transitions are called overtones. The $\Delta v = \pm\, 1$ transition is called the fundamental. From the frequencies of the fundamental and various overtones, the anharmonicity constant $\omega_e x_e$ and the extrapolated vibrational frequency ω_e can be calculated.

To gain a feeling for the magnitude of these effects, the student should work Exercises 5-16 and 5-17.

EXERCISE 5-16   The observed frequencies in cm^{-1} of the fundamental and first three overtones of HCl^{35} are 2885.9, 5668.1, 8347.0, and 10,923.1, respectively.   Calculate the true vibrational frequency and the anharmonicity constant for HCl^{35}.

EXERCISE 5-17   Some of the rotational transitions for HCl^{35} are given in the following table

Transition $J \rightarrow J + 1$	ω_R (cm^{-1})
$3 \rightarrow 4$	83.03
$4 \rightarrow 5$	104.1
$5 \rightarrow 6$	124.30
$6 \rightarrow 7$	145.03
$7 \rightarrow 8$	165.51
$8 \rightarrow 9$	185.86
$9 \rightarrow 10$	206.38
$10 \rightarrow 11$	226.50

Derive a general expression for the energy of a rotational transition with the centrifugal stretching constant included. Calculate a value for B and D for HCl from the above data.

To correct for vibration-rotation coupling, the observed rotational constant B is regarded as a function of the vibrational quantum number v. Thus,

$$B_v = B_e - \alpha \left(v + \frac{1}{2} \right) \qquad (5\text{-}47)$$

where α is the vibration rotation coupling constant and B_e is the (hypothetical) rotational constant in the absence of vibration. The quantity B_v is the effective value of the rotational constant in the v'th vibrational state. In a vibration-rotation spectrum, vibration-rotation coupling causes the lines in the R branch to become more closely spaced and the lines in the P branch to become farther apart as J'' increases. An actual vibration-rotation spectrum of the first overtone band of HCl (Figure 5-4) clearly shows these effects.

The expression for the allowed transitions in an actual vibration-rotation spectrum are more complex than indicated by Equations 5-43a, b. Thus,

$$\omega_{v,R} = \omega_v + B'J'(J' + 1) - B''J''(J + 1) \qquad (5\text{-}48)$$

where a different B value must be used for the upper and lower

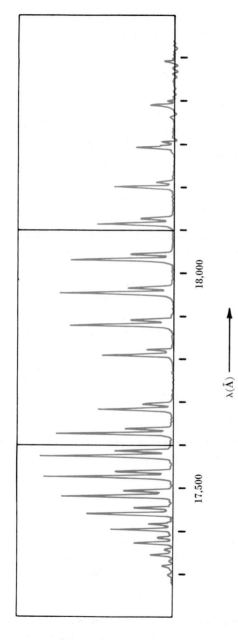

17,500

18,000

$\lambda(\text{Å}) \longrightarrow$

FIG. 5-4 The first overtone band of HCl taken on a Cary model 14 spectrometer. The strong set of lines is from HCl³⁵, the weak set is from HCl³⁷. The unequal spacings between lines shows the effects of vibration-rotation coupling. Each division on the wavelength scale equals 100 Å.

states.   Equation 5-48 leads to the following expressions for the
energy of the lines in the P and R branches.

R branch $\omega_{v,R} = \omega_v + 2B' + (3B' - B'')J''$
$$+ (B' - B'')(J'')^2 \qquad J'' = 0, 1, \ldots \qquad (5\text{-}49a)$$
P branch $\omega_{v,R} = \omega_v - (B' + B'')J''$
$$+ (B' - B'')(J'')^2 \qquad J'' = 1, 2, \ldots \qquad (5\text{-}49b)$$

A consideration of Figure 5-2c shows how B'' and B' can be evaluated from the observed spectrum.   For example, the difference in
energy of $P(2)$ and $R(0)$ gives a spacing $6B''$.

5-7   The Morse function, dissociation energy, and the anharmonicity constant

An empirical equation for the potential energy of a diatomic molecule, which in many cases is quite accurate, was proposed by P. M.
Morse.   It is

$$V = D_e(1 - e^{-\beta q})^2 \qquad (5\text{-}50)$$

where again $q = (r - r_e)$, D_e is the dissociation energy, and β is a
constant which is related to molecular parameters by the relation

$$\beta = \omega_e(2\pi^2 c\mu/D_e h)^{\frac{1}{2}} \qquad (5\text{-}51)$$

It should be noted that for $q = \infty$, $V = D_e$ the dissociation energy.
This dissociation energy differs from the measured dissociation
energy of a molecule, however.   The quantity D_e is the energy
that would be necessary to dissociate the molecule if it could be at
the minimum of the potential energy curve.   Because of the zero
point energy, this is impossible and, therefore,

$$D_e = D_0 + \frac{1}{2}h\nu_0 \qquad (5\text{-}52)$$

where D_0 is the measured dissociation energy.

There is an approximate relationship between the dissociation
energy and the anharmonicity constant that can be derived as
follows: the maximum vibration energy a molecule can have is

$$(E_v)_{\max} = D_e \qquad (5\text{-}53)$$

For large v, the vibrational levels are very closely spaced and, near
dissociation E_v, may be considered a continuous function of v with-

out much error. Converting to wave numbers

$$\epsilon_v = \left(v + \frac{1}{2}\right)\omega_e - \left(v + \frac{1}{2}\right)^2 \omega_e x_e$$

$$\frac{\partial \epsilon_v}{\partial v} = \omega_e - 2\left(v + \frac{1}{2}\right)\omega_e x_e \tag{5-54}$$

At dissociation, the vibrational energy must be a maximum. Therefore

$$\frac{\partial \epsilon_v}{\partial v} = \omega_e - 2\left(v_{max} + \frac{1}{2}\right)\omega_e x_e = 0 \tag{5-55}$$

$$v_{max} = \frac{\omega_e}{2\omega_e x_e} - \frac{1}{2} \tag{5-56}$$

But

$$\epsilon_{max} = D_e = \left(v_{max} + \frac{1}{2}\right)\omega_e - \left(v_{max} + \frac{1}{2}\right)^2 \omega_e x_e \tag{5-57}$$

where D_e is the dissociation energy in cm^{-1}. Substituting Equation 5-56 into 5-57 and rearranging, one obtains

$$D_e = \frac{\omega_e{}^2}{4\omega_e x_e} \tag{5-58}$$

or, in terms of the measured dissociation energy D_0,

$$D_0 = \frac{\omega_e{}^2}{4\omega_e x_e} - \frac{1}{2}\omega_e \tag{5-59}$$

Therefore, from the known dissociation energy and fundamental vibrational frequency, the anharmonicity constant can be estimated or *vice versa*. It should be emphasized that the above treatment is empirical and approximate.

5-8 *Vibrational spectroscopy of complex molecules*

To specify completely the instantaneous state of a molecule containing N atoms, one would have to specify the values of $3N$ coordinates, three coordinates for each atom. It can be said that there is a total of $3N$ degrees of freedom for a molecule containing N atoms. For systems where the potential energy is only a function of the relative positions of the atoms, one can always transform to internal coordinates and separate out the motion of the center of mass. This leaves one with $3N - 3$ internal degrees of freedom and three degrees of freedom for the translational motion of the molecule.

The $3N - 3$ internal degrees of freedom can be further separated into rotational and vibrational degrees of freedom. There will either be two or three rotational degrees of freedom depending on whether the molecule is linear or nonlinear. Thus, for a linear molecule there will be $3N - 5$ vibrational degrees of freedom, whereas for a nonlinear molecule there will be $3N - 6$ vibrational degrees of freedom. For a diatomic molecule (which must be linear), $N = 2$, and there is only one vibrational degree of freedom. This is the displacement coordinate $q = (r - r_e)$ used above. For polyatomic molecules, there will be many vibrational degrees of freedom. The detailed treatment of the vibrational motion of these polyatomic molecules is beyond the scope of this text, but the basic approach to the problem will be summarized.

To a fairly high degree of approximation, it is always possible to separate the translational and rotational motions of a molecule from its vibrational motion. This is done by transforming the $3N$ Cartesian coordinates, with respect to some coordinate system fixed in the laboratory, to a new set of coordinates with respect to a coordinate system whose origin is at the center of mass of the molecule. This molecule-fixed coordinate system is moving with the molecule and is rotating in such a way that the $3N - 6$ coordinates in this moving coordinate system have no displacements which correspond to a translation or a rotation of the molecule. The six coordinates which are needed to account for the original $3N$ can be taken as the three coordinates of the center of mass and the three Eulerian angles describing the configuration of the rotating coordinate system.[9]

The $3N - 6$ ($3N - 5$ for a linear molecule) coordinates which are left may be thought of as vibrational coordinates. If these coordinates are called $q_1, q_2 \cdots q_{3N-6}$, then the potential energy of the molecule for small displacements of the coordinate can be

[9] For a rigorous treatment of this separation, see E. B. Wilson, Jr., J. C. Decius, and P. C. Cross, *Molecular Vibrations*, McGraw-Hill Book Company, Inc., New York (1955) Chapter 11. For a qualitative discussion see Chapter 2.

expanded in a power series

$$V = \sum_{i=1}^{3N-6} \left(\frac{\partial V}{\partial q_i}\right)_0 q_i + \frac{1}{2} \sum_{i,j=1}^{3N-6} \left(\frac{\partial^2 V}{\partial q_i \, \partial q_j}\right)_0 q_i q_j + \text{higher terms}$$

$$(5\text{-}60)$$

In Equation 5-60, the potential energy is taken as zero at the equilibrium nuclear configuration, and all of the derivatives are evaluated at that configuration. Furthermore, at the equilibrium configuration, the potential energy of the system is a minimum, and all of the $\left(\frac{\partial V}{\partial q_i}\right)_0 = 0$. Neglecting terms higher than 2, the potential energy is then

$$V = \frac{1}{2} \sum_{i,j=1}^{3N-6} f_{ij} q_i q_j \qquad (5\text{-}61)$$

where

$$f_{ij} = \left(\frac{\partial^2 V}{\partial q_i \, \partial q_j}\right)_0 \qquad (5\text{-}62)$$

By applying a second coordinate transformation, it is always possible to find a new set of coordinates, called Q_i, that eliminates all of the cross terms in the sum in Equation 5-61. Using these new coordinates, Equation 5-61 becomes

$$V = \frac{1}{2} \sum_{i}^{3N-6} F_i Q_i^2 \qquad (5\text{-}63)$$

In this equation, the potential energy is a sum of terms, each one of which is similar to the harmonic oscillator expression for a one-dimensional oscillator. The F_i are the corresponding force constants. Because the Q_i enable the potential energy to be written in this simple form, they are called normal coordinates, and the modes of vibration which they describe are called normal modes. By deriving the expressions which relate the Q_i to the q_i, these normal modes can be described in terms of various stretch-

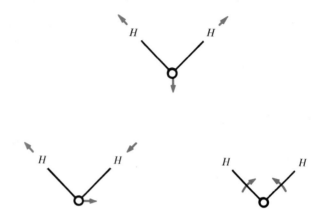

F I G . 5 - 5 *Normal modes of the water molecule.   The frequencies are*
3652, 3756, and 1545 cm^{-1} for the symmetric stretching, asymmetric stretch-
ing and symmetric bending modes, respectively.

ing and bending motions of the atoms.   As an example, the normal
modes for water are shown in Figure 5-5.

It should be emphasized that these normal modes are vibrations
which involve all of the atoms in a molecule.

A complete normal coordinate analysis is only feasible for small
molecules or for larger molecules that have high symmetry.   For
large asymmetric molecules, the number of vibrational degrees of
freedom becomes very large, and an exact analysis of the vibrational motion of such a molecule is impractical, if not impossible.
In the infrared spectrum of such molecules, it is usually possible to
pick out certain group or bond vibrations, however.   These group
or bond vibrations occur at approximately the same frequency
regardless of what the rest of the molecule is like, and the appearance of many bands in an infrared spectrum can be correlated with
the presence of one of these groups or bonds in a molecule.   For
example, a carbonyl group will always give rise to a band in the
infrared between 1650 and 1750 cm^{-1}, and, conversely, the presence
of this band in the spectrum of an unknown compound can be used
to establish the presence of a carbonyl group.   An —OH group
which is not hydrogen bonded occurs at 3600 cm^{-1}.   If the —OH
group is hydrogen bonded, its absorption band occurs at lower
energies (3400–3500 cm^{-1}).   A large amount of data now exists

which correlates IR frequencies with molecular structure, and the interested student may consult other works for more information on this point.[10]

5-9 Raman spectroscopy

In Raman spectroscopy, energy differences between vibrational states are observed so the energetics involved are exactly the same as for infrared spectroscopy. The experimental techniques and selection rules are different, however. In Raman spectroscopy, a beam of monochromatic light, usually visible or ultraviolet light, is passed through a sample, and the frequency of the light scattered at right angles to the incident beam is studied. The theory of Raman scattering is quite complex and will not be discussed here.[11] The important thing about Raman spectroscopy is that the intensity of a Raman line depends not on a change in dipole moment upon vibration, but upon a change in polarizability on vibration. Many times it is possible to observe lines in the Raman spectra of a molecule that are infrared forbidden.

Experimentally, Raman spectroscopy has been very difficult. The basic problem has been that the Raman lines have too small an intensity to be observed. With the development of the laser to give high incident light intensities, a sensitive commercial Raman spectrograph has been developed. This may mean that Raman spectroscopy will soon come into more general use.

5-10 Summary

1. Using the rigid-rotor approximation, the allowed rotational states of a diatomic molecule were found to have energy $\omega_R = BJ(J + 1)$ where J is the rotational quantum number and B is a parameter determined by the molecule.

2. The vibrational states of a diatomic molecule were found to have energy $\omega_v = (v + \frac{1}{2})\omega_0$ where v is the vibrational quantum number.

---

[10] See, for example, L. J. Bellamy, *The Infrared Spectra of Complex Molecules*, John Wiley & Sons, Inc., New York (1954).

[11] The interested student may see G. Herzberg, *Spectra of Diatomic Molecules*, D. Van Nostrand, Inc., Princeton, New Jersey (1950) pages 82 ff.

3. Rotational transitions are only allowed if $\Delta J = \pm 1$, $\Delta m = 0$, ± 1. Within the context of the harmonic oscillator approximation, vibrational transitions are only allowed if $\Delta v = \pm 1$. These restrictions on allowed transitions are called selection rules.

4. In an infrared spectrum, transitions take place between a number of rotational sublevels in the initial and final vibrational states. This leads to sharp vibration-rotation spectra for light diatomic molecules and vibrational band spectra for heavier diatomic and polyatomic molecules.

5. The harmonic-oscillator, rigid-rotor energy expression was corrected for centrifugal stretching, vibrational anharmonicity, and vibration-rotation coupling.

6. A brief discussion of vibrations in polyatomic molecules and Raman spectroscopy was given.

7. The student should be familiar with the terms rotational degeneracy, average internuclear distance, equilibrium internuclear distance, fundamental frequency, overtones, vibrational zero point energy, Morse function, extrapolated dissociation energy, measured dissociation energy, normal mode, and dipole moment.

Chapter 6

THE ELECTRONIC

STRUCTURE OF

ATOMS

IT WAS pointed out in Chapter 3 that the Bohr theory could account for the spectrum of the hydrogen atom, but that it failed to account for the properties of more complex atoms. In this chapter, we will use the postulates given in Chapter 3 to calculate the allowed energies of a hydrogen atom. The structure of more complex atoms will then be discussed in the light of the hydrogen atom results.

6-1 The hydrogen atom and the hydrogen-like ions

It will be convenient to treat the hydrogen atom and the hydrogen-like ions, He^+, Li^{2+}, etc., in one group because they differ from one another only in their nuclear charge. These atoms and ions have a nucleus of charge $+ Ze$ and mass M and one electron of charge $- e$ and mass m. The symbol e represents the electronic charge.

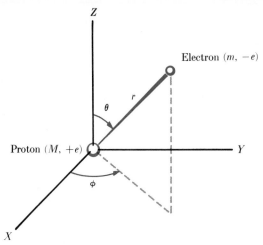

FIG. 6-1 *Quantities used in the discussion of the hydrogen atom. The origin should be at the center of mass, but little error is made if it is put at the proton.*

The potential energy of the system is the attractive energy between the electron and the nucleus. Thus

$$V = -\frac{Ze^2}{r} \qquad (6\text{-}1)$$

where r is the distance between the nucleus and the electron. Since the potential energy is a function only of the internal coordinates, we can immediately separate the coordinates of the center of mass and only concern ourselves with the internal motion of the system.[1] The appropriate Hamiltonian operator is

$$\hat{\mathcal{H}} = -\frac{\hbar^2}{2\mu}\nabla^2 - \frac{Ze^2}{r} \qquad (6\text{-}2)$$

[1] The origin of the coordinate system in Figure 6-1 should be at the center of mass. Since the proton mass is 1846 times the electron mass, the origin can be placed at the proton. In many discussions of the hydrogen atom, the electron mass m is used instead of the reduced mass. Again, very little error is introduced since $\mu = (1846/1847)m$.

To find the allowed energies for the hydrogen atom, the eigenvalue equation

$$\hat{\mathcal{H}}\Psi = E\Psi \qquad (6\text{-}3)$$

must be solved. Since this is a centrosymmetric problem, it will be most convenient to use spherical polar coordinates. Substituting the appropriate form for ∇^2 into Equation 6-3,[2] one obtains the rather formidable looking equation

$$\frac{1}{r^2}\frac{\partial}{\partial r}\left(r^2\frac{\partial\Psi}{\partial r}\right) + \frac{1}{r^2\sin\theta}\frac{\partial}{\partial\theta}\left(\sin\theta\frac{\partial\Psi}{\partial\theta}\right) + \frac{1}{r^2\sin^2\theta}\frac{\partial^2\Psi}{\partial\phi^2}$$
$$+ \frac{2\mu}{\hbar^2}\left(E + \frac{Ze^2}{r}\right)\Psi = 0 \qquad (6\text{-}4)$$

We will follow the same procedure for solving this equation that was followed for the problem of rotational motion. That is, a solution of the form

$$\Psi = R(r)T(\theta)U(\phi) \qquad (6\text{-}5)$$

will be sought. After straightforward algebraic manipulation similar to that used in Chapter 5, the variables in Equation 6-4 can be separated and one obtains three single variable equations.

$$\frac{1}{U}\frac{d^2U}{d\phi^2} = -m^2 \qquad (6\text{-}6)$$

$$\frac{1}{\sin\theta}\frac{d}{d\theta}\left(\sin\theta\frac{dT}{d\theta}\right) - \frac{m^2}{\sin^2\theta}T + \lambda T = 0 \qquad (6\text{-}7)$$

$$\frac{1}{r^2}\frac{d}{dr}\left(r^2\frac{dR}{dr}\right) + \left[\frac{2\mu}{\hbar^2}\left(E + \frac{Ze^2}{r}\right) - \frac{\lambda}{r^2}\right]R = 0 \qquad (6\text{-}8)$$

where the constants m and λ are introduced in the separation procedure (see Section 5-1 if you have forgotten the details of the separation of variables argument). Equations 6-6 and 6-7 are exactly the same as the equations obtained in the discussion of rotational motion, and their solutions have already been given in Section 5-1. In the T function for electronic motion, the quantum number l is used instead of J, however. Thus, the constant $\lambda = l(l + 1)$.

---

[2] The quantity ∇^2 and the volume element $d\tau$ can be transformed to any system of coordinates making use of arguments based on vector analysis. See, for example, II, page 363 ff.

Equation 6-8 can be manipulated to get it in the form of another equation of classical physics, the associated Laguerre equation.[3] For our purposes, we need only know that solutions to Equation 6-8, that are everywhere finite, single valued, and have integrable squares, exist only for the conditions that

$$n^2 = -\frac{Z^2 \mu e^4}{2\hbar^2 E}, \qquad n = 1, 2, 3, 4 \cdots \qquad (6\text{-}9a)$$

and

$$l \leqq n - 1 \qquad (6\text{-}9b)$$

This means that the energy of the electron in a hydrogen atom or hydrogen-like ion is restricted to the values

$$E_n = -\frac{Z^2 \mu e^4}{2\hbar^2} \qquad (6\text{-}10)$$

This is the same as the expression obtained from Bohr theory.

The R functions obtained as solutions of Equation 6-8 are called radial wave functions. Their detailed form depends on the values of the quantum numbers n and l. Some of these radial wave functions are given in Table 6-1.

TABLE 6-1 SOME NORMALIZED RADIAL WAVE FUNCTIONS FOR THE HYDROGEN ATOM. THE NUMBERS IN PARENTHESES ARE THE VALUES OF n AND l. THE QUANTITY a_0 IS THE RADIUS OF THE FIRST BOHR ORBIT, 0.529 Å

$$R(1, 0) = 2 \left(\frac{Z}{a_0}\right)^{\frac{3}{2}} e^{-\sigma}$$

$$R(2, 0) = \left(\frac{Z}{2a_0}\right)^{\frac{3}{2}} (2 - \sigma)e^{-\sigma/2}$$

$$R(2, 1) = 3^{-\frac{1}{2}} \left(\frac{Z}{2a_0}\right)^{\frac{3}{2}} \sigma e^{-\sigma/2} \qquad \sigma = \frac{Zr}{a_0}$$

$$R(3, 0) = \frac{2}{27} \left(\frac{Z}{3a_0}\right)^{\frac{3}{2}} (27 - 18\sigma + 2\sigma^2)e^{-\sigma/3}$$

$$R(3, 1) = \frac{1}{81\sqrt{3}} \left(\frac{2Z}{a_0}\right)^{\frac{3}{2}} (6 - \sigma)\sigma e^{-\sigma/3}$$

[3] For specific details see **I**, pages 77 ff. or **II**, pages 63 ff.

EXERCISE 6-1 Show by direct substitution that R (1, 0) and $R(2, 1)$ are solutions of Equation 6-8.

The total wave function for the hydrogen atom is the product of the suitably normalized radial and angular functions, R and TU. Thus

$$\Psi(n, l, m) = R(n, l)T(l, m)U(m) \tag{6-11}$$

where the explicit dependence on quantum numbers is indicated in parentheses. It can be seen from Equation 6-11 that the allowed states of the hydrogen atom, sometimes called hydrogen-like orbitals, depend on three quantum numbers, n, l, and m. A brief discussion of the significance of each of these quantum numbers will now be given.

The quantum number n is called the principal quantum number. For the hydrogen atom and the hydrogen-like ions, this quantum number determines the energy (for more complex atoms, the energy will also depend on l) and the total number of nodes in the wave function. There will always be $n - 1$ nodes in the total wave function if the node at infinity is neglected.

The quantum number l is called the azimuthal quantum number. It is the quantum number associated with the total angular momentum of the electron. In quantum mechanical language, the functions $T(l, m)U(m)$ are eigenfunctions of the operator $\hat{L}^2$ with eigenvalue $l(l + 1)\hbar^2$. That is

$$\hat{L}^2T(l, m)U(l, m) = l(l + 1)\hbar^2T(l, m)U(l, m) \tag{6-12}$$

The number l is restricted to integral values between 0 and $n - 1$, and it gives the number of nodes in the angular part of the wave function.

The quantum number m is called the magnetic quantum number. It is associated with the component of angular momentum along a specific axis in the atom, usually called the Z axis. Since atoms are spherically symmetric, there is no way to define a specific axis unless the atom is placed in an electric or magnetic field. The quantum number m does not have any effect on the properties of the hydrogen atom unless such fields are present. It does determine the degeneracy of a state, however, since there are $2l + 1$ values of m for a state with quantum number l. The number m is restricted to the values $l, l - 1, \ldots -1 + 1, -l$. The functions $U(m)$ are eigenfunctions of the operator $\hat{L}_z$. Thus

$$\hat{L}_z U(m) = m\hbar U(m) \tag{6-13}$$

In the presence of a magnetic field, the states corresponding to different values of m will have different energies. This splitting of states with different m values by a magnetic field is called the Zeeman effect.

The allowed wave functions for the hydrogen atom are called atomic orbitals. These orbitals are given names according to their values of n and l. The nomenclature for l is: $0 \to s$, $1 \to p$, $2 \to d$, $3 \to f$, etc. The $1s$ orbital is the function $\Psi(1, 0)$. A $3d$ orbital is the function $\Psi(3, 2)$. The quantum number m is not usually specified in this nomenclature and only affects the degeneracy. Thus, there are three $2p$ orbitals, five $3d$ orbitals, etc. When it is necessary to specify the value of m it can be done by adding a subscript to the orbital symbol. Thus, the $2p_{-1}$ orbital is the $2p$ orbital with $m = -1$ or the function $\Psi(2, 1, -1)$.

6-2   The physical significance of hydrogen-like orbitals

It is important that the physical significance of the hydrogen atom solutions be understood because, as will be seen later, these solutions form the building blocks for the solution to more complex problems. The significance of these solutions arises from Postulate I, which states that the function $\Psi^*\Psi \, d\tau$ represents a probability. We will first discuss the radial functions $R(n, l)$ in this context.

There are two ways to discuss the radial functions. The first way makes use of a plot of the function R^2 *versus* r/a_0, the distance from the nucleus in atomic units. Such a plot is shown for several radial functions in Figure 6-2. This quantity $R^2 \, dr$ only has significance for a fixed value of the angular variables θ and ϕ. Fixing θ and ϕ determines a line beginning at the origin. The function $R^2 \, dr$ then is proportional to the probability of finding the electron in a small unit of length dr at different locations along this line. Figure 6-2 shows that, for s orbitals, the electron has a nonvanishing probability of being at the nucleus, whereas for all other orbitals, the value of R^2 at the nucleus is zero. This fact will be

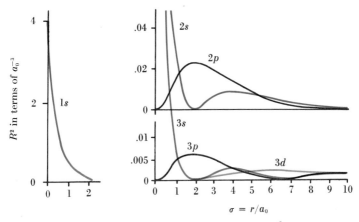

FIG. 6-2 *Plots of the radial probability density, R^2, as a function of the distance r from the nucleus for several atomic orbitals. Note the change in density scale for the different orbitals. Note that R^2 is nonzero at the nucleus only for s orbitals. This fact will be important in the discussion of electron spin resonance in Chapter 9. (Reprinted by permission from K. S. Pitzer, Quantum Chemistry, Prentice-Hall, Inc., Englewood Cliffs, New Jersey, 1953, p. 52.)*

important when electron magnetic resonance spectroscopy is discussed in Chapter 9.

A second way to discuss the significance of the radial wave functions is to integrate over the angular variables and plot the resulting function, F. Thus, we wish to find

$$F = \int_0^\pi \int_0^{2\pi} R^2 r^2 \sin \theta dr \, d\theta \, d\phi$$
$$= 4\pi r^2 R^2 \, dr \tag{6-14}$$

The function $4\pi r^2 R^2$ is called the radial distribution function and gives the probability of finding the electron in a spherical shell of thickness dr at a distance r away from the nucleus. Plots of the radial distribution function for several orbitals are shown in Figure 6-3.

Some other features of the hydrogenic wave functions which should be noted from Figure 6-2 and 6-3 are:

1. There are no nodes in the radial part of the $2p$ function. Since there must be one node in the total wave function, it must be in the angular part of the function. Similar arguments should be considered about the nodes in the other functions.

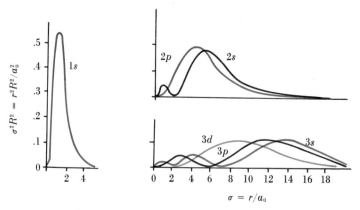

FIG. 6-3 *Plots of the radial distribution function, $4\pi r^2 R^2$, as a function of the distance r from the nucleus for several atomic orbitals. Note that the probability of finding a 2s electron within one Bohr radius of the nucleus is greater than the probability of finding a 2p electron in the same region. This shows why the 1s electrons are more effective in screening 2p electrons from the nuclear charge than 2s electrons. The result is that 2s and 2p orbitals will no longer have the same energy in atoms with more than one electron. (Reprinted by permission from K. S. Pitzer, Quantum Chemistry, Prentice-Hall, Inc., Englewood Cliffs, New Jersey, 1953, p. 52.)*

2. An electron in a 2s orbital has a higher probability of being close to the nucleus than an electron in a 2p orbital. We will use this fact to rationalize the difference in energy between 2s and 2p orbitals in many electron atoms.

Several exercises will be used to illustrate some features of the radial wave functions.

EXERCISE 6-2 Calculate the most probable value of r for an electron in a hydrogen 1s orbital.

EXERCISE 6-3 For an electron in a 1s orbital of a hydrogen atom, calculate: $\langle r \rangle$, and $\langle r^2 \rangle^{\frac{1}{2}}$ (root mean square value of r) and $\langle 1/r \rangle$.

EXERCISE 6-4 Calculate the probability of finding an electron in a 1s orbital outside of the first Bohr orbit (a_0).

A problem of representation arises when discussing the angular dependence of atomic orbitals. The student is probably familiar with the geometrical pictures (such as Figure 6-4a and b) in elementary textbooks. These pictures can be called "charge cloud" drawings. From these pictures, it is easy to jump to the conclusion that the electron is a smeared out charge with the shape shown. This conclusion is misleading, however, for the electron is not a smeared out charge. A more rigorous interpretation of these pictures can be made if one regards the outline of the charge cloud as a line on a contour map. The significance of the charge cloud drawings is that, if an experimentalist could make a large number of measurements of the position of the electron, 90% (or some other chosen fraction) of them would fall inside the contour line. Also, the probability of finding an electron inside this surface is not uniform. This probability will vary along any line starting at the origin as the function $R^2\,dr$ varies. In describing the angular functions, one has the option of either depicting the function $TU(l, m)$ or the function $[TU(l, m)]^2$. The difference (besides slight differences in shape) is that the former function will have different signs in different regions of space whereas the latter func-

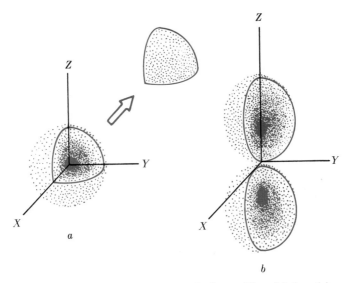

FIG. 6-4 *Angular dependence of hydrogen-like orbitals. (a) 1s orbital; (b) 2p$_z$ orbital. The contour surfaces shown represent a volume wherein the probability of finding the electron will be 0.9.*

tion will be everywhere positive. We will choose to depict $TU(l, m)$ in most cases because the sign of the wave function is useful in discussing symmetry and in the evaluation of certain integrals which will occur in later sections. The student should keep in mind that the sign of the wave function has no physical significance. It is the quantity $[TU(l, m)]^2$ that is related to a probability, and this function is everywhere positive.

With these remarks in mind, some description of the angular dependence of hydrogen-like orbitals will be given. The function $[TU(0, 0)]$ is just a constant (see Table 5-1). The function has the same value regardless of the value of θ and ϕ and, therefore, the electron distribution is spherically symmetrical as shown in Figure 6-4a. The $+$ sign indicates that the function $TU(0, 0)$ is everywhere positive.

A diagram representing a $2p_z$ orbital is shown in Figure 6-4b. This function is

$$TU(1, 0) = \left(\frac{3}{4\pi}\right)^{\frac{1}{2}} \cos \theta \qquad (6\text{-}15)$$

The orbital characterized by this function will have its maximum value at $\theta = 0$ and $\theta = 180°$, and will vanish at $\theta = 90°$. The function is positive on one side of the XY plane and negative on the other side. Whenever an orbital has this property, the orbital is said to be antisymmetric with respect to the XY plane.

Making a drawing of the functions $TU(1, 1)$ and $TU(1, -1)$ presents a problem because both functions have an imaginary part. These functions are

$$TU(1, \pm 1) = \left(\frac{3}{8\pi}\right)^{\frac{1}{2}} \sin \theta e^{\pm i\phi}$$

The functions $|TU(1, 1)|^2$ and $|TU(1, -1)|^2$ are real, however, and are

$$|TU(1, 1)|^2 = |TU(1 - 1)|^2 = \frac{3}{8\pi} \sin^2 \theta \qquad (6\text{-}16)$$

A consideration of Equation 6-16 shows that both functions have the same spatial distribution, and that the spatial distribution has

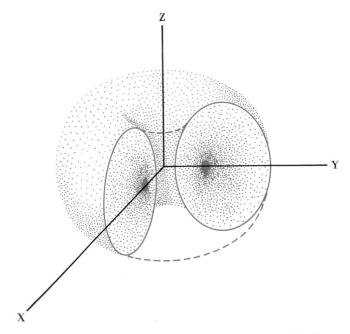

FIG. 6-5   *The angular dependence of the functions $|TU(1,$
$\pm 1)|^2$.   It should be noticed that both functions have the same
probability density.   They are different because the electron in
$TU(1, 1)$ can be thought of as moving counterclockwise about
the Z axis whereas an electron in $TU(1, -1)$ is moving clockwise about the Z axis.*

a maximum in the XY plane ($\theta = 90°$), and is zero along the Z axis
($\theta = 0$).   A picture representing this electron distribution is shown
in Figure 6-5.   In the interpretations of the physical significance
of these functions, it must be kept in mind that the functions
$TU(1, \pm 1)$ are eigenfunctions of $\hat{L}_z$ with eigenvalues $\pm \hbar$, respectively.   In $TU(1, +1)$, therefore, the electron can be thought of
as moving counterclockwise about the Z axis whereas in
$TU(1, -1)$, the electron is moving clockwise.

It is a general property of degenerate wave functions [as
$TU(1, \pm 1)$ are in the absence of fields] that any linear combination of the members of the degenerate set is also an acceptable

wave function and has the same energy as the original functions. We, therefore, construct the two new functions

$$\Psi_1 = \frac{1}{2}[TU(1, 1) + TU(1, -1)] = A \sin \theta \cos \phi \qquad (6\text{-}17a)$$

$$\Psi_2 = \frac{1}{2i}[TU(1, 1) - TU(1, -1)] = A \sin \theta \sin \phi \qquad (6\text{-}17b)$$

where A is the appropriate normalizing factor. These are the functions called p_x and p_y orbitals. They have the same shape as the p_z orbital shown in Figure 6-4b, except that the maximum in the electron density is along the X and Y axes, respectively. These $2p$ orbitals are shown schematically in Figure 6-6. It should be noted that, in this representation, all three p orbitals have a nodal plane perpendicular to the axis of symmetry of the electron distribution.

EXERCISE 6-5   Show that Equations 6-17a and b are true.

A similar procedure can be used for drawing electron distribution pictures of d orbitals except that there will be five orbitals and each will have two nodal planes.

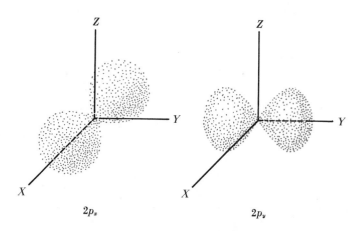

$2p_x$ $2p_y$

FIG. 6-6   *Probability contour drawings for the $2p_x$ and $2p_y$ orbitals. The relative electron density inside the surfaces goes as the radial distribution function for a $2p$ orbital.*

6-3   The spectrum of atomic hydrogen: selection rules

The formula giving the energy of the observed transitions in the hydrogen atom has already been given in Chapter 3. These transitions are now interpreted as transitions between the allowed states of the hydrogen atom, $\Psi(n, l, m)$. We have not said anything about selection rules, however. It will be shown below that these depend on the angular part of the functions Ψ.

The selection rules derived below hold true for all atoms that have only one electron outside of a closed shell—the alkali metals, for example. The selection rules also hold for more complex atoms provided they are interpreted in terms of the eigenvalues with respect to the operator for total electronic angular momentum of the atom. The calculation of these angular momentum eigenvalues is discussed in Section 6-10.

The instantaneous dipole moment of a hydrogen atom is $e\mathbf{r}$ where $\mathbf{r}$ is the vector from the nucleus to the electron. The transition moment is then

$$\mathbf{R} = \langle \Psi^*(n', l', m') | e\mathbf{r} | \Psi(n'', l'', m'') \rangle \tag{6-18}$$

where the primes and double primes have their usual significance. To evaluate this integral, each component must be evaluated separately. Thus Equation 6-17 becomes the three equations,

$$R_x = e \int_0^\infty \int_0^\pi \int_0^{2\pi} \Psi^*(n', l', m')(r \sin\theta \cos\phi) \\ \Psi(n'', l'', m'') r^2 \sin\theta \, dr \, d\theta \, d\phi \tag{6-19a}$$

$$R_y = e \int_0^\infty \int_0^\pi \int_0^{2\pi} (\Psi^*)'(\Psi)'' r \sin\theta \sin\phi \, r^2 \sin\theta \, dr \, d\theta \, d\phi \tag{6-19b}$$

$$R_z = e \int_0^\infty \int_0^\pi \int_0^{2\pi} (\Psi^*)'(\Psi)'' r \cos\theta \, r^2 \sin\theta \, dr \, d\theta \, d\phi \tag{6-19c}$$

These integrals may be evaluated for general Legendre polynomials to obtain the selection rules: [4]

$$\Delta l = \pm 1$$
$$\Delta m = 0, \pm 1 \tag{6-20}$$
$$\Delta n\text{—no restriction}$$

---

[4] See **I**, pages 102–104 or **II**, pages 59 ff. for the recurrence relations necessary to evaluate these integrals.

We will not go through this mathematical procedure; rather, several exercises will be given to illustrate the use of these selection rules.

EXERCISE 6-6 Show that, for a hydrogen atom, the transition $\Psi_{1s} \rightarrow \Psi_{2s}$ is not allowed.

EXERCISE 6-7 Show that the transition $\Psi_{1s} \rightarrow \Psi_{3p}$ is allowed.

EXERCISE 6-8 What is the ionization potential of an electron in a $1s$ orbital of hydrogen?

6-4 Atomic units

To save writing down a lot of constants, it is customary to use atomic units in atomic and molecular calculations. These units are as follows:

$$\text{Unit of length: } a_0 \text{(radius of first Bohr orbit)} = \frac{\hbar^2}{me^2} = 0.529 \text{ Å}$$

$$\text{Unit of energy: } H \text{(Hartree)} = \frac{e^2}{a_0} = 27.2 \text{ ev}$$

In terms of atomic units, the energy of a hydrogen atom in its ground state is $- 13.6$ ev or

$$E = -\frac{me^4}{2\hbar^2} = -\frac{1}{2}\frac{e^2}{a_0} = -\frac{1}{2} H$$

The Hamiltonian operator in atomic units can be derived from the corresponding operator in cgs units by changing $-\frac{\hbar^2}{2m}\nabla^2$ to $-\frac{1}{2}\nabla^2$, and by changing the potential energy terms from Ze^2/r to Z/r. To see how this comes about, consider the Hamiltonian for the hydrogen atom

$$\hat{\mathcal{H}}(\text{cgs}) = -\frac{\hbar^2}{2m}\nabla^2 - \frac{Ze^2}{r}$$

We now let $r(\text{cm}) = a_0 r'(\text{au})$, and take advantage of the fact that

$$\frac{\partial^2}{\partial r^2} = \frac{1}{a_0^2}\frac{\partial^2}{\partial (r')^2}$$

Making these substitutions, the Hamiltonian in cgs units is converted to the Hamiltonian in au multiplied by e^2/a_0.

$$\hat{\mathfrak{K}}(\text{cgs}) = \frac{\hbar^2}{2m}\frac{1}{a_0{}^2}\nabla^2(\text{au}) - \frac{Ze^2}{a_0 r'}$$

$$= \left[\frac{1}{2}\nabla^2 - \frac{Z}{r'}\right]\frac{e^2}{a_0} = \hat{\mathfrak{K}}(\text{au})(e^2/a_0)$$

The atomic unit of angular momentum is $\hbar$. This means that the quantum numbers l and m are angular momenta in atomic units. For example, the function $e^{-2i\phi}$ is an eigenfunction of $\hat{L}_z$ with eigenvalue -2.

6-5   The helium atom

Now that the quantum mechanical problem of the hydrogen atom has been solved, the next step is to find the allowed energy states and wave functions for more complex atoms. The simplest of these is the helium atom. The helium atom contains a nucleus with charge $+2$ and two electrons which, for convenience, will be designated 1 and 2 (see Figure 6-7). Using our common

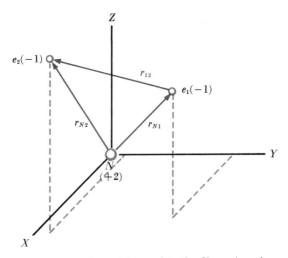

FIG. 6-7 *Quantities used in the discussion of the helium atom. The quantities in parentheses are the charges on the particles.*

procedure, we can immediately write down the appropriate Hamiltonian operator, which, in atomic units, is

$$\hat{\mathcal{H}} = -\frac{1}{2}[\nabla^2(1) + \nabla^2(2)] - \frac{2}{r_{N1}} - \frac{2}{r_{N2}} + \frac{1}{r_{12}} \tag{6-21}$$

The term in brackets contains the kinetic energy operators for electrons 1 and 2, respectively, and the remainder is the potential energy for the system. Note that there are three terms in the potential energy. These correspond to the nuclear attraction for electron 1, the nuclear attraction for electron 2, and the mutual repulsion between the two electrons, respectively.

One now has to solve the eigenvalue equation

$$\hat{\mathcal{H}}\Psi = E\Psi \tag{6-22}$$

for $\hat{\mathcal{H}}$ given in Equation 6-21, and the problem is completed. Unfortunately, the task is frustrated at this point because Equation 6-22 is now insoluble. That is, there are no known analytic functions Ψ which, when operated on by the Hamiltonian operator of Equation 6-21, will give a number times the function back again. The failure to obtain solutions to Equation 6-22 is due to the presence of the $1/r_{12}$ term in the Hamiltonian. This term is called the electron repulsion or electron correlation term, and much present research in quantum chemistry is devoted to trying to find a satisfactory way to take this term into account. This problem is called the "electron correlation" problem.[5]

Since the $1/r_{12}$ term is the bottleneck in the solution, the first and most naïve approach to the problem is to leave this term out. The effects of electron repulsion can then be partially taken into account by introducing an effective nuclear charge. This effective nuclear charge is the nuclear charge minus the screening charge of the other electron. We, thus, write the approximate Hamiltonian

$$\hat{\mathcal{H}}_0 = -\frac{1}{2}(\nabla_1{}^2 + \nabla_2{}^2) - \frac{Z'}{r_{N1}} - \frac{Z'}{r_{N2}} \tag{6-23}$$

[5] There has been some confusion about the meaning of the term electron correlation. Many quantum mechanical methods lead to wave functions that include an *electron repulsion effect*. These wave functions are still inadequate because they do not include instantaneous correlation of the electrons. The commonly accepted definition of the "electron correlation energy" is the difference in energy between a wave function taking the average electron repulsion into account and one taking both the average and instantaneous correlations into account.

where the value of Z' is the effective nuclear charge to be determined later.

It should be noted that the Hamiltonian in Equation 6-22 can be written in the form

$$\hat{\mathcal{K}}_0 = \hat{h}_0(1) + \hat{h}_0(2)$$

where $\hat{h}_0(1)$ depends only on the coordinates of electron 1, and $\hat{h}_0(2)$ depends only on the coordinates of electron 2. Recalling our previous discussion at the end of Chapter 3 about the separation of variables, we know that a solution to the equation

$$\hat{\mathcal{K}}_0 \Psi_0 = E_0 \Psi_0 \qquad (6\text{-}24)$$

can be found using

$$\Psi = \phi_0(1)\phi_0(2) \qquad (6\text{-}25)$$

We know further that the total energy E is the sum of the two "one-electron" energies ϵ_1 and ϵ_2. Substituting Equation 6-25 into 6-24 and separating variables, one obtains two identical equations

$$\hat{h}_0(1)\phi_0(1) = -\frac{1}{2}\nabla_1^2\phi_0(1) - \frac{Z'}{r_{N1}}\phi_0(1) = \epsilon_1{}^0\phi_0(1) \qquad (6\text{-}26a)$$

$$\hat{h}_0(2)\phi_0(2) = -\frac{1}{2}\nabla_2^2\phi_0(2) - \frac{Z'}{r_{N2}}\phi_0(2) = \epsilon_2{}^0\phi_0(2) \qquad (6\text{-}26b)$$

These are the same as the eigenvalue equations for a hydrogen atom with nuclear charge Z', however, and the solutions to these are known. Thus, we can immediately write

$$\phi_0(1) = R(n,\,l)\,T(l,\,m)\,U(m)(1)$$
$$\phi_0(2) = R(n,\,l)\,T(l,\,m)\,U(m)(2)$$

and the energies in atomic units are

$$\epsilon_1 = -\frac{Z'^2}{2}\left(\frac{1}{n_1{}^2}\right)$$

$$\epsilon_2 = -\frac{Z'^2}{2}\left(\frac{1}{n_2{}^2}\right)$$

$$E_0 = -\frac{Z'^2}{2}\left(\frac{1}{n_1{}^2} + \frac{1}{n_2{}^2}\right)$$

At this level of approximation, the energy of the helium atom in its ground, or lowest energy, state ($n_1 = n_2 = 1$) is

$$E_0 = 2Z'^2E(H) \tag{6-27}$$

where $E(H)$ is the energy of a hydrogen atom in its ground state, $-\frac{1}{2}H$ or -13.6 ev.

There are two ways in which calculated results may be compared with experimental results for helium. One is to compare values of the total binding energy, E_{He}. The other is to compare values of the first ionization potential (IP). The first ionization potential is equal to the energy of a helium atom minus the energy of the helium positive ion, He^+. The energy of He^+ can be calculated exactly since it is a hydrogen-like ion. Thus,

$$IP = -(E_{He} - E_{He^+}) \tag{6-28}$$

and

$$E_{He^+} = 4E(H) = -2H = -54.4 \text{ ev} \tag{6-29}$$

The experimental values of E_{He} and IP are $-2.905H$ (-78.98 ev) and $0.904H$ (24.6 ev), respectively.

These experimental values will now be compared with values calculated using different levels of approximation.

The first calculation uses the approximate wave function, 6-25, with $Z' = Z = 2$, the actual nuclear charge, and the approximate Hamiltonian to calculate the expectation value of the energy. Thus, using Equation 6-27,

$$\langle E \rangle_0 = 2(4)E(H) = -4H = -109 \text{ ev}$$

and

$$IP = -(-4H + 2H) = 2H = 54.4 \text{ ev}$$

It can be seen that the energy is in error by 38%, the ionization potential by 100%. This calculation is not very satisfying.

The next step is to use the approximate wave function 6-25 with $Z = Z' = 2$, and the exact Hamiltonian 6-23, to calculate the expectation value of the energy $\langle E \rangle$. The student may verify that this leads to

$$\langle E \rangle = 2Z^2E(H) + \left(\Psi_0 \left| \frac{1}{r_{12}} \right| \Psi_0 \right) \tag{6-30}$$

The second integral is algebraically difficult to evaluate, and we will give its value without further discussion. It is

$$\left(\Psi_0 \left| \frac{1}{r_{12}} \right| \Psi_0\right) = \frac{5}{8} Z' \tag{6-31}$$

where Z' is the nuclear charge used in the functions $\phi_0(1)$ and $\phi_0(2)$. Using $Z' = 2$, one then obtains

$$\langle E \rangle = -4H + \frac{5}{4} H = -\frac{11}{4} H = -74.8 \text{ ev}$$

$$IP = -(-74.8 + 54.4) = 20.4 \text{ ev}$$

These are much more satisfactory answers, being off by only 5% and 17%, respectively. It can be seen that the ionization potential is a much more sensitive criterion of the "goodness" of our calculation than is the total binding energy.

The final calculation which can be done using a wave function of the form of Equation 6-25 is the calculation of $\langle E \rangle$ using the exact Hamiltonian, and an orbital function ϕ_0 with an effective nuclear charge Z'. Thus, the function ϕ_0 is

$$\phi_0 = A e^{-Z'r/a_0} \tag{6-32}$$

The effective nuclear charge will then be chosen to give the best possible value of $\langle E \rangle$. Carrying out the calculation, it can be shown that in atomic units [6]

$$\langle E \rangle = (Z')^2 - 2ZZ' + \frac{5}{8} Z' \tag{6-33}$$

It will be shown in Chapter 7 that, to find the best value of the energy that can be obtained from a function containing one or more arbitrary parameters, the parameters are chosen so as to make the energy a minimum. To calculate the value of Z' which minimizes $\langle E \rangle$, therefore, we calculate

$$\frac{dE}{dZ'} = 2Z' - 2Z + \frac{5}{8} = 0$$

$$Z' = Z - \frac{5}{16}$$

[6] **II,** page 105.

Using this result in Equation 6-33 gives

$$\langle E \rangle = \left(Z - \frac{5}{16} \right)^2 - 2Z \left(Z - \frac{5}{16} \right) + \frac{5}{8} \left(Z - \frac{5}{16} \right)$$

which, for $Z = 2$, gives

$$\langle E \rangle = - \left(\frac{27}{16} \right)^2 = - 77.45 \text{ ev}$$

and

$$\text{IP} = 23.05 \text{ ev}$$

These values differ from the experimental ones by only 2% and 6%, respectively. This final calculation is the best that can be done using the independent electron approximation and a simple exponential function with the form of Equation 6-25.

It is interesting to note that, at this level of approximation, each electron is screened from the full nuclear charge of $+ 2$ by $\frac{5}{16}$. This latter number is a measure of the screening effect that the average distribution of one electron has upon the nuclear charge "seen" by the other electron.

A great deal of effort has been spent on improving calculations for the helium atom. In the best calculation, the interelectron distance is explicitly included in the wave function, and the binding energy can be calculated to greater accuracy than it can be measured.[7]

6-6   *Orbital angular momentum*

We have already seen how eigenfunctions of the operators $\hat{L}^2$ and $\hat{L}_z$ arise in the cases of molecular rotation and atomic structure. These are just two examples of the important role which angular momentum plays in quantum mechanics. In this section, the subject of orbital angular momentum is discussed in some detail. This treatment serves a dual purpose in that it gives the student some familiarity with quantum mechanical operator algebra, and it lays the groundwork for the discussion of electron spin in Section 6-7.

[7] See **III**, pages 289 ff. for more discussion of the helium atom.

Before proceeding, we need to discuss some additional quantum mechanical theorems. These theorems will then be used to simplify our discussions of angular momentum.

Theorem I.   Eigenfunctions belonging to different eigenvalues of a Hermitian operator are orthogonal.

Proof: Let $\hat{F}$ be a Hermitian operator with eigenfunctions Ψ_i and Ψ_j such that

$$\hat{F}\Psi_i = f_i\Psi_i \qquad \hat{F}\Psi_j = f_j\Psi_j \qquad\qquad (6\text{-}34a \text{ and } b)$$

and our postulate is that $f_i \neq f_j$.   We next perform the following operations

1. Multiply Equation 6-34a from the left by $\Psi_j{}^*$ and integrate.

2. Take the complex conjugate of Equation 6-34b, multiply from the left by Ψ_i, and integrate.

This gives

$$(\Psi_j{}^*|\hat{F}|\Psi_i) = f_i(\Psi_j{}^*|\Psi_i) \qquad\qquad (6\text{-}35a)$$
$$(\Psi_i|\hat{F}|\Psi_j{}^*) = f_j{}^*(\Psi_i|\Psi_j{}^*) = f_j(\Psi_i|\Psi_j{}^*) \qquad\qquad (6\text{-}35b)$$

Subtracting Equation 6-34b from 6-34a, one obtains

$$(\Psi_j{}^*|\hat{F}|\Psi_i) - (\Psi_i|\hat{F}{}^*|\Psi_j{}^*) = (f_i - f_j)(\Psi_j{}^*|\Psi_i) \qquad\qquad (6\text{-}36)$$

Since $\hat{F}$ is Hermitian, the left-hand side of Equation 6-36 is zero because of Equation 3-18.   The quantity $(f_i - f_j)$ cannot be zero by postulate, therefore

$$(\Psi_j{}^*|\Psi_i) = 0$$

and the two functions Ψ_j and Ψ_i are orthogonal.

Example of use.   For a hydrogen atom, the functions $\Psi(2, 1, 0)$ and $\Psi(2, 0, 0)$ are both eigenfunctions of the operator $\hat{L}^2$, the first with eigenvalue $2\hbar^2$ and the second with eigenvalue $0\hbar^2$.   Theorem 1 states that these two functions must be orthogonal.   We can thus immediately write that

$$\langle\Psi^*(2, 1, 0)|\Psi(2, 0, 0)\rangle = 0$$

without evaluating the integral.

EXERCISE 6-9   Using a technique similar to that used to prove Theorem 1, prove that if the two operators $\hat{F}$ and $\hat{G}$ are Hermitian, their product $\hat{F}\hat{G}$ is Hermitian only if $\hat{F}$ and $\hat{G}$ commute.

Theorem II. If two operators $\hat{F}$ and $\hat{G}$ commute, then there exists a set of functions that are simultaneous eigenfunctions of both operators.

Proof: Suppose we have a set of eigenfunctions of the operator $\hat{F}$. That is,

$$\hat{F}\Psi_i = f_i\Psi_i \tag{6-37}$$

We further have the postulate that $\hat{F}\hat{G} - \hat{G}\hat{F} = 0$. We will restrict ourselves to the case that none of the f_i are equal. That is, there is no degeneracy. The theorem can also be proved without this restriction. Operating on Equation 6-37 from the left by $\hat{G}$ and taking advantage of the commutative property of $\hat{F}$ and $\hat{G}$, we write

$$\hat{G}\hat{F}\Psi_i = \hat{F}(\hat{G}\Psi_i) = f_i(\hat{G}\Psi_i) \tag{6-38}$$

Considering the last equality, Equation 6-37 shows that the function $(\hat{G}\Psi_i)$ must also be an eigenfunction of F with eigenvalue f_i. The only way that this result can be consistent with our assumption that Ψ_i was the only function with eigenvalue f_i is if the function $\hat{G}\Psi_i$ is a simple multiple of Ψ_i. Any other functional form of $\hat{G}\Psi_i$ would be a new function. Thus, the equation

$$\hat{G}\Psi_i = g_i\Psi_i$$

must hold, and we have the result that Ψ_i is also an eigenfunction of the operator $\hat{G}$ with eigenvalue g_i. If there is degeneracy, that is if there is more than one function Ψ_i with eigenvalue f_i, it is always possible to construct a linear combination of these functions which is an eigenfunction of the operator $\hat{G}$. This will not be proved, however.

Example: It can be shown that for the hydrogen atom the operators $\mathfrak{K}$, $\hat{L}^2$, and $\hat{L}_z$ commute with one another. According to Theorem II, it should be possible to find a set of functions which are simultaneous eigenfunctions of all three operators. The functions first listed in this chapter were, indeed, chosen to be these simultaneous eigenfunctions. The student may remember, however, that the functions derived for the p_x and p_y orbital descriptions were not eigenfunctions of $\hat{L}_z$. These latter functions could equally well have been used in the solution of Equation 6-6, and the resulting hydrogen orbitals would only have been eigenfunctions of $\mathfrak{K}$ and $\hat{L}^2$. Of course, the p_x and p_y functions could have then been made into eigenfunctions of $\hat{L}_z$ by taking appropriate linear combinations.

This theorem, in conjunction with Postulate III, has important implications for experimental measurements. Since the only quantities that can be precisely and simultaneously measured are those for which the system is in an eigenstate of the corresponding operators, it follows that, to measure precisely and simultaneously two or more quantities, the operators corresponding to these quantities must commute. Conversely, quantities whose corresponding operators do not commute (such as x and p_x) cannot be precisely and simultaneously measured under any conditions. In fact, a general statement of the uncertainty principle can be derived involving the commutator of the two operators involved.[8]

Theorem III. Given a pair of commuting Hermitian operators, $\hat{F}$ and $\hat{G}$, and a set of functions such that

$$\hat{F}\Psi_i = f_i\Psi_i$$

then all integrals of the type $(\Psi_i{}^*|\hat{G}|\Psi_j) = 0$ unless $f_i = f_j$. The proof of Theorem III is left as an exercise for the student. Theorem III is an extremely valuable one in many quantum mechanical problems because it allows one to set many integrals equal to zero without evaluating them. For example, the integral $\langle\Psi^*(2, 1, 0)|\hat{L}^2|\Psi(3, 1, 0)\rangle$, where the Ψ's are the appropriate hydrogen atom functions, is zero because the operators $\hat{\mathcal{H}}$ and $\hat{L}^2$ commute and $\Psi(2, 1, 0)$ and $\Psi(3, 1, 0)$ belong to different eigenvalues of $\hat{\mathcal{H}}$.

Many of the properties of angular momentum operators have been introduced in previous chapters, usually in the form of exercises. The results that should be familiar are:

$$\mathbf{L} = \mathbf{r} \times \mathbf{P} \tag{6-39a}$$

$$\mathbf{L} = L_x\mathbf{i} + L_y\mathbf{j} + L_z\mathbf{k} \tag{6-39b}$$

$$\hat{L}_x = y\hat{p}_z - z\hat{p}_y = -i\hbar\left(y\frac{\partial}{\partial z} - z\frac{\partial}{\partial y}\right) \tag{6-39c}$$

$$\hat{L}_y = z\hat{p}_x - x\hat{p}_z = -i\hbar\left(z\frac{\partial}{\partial x} - x\frac{\partial}{\partial z}\right) \tag{6-39d}$$

$$\hat{L}_z = x\hat{p}_y - y\hat{p}_x = -i\hbar\left(x\frac{\partial}{\partial y} - y\frac{\partial}{\partial x}\right) \tag{6-39e}$$

$$\hat{L}^2 = \hat{\mathbf{L}}\cdot\hat{\mathbf{L}} = \hat{L}_x{}^2 + \hat{L}_y{}^2 + \hat{L}_z{}^2 \tag{6-39f}$$

---

[8] **I,** page 332 ff.

The student should also know the appropriate expressions in polar coordinates. These are

$$\hat{L}_x = -i\hbar \left(-\sin\phi \, \frac{\partial}{\partial\theta} - \cot\theta \cos\phi \, \frac{\partial}{\partial\phi} \right) \qquad (6\text{-}40a)$$

$$\hat{L}_y = -i\hbar \left(\cos\phi \, \frac{\partial}{\partial\theta} - \cot\theta \sin\phi \, \frac{\partial}{\partial\phi} \right) \qquad (6\text{-}40b)$$

$$\hat{L}_z = -i\hbar \, \frac{\partial}{\partial\phi} \qquad (6\text{-}40c)$$

$$\hat{L}^2 = -\hbar^2 \left(\frac{1}{\sin\theta} \frac{\partial}{\partial\theta} \sin\theta \frac{\partial}{\partial\theta} + \frac{1}{\sin^2\theta} \frac{\partial}{\partial\phi^2} \right) \qquad (6\text{-}40d)$$

EXERCISE 6-10 Derive Equations 6-40. This may be done by using the relations

$$r^2 = x^2 + y^2 + z^2$$

$$\cos\theta = \frac{z}{(x^2 + y^2 + z^2)^{\frac{1}{2}}}$$

$$\tan\phi = y/x$$

and the result from calculus that, for example,

$$L_x = -i\hbar \left(y \, \frac{\partial}{\partial z} - z \, \frac{\partial}{\partial y} \right)$$

$$= -i\hbar \left[r\sin\theta\sin\phi \left(\frac{\partial r}{\partial z}\frac{\partial}{\partial r} + \frac{\partial\theta}{\partial z}\frac{\partial}{\partial\theta} + \frac{\partial\phi}{\partial z}\frac{\partial}{\partial\phi} \right) \right.$$

$$\left. - r\cos\theta \left(\frac{\partial r}{\partial y}\frac{\partial}{\partial r} + \frac{\partial\theta}{\partial y}\frac{\partial}{\partial\theta} + \frac{\partial\phi}{\partial y}\frac{\partial}{\partial\phi} \right) \right]$$

Some of the most important properties of angular momentum operators are the commutation relations. It can be shown that $\hat{L}^2$ commutes with any component of angular momentum. That is

$$[\hat{L}^2, \hat{L}_x] = [\hat{L}^2, \hat{L}_y] = [\hat{L}^2, \hat{L}_z] = 0 \qquad (6\text{-}41)$$

No two components commute with each other, however. In fact,

$$[\hat{L}_x, \hat{L}_y] = \hat{L}_x\hat{L}_y - \hat{L}_y\hat{L}_x = i\hbar\hat{L}_z \qquad (6\text{-}42a)$$
$$[\hat{L}_y, \hat{L}_z] = i\hbar\hat{L}_x \qquad (6\text{-}42b)$$
$$[\hat{L}_z, \hat{L}_x] = i\hbar\hat{L}_y \qquad (6\text{-}42c)$$

EXERCISE 6-11 Prove that $[\hat{L}^2, \hat{L}_z] = 0$ and that $[\hat{L}_x, \hat{L}_y] = i\hbar L_z$. The proof is most convenient in Cartesian coordinates.

The physical significance of these commutation relations is that it is only possible to measure simultaneously and precisely the square of the angular momentum and *one* component. That is, it is impossible to know exactly at a given time more than one component of angular momentum. By convention, the measurable component is usually taken to be the z component, and the Z axis is usually defined by an electric or a magnetic field. For more information about the use of magnetic fields to study electronic states, the student is referred to Chapter 9.[9]

Two other operators of interest are the so-called raising and lowering or ladder operators. These operators, called $\hat{L}_+$ and $\hat{L}_-$, are defined as

$$\hat{L}_+ = \hat{L}_x + i\hat{L}_y$$
$$\hat{L}_- = \hat{L}_x - i\hat{L}_y$$

These operators have an important effect on the functions $T(\theta)U(\phi)$. They will also be important in problems involving electron and nuclear spin. We now introduce the notation that

$$S_{l,m} \equiv T(l, m)U(m) \tag{6-43}$$

The operators $\hat{L}_+$ and $\hat{L}_-$ have the property that

$$\hat{L}_+ S_{l,m} = \hbar[l(l + 1) - m(m + 1)]^{\frac{1}{2}}S_{l,m+1} \tag{6-44}$$
$$\hat{L}_- S_{l,m} = \hbar[l(l + 1) - m(m - 1)]^{\frac{1}{2}}S_{l,m-1} \tag{6-45}$$

The easiest way to see the effect of these operators is to substitute some of the functions $S_{l,m}$ into Equations 6-44 and 6-45. It can be seen that the effect of $\hat{L}_+$ or $\hat{L}_-$ is to either raise or lower the eigenvalue with respect to $\hat{L}_z$, keeping the eigenvalue with respect to $\hat{L}^2$ the same. If the eigenvalue of $S_{l,m}$ with respect to $\hat{L}_z$ already has its maximum value, $m = l$, then $\hat{L}_+$ annihilates the function. That is

$$\hat{L}_+ S_{l,l} = 0$$

These properties can best be illustrated by some specific examples.

EXERCISE 6-12 Show that $\hat{L}_+ S_{1,-1} = +\hbar\sqrt{2}\,S_{1,0}$, and that $\hat{L}_+ S_{1,1} = 0$. Likewise, show that $\hat{L}_- S_{1,0} = \hbar\sqrt{2}\,S_{1,-1}$, and that

[9] See, also, **III**, pages 261–270.

$L_-S_{1,-1} = 0$. That is, show that

$$(\hat{L}_x + i\hat{L}_y)\left(\frac{3}{8}\pi\right)^{\frac{1}{2}} \sin\theta e^{-i\phi} = +\hbar\sqrt{2}\left(\frac{3}{4}\pi\right)^{\frac{1}{2}}\cos\theta\, e^\circ$$

One of the most useful properties of the ladder operators is that they permit the expression for $\hat{L}^2$ to be written in a form which makes computation much simpler. It is known that

$$\hat{L}^2 = \hat{L}_x{}^2 + \hat{L}_y{}^2 + \hat{L}_z{}^2 \tag{6-46}$$

but

$$\hat{L}_+\hat{L}_- = (\hat{L}_x + i\hat{L}_y)(\hat{L}_x - i\hat{L}_y) = \hat{L}_x{}^2 - i\hat{L}_x\hat{L}_y + i\hat{L}_y\hat{L}_x + \hat{L}_y{}^2$$

(note that we have been careful to maintain the order of operations)

$$= \hat{L}_x{}^2 + \hat{L}_y{}^2 - i(\hat{L}_x\hat{L}_y - \hat{L}_y\hat{L}_x) \tag{6-47}$$

The term $(\hat{L}_x\hat{L}_y - \hat{L}_y\hat{L}_x)$ is the commutator of $\hat{L}_x$ and $\hat{L}_y$, however, and is given by Equation 6-42a as $i\hbar\hat{L}_z$. Therefore,

$$\hat{L}_+\hat{L}_- = \hat{L}_x{}^2 + \hat{L}_y{}^2 + \hbar\hat{L}_z \tag{6-48}$$

and

$$\hat{L}_x{}^2 + \hat{L}_y{}^2 = \hat{L}_+\hat{L}_- - \hbar\hat{L}_z \tag{6-49}$$

Therefore, we can write the operator L^2 in the form

$$\hat{L}^2 = \hat{L}_+\hat{L}_- + \hat{L}_z{}^2 - \hbar\hat{L}_z \tag{6-50}$$

Likewise, it can also be shown that

$$\hat{L}^2 = \hat{L}_-\hat{L}_+ + \hat{L}_z{}^2 + \hbar\hat{L}_z \tag{6-51}$$

EXERCISE 6-13   Derive Equation 6-51 making use only of definitions and commutation relations.

All of the above relations have been for a system with only one electron. For systems with more than one electron, the angular momentum must be calculated vectorially. For example, if a two-electron system is considered, we can write

$$\mathbf{L}_T = \mathbf{L}(1) + \mathbf{L}(2) \tag{6-52}$$

where $\mathbf{L}_T$ is the total angular momentum of the system, and $\mathbf{L}(1)$ and $\mathbf{L}(2)$ are the angular momenta of electrons one and two, respectively. The square of the total angular momentum is, therefore,

$$L_T{}^2 = \mathbf{L}_T \cdot \mathbf{L}_T = L^2(1) + L^2(2) + 2\mathbf{L}(1) \cdot \mathbf{L}(2) \qquad (6\text{-}53)$$

Calculations of $L_T{}^2$ for many electron systems are most conveniently performed with an expression analogous to Equations 6-50 or 6-51. Thus,

$$\hat{L}_T{}^2 = \hat{L}_+(T)\hat{L}_-(T) + \hat{L}_z{}^2(T) - \hbar\hat{L}_z(T) \qquad (6\text{-}54)$$

where

$$\hat{L}_+(T) = \hat{L}_x(T) + i\hat{L}_y(T) \qquad (6\text{-}55a)$$
$$\hat{L}_-(T) = \hat{L}_x(T) - i\hat{L}_y(T) \qquad (6\text{-}55b)$$
$$\hat{L}_\alpha(T) = \sum_i \hat{L}_\alpha(i) \qquad (6\text{-}55c)$$

The subscript α in Equation 6-55c goes over the three components x, y, and z. The use of these equations is illustrated in Exercise 6-14.

EXERCISE 6-14 For a two-electron system, show that Equation 6-54 is identical to Equation 6-53. To do this, write each equation in terms of the components of angular momentum and compare.

6-7 Electron spin

Shortly before quantum mechanics was developed, Goudsmit and Uhlenbeck postulated that an electron had an intrinsic angular momentum which they called "spin angular momentum." This new property, many times just called "spin," has some unusual characteristics. In part, these characteristics seem unusual because *there is no classical analogue of spin.*

The experimental evidence supporting the spin hypothesis is quite large. Some examples of things which can be explained by the concept of spin are:

1. Stern-Gerlach experiments
2. Electron and nuclear spin resonance spectroscopy
3. The degeneracy of the excited states of atoms and molecules
4. The anomalous Zeeman effect
5. The fine structure splittings of atomic spectra

To discuss each of these experiments is beyond the scope of this text, and good discussions are already available.[10]

Since there is no classical analogue of spin, we cannot follow our standard procedure, starting with writing down the classical expression, for finding the appropriate quantum mechanical operators, commutation rules, etc. We, therefore, introduce spin by a series of postulates.[11] These postulates are justified by the fact that they give the right answers in experiments such as those listed above. The postulates are:

I. The operators for spin angular momentum commute and combine in the same way as those for ordinary angular momentum.

We, therefore, have operators $\hat{S}^2$, $\hat{S}_x$, $\hat{S}_y$, $\hat{S}_z$, $\hat{S}_+$, $\hat{S}_-$, which are exactly analogous to the operators $\hat{L}^2$, $\hat{L}_x$, $\hat{L}_y$, $\hat{L}_z$, $\hat{L}_+$, and $\hat{L}_-$ discussed in Section 6-6.

II. For a single electron there are only two simultaneous eigenfunctions of $\hat{S}^2$ and $\hat{S}_z$. These are called α and β and have eigenvalues

$$\hat{S}_z\alpha = \frac{1}{2}\hbar\alpha \qquad S^2\alpha = \frac{1}{2}\left(\frac{1}{2}+1\right)\hbar^2\alpha$$

$$\hat{S}_z\beta = -\frac{1}{2}\hbar\beta \qquad S^2\beta = \frac{1}{2}\left(\frac{1}{2}+1\right)\hbar^2\beta \tag{6-56}$$

Spin, like orbital angular momentum, can be expressed in atomic units of $\hbar$. The functions α and β are then said to be eigenfunctions of $\hat{S}_z$ with eigenvalue $\frac{1}{2}$ and $-\frac{1}{2}$, respectively. The functions α and β are taken to be normalized. That is, the integrals of α^2 and β^2 over all *spin* space equal 1. They are also orthogonal because of Theorem I, Section 6-6.

III. The spinning electron acts like a magnet, the magnetic dipole moment of which is

$$\hat{\mathbf{\mu}} = -g_0\beta_m\hat{\mathbf{S}} \tag{6-57}$$

The quantities g_0 and β_m are the Lande g factor, or spectroscopic splitting factor, and the Bohr magneton, respectively. These quantities have the values 2.0023 and 9.2732×10^{-21} erg gauss^{-1}.

---

[10] III, page 283 ff.

[11] This form of the spin postulate is essentially that of III, page 306 ff.

The minus sign indicates that the direction of the dipole moment vector is antiparallel to the spin vector. From Equation 6-57 it can easily be seen that the operator for the z component of the magnetic moment is

$$\hat{\mu}_z = - g_0 \beta_m \hat{S}_z \tag{6-58}$$

Since the spin operators affect only "spin coordinates," they commute with all operators that are a function only of orbital coordinates. The operators $\hat{S}^2$ and $\hat{S}_z$ will, therefore, commute with the operators $\mathcal{R}$, $\hat{L}^2$, and $\hat{L}_z$ as long as $\mathcal{R}$ contains no spin terms. We can choose our atomic wave functions, then, to be simultaneous eigenfunctions of all five of these operators. It is customary, therefore, to characterize atomic wave functions by four quantum numbers, n, l, m, and S_z. A single electron can be thought of as moving in a four-dimensional space described by three regular coordinates and a spin coordinate.

EXERCISE 6-15   Using the definitions of $\hat{S}_+$ and $\hat{S}_-$, calculate the results of operating on the functions α and β with the operators $\hat{S}_x$ and $\hat{S}_y$. Can you construct two functions from α and β which are eigenfunctions of $\hat{S}_x$?

EXERCISE 6-16   For more than one electron, the operators for the *total* spin angular momentum can be constructed vectorially. Thus, for two electrons, $\hat{\mathbf{S}}_T = \hat{\mathbf{S}}_1 + \hat{\mathbf{S}}_2$, $\hat{S}_z^T = \hat{S}_z(1) + \hat{S}_z(2)$, etc. For the two-electron case, write the operators $\hat{S}_+^T$ and $\hat{S}_-^T$ and then write $\hat{S}_T^2$ in terms of these and $\hat{S}_z^T$. Show that the functions

$$\alpha(1)\alpha(2)$$
$$1/\sqrt{2}\,[\alpha(1)\beta(2) + \beta(1)\alpha(2)]$$
$$\beta(1)\alpha(2)$$

are simultaneous eigenfunctions of $\hat{S}^2_T$ and $\hat{S}_z^T$. What are the eigenvalues? These spin functions are the spin functions for a *triplet* state.

6-8   Identical particles and the Pauli principle

We now wish to consider some aspects of systems containing two or more identical particles. By identical particles, we mean that the particles possess exactly the same properties, and they cannot, therefore, be distinguished from one another by physical measurements. All of the conclusions that we draw about systems containing identical particles must be independent of the labeling on the particles. For example, consider the case of a pair of non-interacting particles in a one-dimensional box. The Hamiltonian operator for the system will be

$$\hat{\mathfrak{K}} = -\frac{\hbar^2}{2m}[\nabla^2(1) + \nabla^2(2)] \tag{6-59}$$

and it is clear that the Hamiltonian is symmetric in the two particles. That is, interchanging the labels (1) and (2) leaves the Hamiltonian in Equation 6-59 unchanged. In the eigenvalue equation using the Hamiltonian of Equation 6-59, the variables for electrons (1) and (2) are separable and the solutions are

$$\Psi_1 = A \sin \frac{n_1 \pi x}{a} \tag{6-60a}$$

$$\Psi_2 = A \sin \frac{n_2 \pi x}{a} \tag{6-60b}$$

Suppose we consider the case where one particle is in the lowest energy orbital and the second is in the next to lowest energy orbital. An acceptable mathematical solution to the two-particle eigenvalue equation would then be

$$\Psi_{tot} = \Psi_1(1)\Psi_2(2) \tag{6-61}$$

where the subscripts 1 and 2 refer to the values of the quantum numbers n_1 and n_2. Such a wave function is physically unacceptable, however, because it implies that we can separately locate particles (1) and (2). That is, it unequivocally states that particle (1) is in state Ψ_1 and particle (2) is in state Ψ_2. Such an assertion is impossible to verify experimentally. The only thing that can be experimentally verified is that there is *a* particle in state Ψ_1 and *a* particle in state Ψ_2.

It is a straightforward procedure to construct wave functions which will take this indistinguishability into account. Since the Hamiltonian operator of Equation 6-59 is symmetric in the two electrons, an equally good solution to Equation 6-61 is

$$\Psi_{tot} = \Psi_2(1)\Psi_1(2) \tag{6-62}$$

Also, any linear combinations of Equations 6-61 and 6-62 will be an equally good solution. Two of these linear combinations will be of special interest.   They are

$$\Psi_+ = 1/\sqrt{2}\,[\Psi_1(1)\Psi_2(2) + \Psi_2(1)\Psi_1(2)] \qquad (6\text{-}63a)$$

$$\Psi_- = 1/\sqrt{2}\,[\Psi_1(1)\Psi_2(2) - \Psi_2(1)\Psi_2(2)] \qquad (6\text{-}63b)$$

Equation 6-59a is a symmetrical linear combination.   That is, it remains unchanged when the labels on particles (1) and (2) are interchanged.   Equation 6-63b is an antisymmetrical linear combination.   It changes sign when the labels on particles (1) and (2) are interchanged.   In operator language, we can introduce a permutation operator $\hat{P}_{12}$ which tells one to interchange the coordinates on particles (1) and (2) in the function that follows.   Equations 6-63a and 6-63b will both be eigenfunctions of the operator $\hat{P}_{12}$ with eigenvalues $+1$ and -1, respectively.   The important thing about Equations 6-63a and b is that they are consistent with the fact that we can tell that there is a particle in state Ψ_1 and state Ψ_2, but we cannot tell which particle it is.

EXERCISE 6-17   The factor $1/\sqrt{2}$ in Equations 6-63a and b is a normalizing constant.   Given Ψ_1 and Ψ_2 are normalized functions for a particle in a one-dimensional box, show that the functions 6-63a and b are normalized.

It will be a general property of wave functions for systems containing many identical particles that they must be properly symmetrized to take the indistinguishability of the identical particles into account.   This can be taken to be an additional postulate to those given in Chapter 3.   To complete the postulate, the particular kind of symmetrized wave function to use must be stated.   This choice is determined by experimental observation. The Pauli exclusion principle, which originally was given for electrons, but which applies to all particles with half integral spin (i.e., protons, C^{13} nuclei, etc.), is one form of this postulate.   It states

All acceptable wave functions for half-integral spin particles must be antisymmetric upon permutation of the coordinates of any two particles.

For particles with even spin (photons have spin 1, as do deuterons and N^{14} nuclei, to mention only a few) the postulate requires that the acceptable wave functions be symmetric with respect to the permutation of the coordinates of any two particles.

To illustrate the application of the Pauli principle to a specific case, let us write down all of the possible functions of the form of Equation 6-25 that are approximate solutions for the ground state of the helium atom. These solutions will also include the electron spin coordinate. The four possible functions are

$$
\begin{aligned}
\Psi_1 &= \phi_{1s}(1)\phi_{1s}(2)\alpha(1)\alpha(2) \\
\Psi_2 &= \phi_{1s}(1)\phi_{1s}(2)\alpha(1)\beta(2) \\
\Psi_3 &= \phi_{1s}(1)\phi_{1s}(2)\beta(1)\alpha(2) \\
\Psi_4 &= \phi_{1s}(1)\phi_{1s}(2)\beta(1)\beta(2)
\end{aligned}
\qquad (6\text{-}64)
$$

All four of these functions are correct solutions to the eigenvalue Equation 6-24, but none of the four satisfy the Pauli principle. This can be seen by actually operating on the four functions with the permutation operator $\hat{P}_{12}$. The functions Ψ_1 and Ψ_4 are eigenfunctions of $\hat{P}_{12}$ with eigenvalue $+1$, and Ψ_2 and Ψ_3 are not eigenfunctions of $\hat{P}_{12}$. In fact,

$$
\begin{aligned}
\hat{P}_{12}\Psi_2 &= \Psi_3 \\
\hat{P}_{12}\Psi_3 &= \Psi_2
\end{aligned}
\qquad (6\text{-}65)
$$

In order to preserve the indistinguishability of the electrons, we must, therefore, take linear combinations of Ψ_2 and Ψ_3. The appropriate ones are those similar to Equations 6-63 and are,

$$
\Psi_+ = 1/\sqrt{2}\,\{\phi_{1s}(1)\phi_{1s}(2)[\alpha(1)\beta(2) + \beta(1)\alpha(2)]\} \qquad (6\text{-}66a)
$$
$$
\Psi_- = 1/\sqrt{2}\{\phi_{1s}(1)\phi_{1s}(2)[\alpha(1)\beta(2) - \beta(1)\alpha(2)]\} \qquad (b)
$$

with Ψ_+ having the eigenvalue $+1$ with respect to $\hat{P}_{12}$, and Ψ_- having the eigenvalue -1. We, therefore, see that the only acceptable ground state wave function for the helium atom at this level of approximation is given by Equation 6-66b. If one were to calculate the eigenvalue with respect to the total spin angular momentum operator $S_T{}^2$, for the function Ψ_- in Equation 6-66b, this eigenvalue would be zero. The state characterized by Equation 6-66b would, therefore, have a spin degeneracy of $(2S_T + 1) = 1$. The spin degeneracy, in turn, determines the multiplicity of a state. For $S_T = 0$, the multiplicity of the state is *one* and the state is called a singlet state. For the case that $S_T = 1$, $(2S_T + 1)$ equals *three*, and the state is called a *triplet* state.

6-9 Independent electron theory of complex atoms

Following the same procedure as that used for the helium atom, we can immediately write down the Hamiltonian operator for any atom. This operator is

$$\hat{\mathcal{3C}} = -\frac{1}{2} \sum_i \nabla_i^2 - \sum_i \frac{Z_N}{r_{iN}} + \sum_{i<j}\sum \frac{1}{r_{ij}} \tag{6-67}$$

The first term is the sum of the kinetic energy operators for the electrons. The second term is the attractive energy of the electrons for the nucleus. The third term is the electron repulsion energy. Of course, the eigenvalue equation, using Equation 6-67 for the operator, is impossible to solve exactly in terms of analytical functions.

To find approximate solutions, we again follow the procedure that was used for helium. This involves finding functions which are eigenfunctions of an approximate Hamiltonian that leaves out the electron repulsion terms explicitly, and tries to account for them, in part, by introducing an effective nuclear charge for each electron. We, therefore, seek solutions to the Hamiltonian

$$\hat{\mathcal{3C}}_0 = -\frac{1}{2} \sum_i \nabla_i^2 - \sum_i \frac{Z'}{r_{iN}} \tag{6-68}$$

where Z' is now an effective nuclear charge. This is a Hamiltonian of the form

$$\hat{\mathcal{3C}}_0 = \sum_i \hat{h}(i) \tag{6-69}$$

where $\hat{h}(i)$ is a single-electron Hamiltonian. We can, therefore, use a product function of the type

$$\Psi = \prod_{i=1}^{N} \phi_i(i) \tag{6-70}$$

where ϕ_i is the space orbital occupied by the i'th electron, to reduce an N electron problem to N one-electron problems *to which we already know the solution*. These solutions are the solutions to the hydrogen atom problem with the effective nuclear charge Z' replacing the actual charge in the energy and wave functions.

At this point, the meaning of the word orbital should be made clear because the concept of an orbital plays an important part in the remainder of the text. An orbital is a one-electron wave function. That is, it is a solution to an eigenvalue equation in which the Hamiltonian depends only on the coordinates of a single electron. Orbitals are equivalent to atomic and molecular states only for systems that contain a single electron such as H, He^+, and the hydrogen molecule ion H_2^+, to be discussed in the next chapter. In more complex systems, the states of the atom or molecule can be expressed as products or sums of products of orbitals, but it must be kept in mind that such descriptions are approximations to the true state of affairs. The orbital concept has great value for the chemist, however, in spite of the fact that numerical results calculated using wave functions based on the orbital approximation are, in general, poor. The fact that the orbital concept correctly rationalizes most observations connected with the valence of atoms and the periodicity of the elements is an outstanding achievement and its importance should not be minimized.

It should be noted that, although Equation 6-70 is a solution to the approximate eigenvalue equation using the Hamiltonian of Equation 6-68, it is like one of the simple product functions written down above for the helium atom in that it does not satisfy the Pauli principle. In order to construct a function that does satisfy the Pauli principle, we must take a linear combination of product functions of the type in Equation 6-70 so that the resulting function will change sign upon the permutation of the coordinates of any two electrons.

Instead of discussing this procedure in general, let us consider the specific case of the lithium atom, a three-electron problem. Including spin, the independent electron orbitals and their orbital energies are

$$
\begin{array}{ll}
\chi_i & \epsilon_i \\
\chi_1 = \phi(1,\,0,\,0)\alpha & \epsilon_{1s} \\
\chi_2 = \phi(1,\,0,\,0)\beta & \epsilon_{1s} \\
\chi_3 = \phi(2,\,0,\,0)\alpha & \epsilon_{2s} \\
\chi_4 = \phi(2,\,0,\,0)\beta & \epsilon_{2s} \\
\quad\cdot & \cdot \\
\quad\cdot & \cdot \\
\quad\cdot & \cdot
\end{array}
\qquad (6\text{-}71)
$$

We now must place the three electrons in these orbitals to form product functions and then find a linear combination of the product functions that is a simultaneous eigenfunction of $\hat{P}_{12}$, $\hat{P}_{13}$, and $\hat{P}_{23}$ with eigenvalues -1. We first investigate what happens when all three electrons are placed into one of the lowest energy orbitals χ_1 or χ_2. The student may easily verify that such a product function is symmetric with respect to the interchange of the coordinates of any two electrons. Hence, all such configurations may be ruled out. A similar argument can be used to rule out configurations with *two* electrons in any one orbital. We are, thus, left with the fact that the lowest energy state for the lithium atom must have one electron in each of χ_1, χ_2, and χ_3.[12] The final antisymmetric wave function must, therefore, be a linear combination of product functions involving these three independent electron orbitals.

There is an elegant way to construct such a wave function which was introduced by J. C. Slater. This method makes use of the property of determinants that requires that a determinant change sign upon interchange of any two rows or columns. We, thus, label the columns of a determinant with the electron number and the rows with the orbital number, and the determinant automatically gives an antisymmetric wave function. Thus, for lithium we have

$$
\Psi = \begin{array}{c} \\ 1 \\ 2 \\ 3 \end{array} \overset{\begin{array}{ccc} 1 & 2 & 3 \leftarrow \text{electron number} \end{array}}{\begin{vmatrix} \chi_1(1) & \chi_1(2) & \chi_1(3) \\ \chi_2(1) & \chi_2(2) & \chi_2(3) \\ \chi_3(1) & \chi_3(2) & \chi_3(3) \end{vmatrix}} \frac{1}{(3!)^{\frac{1}{2}}}
$$

$$\text{orbital} \uparrow \text{number}$$

(6-72)

The $1/(3!)^{\frac{1}{2}}$ is a normalizing factor because an $N \times N$ determinant will have $N!$ terms. Such determinants are called Slater determinants and are usually abbreviated by only writing the diagonal term $|\chi_1(1)\chi_2(2)\chi_3(3)|$. In the future, when we write a product wave function, we will assume that we are writing a Slater determinant.

EXERCISE 6-18 Evaluate the determinant given in Equation 6-72 and show that it is an eigenfunction of P_{13} with eigenvalue -1.

[12] One electron can also be placed in χ_1, χ_2, and χ_4 to give a state with the same energy in the absence of external fields.

It is of interest to use the properties of Slater determinants to rule out the product functions that would result if we tried to place two or more electrons into one of the orbitals, say χ_1. If the Slater determinant is written down for such a case, it can immediately be seen that two or more rows will be identical. Such a determinant must vanish (see Section 1-3). This result allows us to make a more useful statement of the Pauli principle for problems involving the independent electron approximation. Since, if two electrons are in the same orbital, they must have the same set of four quantum numbers (3 space and 1 spin), the Pauli principle can be stated in the form:

> *No two electrons can have the same set of four quantum numbers.*

Such a statement of the Pauli principle is a logical consequence of the more general statement given in Section 6-7 and can be used whenever the independent electron model is employed.

6-10   *The Aufbau principle and the periodic table*

Using the above statement of the Pauli principle and the independent electron model, we can rationalize the properties of atoms and their position in the periodic table with their electronic structure. A schematic drawing of the allowed orbitals of an atom in order of increasing energy is given in Figure 6-8. It should be noticed that the three $2p$ orbitals are now given a higher energy than the $2s$ orbital. This occurs because an electron in a $2p$ orbital will experience a different effective nuclear charge than an electron in a $2s$ orbital. A consideration of Figure 6-3 shows why this is the case. In this figure, it is seen that the probability of finding a $2p$ electron in the region where the $1s$ electrons have their maximum density is less than the probability of finding a $2s$ electron in the same region. When such a situation exists, the $2s$ electron is said to have better penetration into the $1s^2$ shell. As a result of this better penetration, a $2s$ electron will experience a greater effective nuclear charge than a $2p$ electron and will have a lower energy.

The levels shown in Figure 6-8 represent the space part of the orbitals. For each space orbital there are two possible values of the spin quantum number. According to the Pauli principle, we can,

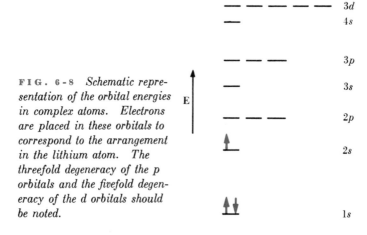

FIG. 6-8 *Schematic representation of the orbital energies in complex atoms. Electrons are placed in these orbitals to correspond to the arrangement in the lithium atom. The threefold degeneracy of the p orbitals and the fivefold degeneracy of the d orbitals should be noted.*

therefore, put a maximum of 2 electrons in each of the space orbitals. The electronic structures and approximate energies of the ground states of the first few atoms in the periodic table are given in Table 6-2.

When we come to the structure of the carbon atom a difficulty arises because there are a number of ways that the sixth electron can be put into the available orbitals. By writing down all possibilities, it is seen that there are 15 possible wave functions for the configuration $(2p)^2$. These are given in Table 6-3. The core electrons $(1s)^2$ and $(2s)^2$ are not specified because their only effect is to screen the $2p$ electrons. The student should keep in mind that, for these functions to satisfy the Pauli principle, they must be Slater determinants.

TABLE 6-2 THE ELECTRONIC STRUCTURES OF THE GROUND STATES He, Li, Be, AND B WITHIN THE CONTEXT OF THE INDEPENDENT ELECTRON MODEL

Atom	Wave Function (space part only)	Approximate Energy
He	$(1s)(1s) \equiv (1s)^2$	$2\epsilon_{1s}$
Li	$(1s)^2 (2s)$	$2\epsilon_{1s} + \epsilon_{2s}$
Be	$(1s)^2 (2s)^2$	$2\epsilon_{1s} + 2\epsilon_{2s}$
B	$(1s)^2 (2s)^2 2p$	$2\epsilon_{1s} + 2\epsilon_{2s} + \epsilon_{2p}$

TABLE 6-3 POSSIBLE WAVE FUNCTIONS FOR THE CONFIGURATION $(2p)^2$

i	Function x_i	L_T	L_z	S_T	S_z
1	$(2p_1\alpha)(2p_1\beta)$	2	2	0	0
2	$(2p_1\alpha)(2p_0\alpha)$	1	1	1	1
3	$(2p_1\alpha)(2p_0\beta)$	—	1	—	0
4	$(2p_1\beta)(2p_0\alpha)$	—	1	—	0
5	$(2p_1\beta)(2p_0\beta)$	1	1	1	−1
6	$(2p_1\alpha)(2p_{-1}\alpha)$	1	0	1	1
7	$(2p_1\alpha)(2p_{-1}\beta)$	—	0	—	0
8	$(2p_1\beta)(2p_{-1}\alpha)$	—	0	—	0
9	$(2p_1\beta)(2p_{-1}\beta)$	1	0	1	−1
10	$(2p_0\alpha)(2p_0\beta)$	—	0	—	0
11	$(2p_0\alpha)(2p_{-1}\alpha)$	1	−1	1	1
12	$(2p_0\alpha)(2p_{-1}\beta)$	—	−1	—	0
13	$(2p_0\beta)(2p_{-1}\alpha)$	—	−1	—	0
14	$(2p_0\beta)(2p_{-1}\beta)$	1	−1	1	−1
15	$(2p_{-1}\alpha)(2p_{-1}\beta)$	2	−2	0	0

In Table 6-3, the following nomenclature was used

α and β	Spin functions
$2p_1$	The function $\Psi(2, 1, 1)$
$2p_0$	The function $\Psi(2, 1, 0)$
$2p_{-1}$	The function $\Psi(2, 1, -1)$
L_T	The eigenvalue in atomic units with respect to $\hat{L}_T^2$; that is $\hat{L}_T^2\Psi = L_T(L_T + 1)\hbar^2\Psi$. If no number is given, the function is not an eigenfunction of $\hat{L}_T^2$
S_T	Same as above except for spin angular momentum
L_z and S_z	The eigenvalue in atomic units of the function with respect to $\hat{L}_z(T)$ and $\hat{S}_z(T)$, respectively.

In order to find the appropriate states of the carbon atom with configuration $2p^2$ (1s and 2s electrons neglected), a set of simultaneous eigenfunctions of the operators $\hat{L}_T^2$, $\hat{L}_z(T)$, $\hat{S}_T^2$, and $\hat{S}_z(T)$ must be constructed. Before doing this, some features of the symbolism for atomic states must be considered. The symbol used to designate an atomic state is based on the eigenvalues which the wave function characterizing that state has with respect to $\hat{L}_T^2$ and $\hat{S}_T^2$. The capital letter designations S, P, D, etc., are used for the eigenvalues $L_T = 0, 1, 2, \ldots$, respectively. The eigenvalue with respect to $S_T{}^2$ determines the multiplicity of the state, and the multiplicity is designated by a left superscript. It will be shown below that, for a carbon atom with the $2p^2$ configuration, the fifteen functions in Table 6-3 lead to a ^3P (triplet P) state with a total degeneracy of nine, a ^1D (singlet D) state with a total degeneracy of five, and a ^1S (singlet S) state with a total degeneracy of one.

The fifteen functions in Table 6-3 are already eigenvalues of $\hat{L}_z(T)$ and $\hat{S}_z(T)$, and use can be made of the eigenvalues with respect to these two operators to predict the states that can occur for this configuration. It should be recalled that, if a state has angular momentum of L_T, then all the values of $L_z(T)$ between $+ L_T$ and $- L_T$ can occur. In Table 6-3, the maximum value of $L_z(T)$ is two, and this means that a D state must occur. Since the maximum value of $S_z(T)$ occurring with the $L_z(T) = 2$ functions is zero, the D state must be a ^1D.[13] The function χ_1 is, therefore, one of the five degenerate functions comprising the ^1D state. These five degenerate functions will be characterized by their $L_z(T)$ values of 2, 1, 0, $- 1$, $- 2$, and they all must have $S_T = 0$. It is clear that χ_{15} is another member of the degenerate set. To obtain the detailed wave functions for the remaining three members of the five-fold degenerate ^1D state, a quantum mechanical calculation must be carried out.[14]

[13] The functions χ_1 and χ_{15} are already simultaneous eigenfunctions of $\hat{L}_T{}^2$ and $\hat{S}_T{}^2$ with eigenvalues $L_T = 2$ and $S_T = 0$, showing that a ^1D state exists. The above discussion shows how to proceed if this had not been the case.

[14] The interested student may derive the wave functions corresponding to the missing components of the above states by the following procedure:

1. Write the operator for the square of the total angular momentum $\hat{L}_T{}^2$ for a system with two electrons. For what follows, it will be most convenient to express it in terms of the ladder operators $\hat{L}_+$ and $\hat{L}_-$. A similar expression holds for $\hat{S}_T{}^2$.

2. Divide the functions into groups according to their simultaneous eigenvalues with respect to $\hat{L}_z(T)$ and $\hat{S}_z(T)$. In some groups there will only be one function and this function will already be an eigenfunction of $\hat{L}_T{}^2$ and $\hat{S}_T{}^2$.

3. Form linear combinations of the members of each group so that they are simultaneous eigenfunctions of $\hat{L}_T{}^2$ and $\hat{S}_T{}^2$. The procedure for doing this is identical with that discussed in Section 8-2.

4. Performing step 3 will lead to two 2×2 and one 3×3 determinant for each operator. Why doesn't one have to worry about cross terms between members of different groups?

5. Solving these secular determinants and finding the coefficients will yield the desired functions.

A similar argument using the maximum values of $L_z(T)$ and $S_z(T)$ among the *remaining* functions can be used to show that there must be a ^3P state.

The ^1D and ^3P states account for 14 functions and, therefore, one function remains of the original 15. This function must be a ^1S state. To show the reasoning behind this last conclusion, the following points should be considered:

1. Since χ_7, χ_8, and χ_{10} all have the same eigenvalues with respect to $\hat{L}_z(T)$ and $\hat{S}_z(T)$, any linear combination of these states will also have these eigenvalues.

2. From these three functions, three new functions can be constructed that are mutually orthogonal and are also simultaneous eigenfunctions of $\hat{L}_T{}^2$ and $\hat{S}_T{}^2$.

3. Two of the three functions formed in step 2 will be the $L_z(T) = 0$, $S_z(T) = 0$ components of the ^1D and ^3P states.

4. There will be one function left of the three and, since both $L_z(T)$ and $S_z(T) = 0$, this remaining function must correspond to a ^1S state.

To determine which of the three states for the configuration $2p^2$ has the lowest energy, we must appeal to two working postulates known as Hund's rules. Hund's first rule states:

> *Other things being equal, the state of highest multiplicity will be the most stable.*

Hund's second rule is

> *Among levels having the same electronic configuration and the same multiplicity, the most stable level is the one with the largest angular momentum.*

Thus, for a carbon atom, the group of ^3P states will have the lowest energy because it has the highest multiplicity (3). Among the ^1D and ^1S states, the ^1D will be the most stable because it has the largest total angular momentum.

The physical basis for Hund's first rule may be seen by considering the properties of two-electron triplet and singlet wave functions. From advanced quantum mechanical considerations, it can be shown that the probability of finding two electrons with the *same* spin at the same point in space is *zero*. No such restriction applies to electrons with opposite spins, however. These statements are another form of the Pauli principle. Since, in a triplet state, the electrons have the same spin, they cannot be allowed to come into the same region of space if the Pauli principle is to be obeyed. This keeping of the electrons apart in a triplet wave function is accomplished by virtue of the fact that the space part of the function must be antisymmetric.[15] Since the electrons are kept apart in this function, the electron repulsion energy is smaller than if the electrons were allowed to come close together.

In a singlet wave function, the electrons have opposite spins and there is nothing in the Pauli principle which keeps these electrons from being in the same region of space. This is consistent with the fact that the space part of a two-electron singlet function is always symmetric with respect to exchange of the two electrons. Since the electrons can come close to one another, the electron repulsion energy between them will be relatively large. As a consequence of this difference in the space parts of the triplet and singlet wave functions, the triplet state for a given configuration will tend to have a lower energy than the singlet state for that configuration.

EXERCISE 6-19 Let ψ_1 and ψ_2 be the functions for a particle in a one-dimensional box with $n = 1$ and $n = 2$. If one electron were in each of these orbitals, the space part of the triplet and singlet wave functions would be $\Psi_A = 1/\sqrt{2} \, [\psi_1\psi_2 - \psi_2\psi_1]$ and $\Psi_S = 1/\sqrt{2} \, [\psi_1\psi_2 + \psi_2\psi_1]$, respectively. Suppose that particle *one* is in a small element of length dx at $x = 0.250a$ and particle *two* is in a small element of length dx at $x = 0.255a$. The quantity a is the length of the box. Show that Ψ_A has a very small value under these conditions while Ψ_S can be large. What happens to Ψ_A if both electrons are at $x = 0.250a$? This problem shows how an antisymmetric space function keeps the electrons apart.

The second rule can be rationalized in the following way: If the electrons in an atom have a large total angular momentum, it is an indication that the electrons tend to move around the nucleus in the same direction. They, therefore, are better able to keep out of each other's way than if they were going in opposite or random directions. Kauzmann's example [16] is a good one to illustrate this point. Think about people emptying a football

---

[15] In Exercise 6-17 it was shown that the spin functions for a triplet state were symmetric. The space part of a function for a triplet state must, therefore, be antisymmetric in order for the total wave function to be antisymmetric.

[16] **III,** p. 343.

stadium by walking out around the track. The "repulsion inter-action" will be much smaller if they are all going in the same direction around the track then if they are going in random directions.

Similar arguments can be used to predict that the ground states of a nitrogen, oxygen, and fluorine atom should be a ^4S, ^3P, and ^2P, respectively. All of these predictions are confirmed by experiment.

Much of the chemical behavior of the elements as well as the arrangement of the elements in the periodic table can be rationalized using this simple model.[17]

6-11 *Summary*

1. The energy levels and wave functions for the hydrogen atom and the hydrogen-like ions were found. The wave functions were found to depend on three quantum numbers n, l, and m, and the significance of these quantum numbers was discussed.

2. The selection rules for transitions between hydrogen-like orbitals were derived. They are $\Delta l = \pm 1$, $\Delta m = 0, \pm 1$, Δn—no restriction.

3. Atomic units were introduced. Using these units, distances are measured in Bohr radii and energy in Hartrees. One Hartree = 27.2 ev.

4. The electronic structure of the helium atom was discussed. It was found that exact analytical solutions to the helium problem could not be obtained because of the electron repulsion term in the Hamiltonian. Various approximate solutions to the helium problem were discussed.

5. Some properties of orbital angular momentum operators were introduced.

6. The existence of electron spin angular momentum was postulated. The operators for spin angular momentum combine and commute in the same way as the corresponding ones for orbital angular momentum.

---

[17] For more information on the structure of atoms, the student may wish to consult references B3 and D1 in the Bibliography.

7. The restrictions placed on wave functions for systems containing many identical particles were discussed.   For electrons and other spin $\frac{1}{2}$ particles, acceptable wave functions must be antisymmetric upon interchange of the coordinates of any two particles.   For even spin particles, acceptable wave functions must be symmetric upon interchange of the coordinates of any two particles.

8. The independent electron theory of complex atoms was developed, and it was shown that an antisymmetrized wave function for such atoms could be written in the form of a Slater determinant.

9. The properties of some of the atoms in the first row of the periodic table were discussed in terms of this independent electron theory.

10. The student should be familiar with the terms principal quantum number, azimuthal quantum number, magnetic quantum number, radial distribution function, node, electron repulsion term, raising and lowering operator, antisymmetric wave function, permutation operator, Slater determinant, multiplicity, Aufbau principle, Hund's first and second rules, orbital, Lande g factor, and Bohr magneton.

Chapter 7

MOLECULES AND THE
CHEMICAL BOND

THE PROBLEM of molecular electronic structure is one of the most fundamental to the chemist because the great majority of chemical experiments today involve molecules. A successful theory of molecular electronic structure must, first of all, answer several fundamental questions about molecules. Only when these questions have been answered should the theory be examined to see how well it explains the details of molecular structure.

There are at least three fundamental questions that we seek to answer by a theory of molecular electronic structure.

1. Why do molecules form at all? Why, for example, do a pair of halogen atoms combine to form a halogen molecule while a pair of inert gas atoms do not? An alternate way to phrase this same question is to ask, "What is a chemical bond?"

2. Why do molecules have the formulas that they do? Can a quantum mechanical description be provided for the Law of Multiple Proportions?

3. Why do molecules form with their characteristic stereo-chemical arrangement? For example, why is CO_2 a linear molecule while SO_2 is bent?

In this chapter, we will attempt to answer these questions, at least in part. The student must keep in mind, however, that even though much progress has been made in answering these questions, a great deal remains to be done. Perhaps this chapter will induce some of the readers to contribute to the answers.

7-1 *The hydrogen molecule ion, H_2^+*

The simplest molecule is one containing two protons and one electron. This molecule, H_2^+, is called the hydrogen molecule ion. It was discovered by J. J. Thomson in cathode rays, and has been found to have an equilibrium internuclear distance of 1.060 Å and a binding energy of 2.791 ev. The eigenfunctions and eigenvalues to the problem of H_2^+ are very important because they can be used to develop an approximate theory of the structure of more complex diatomic molecules in the same way as the solutions to the hydrogen atom problem were used in constructing an approximate theory of the structure of complex atoms.

The nomenclature used in discussing H_2^+ is shown in Figure 7-1. The quantities r_A and r_B are the electronic distances from nucleus A and B, respectively, and R_{AB} is the internuclear distance.

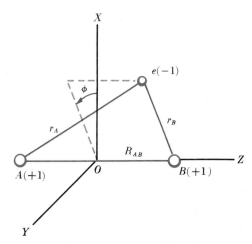

FIG. 7-1 *Quantities used in the discussion of H_2^+. The angle ϕ is the angle between the X axis and the projection of the line Oe in the XY plane.*

The Hamiltonian operator in atomic units is

$$\hat{\mathfrak{H}} = -\frac{1}{2}\nabla^2 - \frac{m}{M_A}\frac{1}{2}\nabla_A{}^2 - \frac{m}{M_B}\frac{1}{2}\nabla_B{}^2 - \frac{1}{r_A} - \frac{1}{r_B} + \frac{1}{R_{AB}}$$

$$(7\text{-}1)$$

where the terms represent, respectively, the kinetic energies of the electron, nucleus A and nucleus B, the potential energy of attraction between the electron and the two nuclei, and the nuclear repulsion energy. The allowed energies and wave functions are found by the solution to the eigenvalue equation

$$\hat{\mathfrak{H}}\Psi_i = E_i\Psi_i \qquad\qquad (7\text{-}2)$$

The student will immediately notice that the problem of $H_2{}^+$ is a three-body problem like that of the helium atom. The three-body problem is insoluble in its most general form, but, fortunately, a very good approximation can be made that renders Equation 7-2 soluble to any degree of accuracy required. This approximation is called the Born-Oppenheimer approximation. It states that the motions of the electrons in a molecule are so rapid that in studying the electronic properties of molecules the nuclei may be regarded as fixed. This means that the electronic energy can be found at a set of fixed internuclear distances, and then plotted as a function of R_{AB}. When this procedure is followed for $H_2{}^+$, a plot such as that shown in Figure 7-2 is obtained. A minimum in the curve corresponds to the formation of a stable molecule, and the depth of the minimum is the dissociation or binding energy.[1] Curves such as that of Figure 7-2 have a double interpretation. First, they give the electronic energy as a function of internuclear distance. Second, they give the potential energy of the nuclei as a function of the displacement from the equilibrium internuclear distance. Thus, it is the change in electronic energy upon increasing or decreasing the internuclear distance that gives rise to the vibrational force constant discussed in Chapter 5.

Mathematically, the Born-Oppenheimer approximation allows us to drop the nuclear kinetic energy terms from the Hamiltonian in Equation 7-1. The problem of $H_2{}^+$ is then exactly soluble because it is reduced to a one-electron problem.

[1] The student will recall that the binding energy is the same as the energy D_e discussed in Chapter 5. Thus, the binding energy is equal to the measured dissociation energy, D_0, plus the zero point energy.

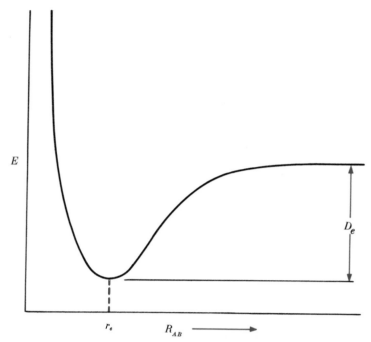

FIG. 7-2 *A plot of electronic energy versus internuclear distance for a diatomic molecule. The quantity r_e is the internuclear distance, and D_e is the dissociation or binding energy. The quantity D_e is the observed dissociation energy of a molecule plus the vibrational zero point energy.*

If elliptical coordinates are used, it is possible to separate variables and find a solution to Equation 7-2 of the form

$$\Psi = U(\mu)V(\nu)\Phi(\phi) \tag{7-3}$$

where the three functions U, V, and Φ, are a function only of the variables μ, ν, and ϕ, respectively.[2] We will not be concerned about this exact solution to the H_2^+ problem except to make a few remarks about the Φ part of the wave function.

From Figure 7-1, it can be seen that the potential energy of H_2^+ has rotational symmetry about the A—B axis. That is, the Hamiltonian in Equation 7-1 does not depend on the location of

---

[2] The detailed form of the solutions U, V, can be found in D. R. Bates, K. Ledsham, and A. L. Stewart, *Phil. Trans. Roy. Soc.*, **A246**, 215 (1953).

the X and Y axes. The Φ part of the eigenvalue Equation 7-2 reflects this and leads to

$$\frac{d^2\Phi}{d\phi^2} = -m^2\Phi \tag{7-4}$$

which has the familiar solutions

$$\Phi = Ae^{im\phi} \tag{7-5}$$

where $m = 0, \pm 1, \pm 2 \cdots$. These solutions have a physical interpretation based on the fact that they are eigenfunctions of the operator $\hat{L}_z$ where now the Z axis is defined by the direction of the A—B bond.

In the case of H_2^+, the energy will depend on m, except that states for $\pm m$ will have the same energy. Thus, considering only angular degeneracy, we have a singly degenerate level for $m = 0$, and doubly degenerate levels for $m = \pm 1, \pm 2$, etc. The Φ solutions have been discussed mainly so as to introduce a nomenclature to describe the states of diatomic molecules. This nomenclature is similar to the s, p, d, f nomenclature used in atomic orbitals except that Greek letters are used. Thus, for various values of m, the orbitals are labeled as follows:

m	Orbital Designation
0	σ
± 1	π
± 2	δ

Similar to the situation encountered with the $TU(1, 1)$ functions for atoms, it may not always be convenient to use orbital functions of the form of Equation 7-5. Thus, orbitals analogous to the p_x and p_y orbitals for atoms can be constructed by taking appropriate linear combinations of the $\pm m$ functions in Equation 7-5. The same orbital designations given above are used for these linear combinations.

EXERCISE 7-1   Describe the angular properties of the function

$$\Phi_\pi = \frac{1}{(2)^{\frac{1}{2}}}[Ae^{+i\phi} + Ae^{-i\phi}] \text{ for } H_2^+.$$

It will now be instructive to investigate some of the approximate solutions for H_2^+. These approximate solutions will then be used in the remainder of our discussion of diatomic molecules.

7-2 *The variation principle and the LCAO method*

One of the most powerful approximation methods of quantum mechanics rests on a result that can be proved from classical physics. This result, which we will give without proof, is called the variation principle. In the form that we will use, it states:

> *Given any approximate wave function satisfying the boundary conditions of the problem, the expectation value of the energy calculated from this function will always be higher than the true energy of the ground state.*[3]

This principle suggests a procedure for solving quantum mechanical problems. This procedure is to guess several functions, called trial functions, calculate the expectation value of the energy for each one, choose the one with the lowest energy, and conclude that this is the best function that can be obtained from the original guesses.

Scientists like to use a more systematic procedure than the above. One way to be more systematic is to start with a trial function containing several arbitrary parameters. The expectation value of the energy is then calculated and is minimized with respect to the arbitrary parameters. In this way, a large number of "guesses" can be made with a single function. The resulting wave function is then the best available with the particular parametric form chosen.

The usual way to carry out such a calculation is to make use of a linear variation function, and this is the basis for the "linear combination of atomic orbitals" or LCAO method. Since molecules are made up of atoms, it is fairly reasonable to assume that the electron distribution in a molecule can be approximately represented as a sum of atomic electron distributions. This is the physical basis for the "molecular orbital" or MO method of solving

---

[3] The variation principle can be applied to finding approximate wave functions for excited states, but there are many problems involved in such an application. The variation principle is rigorously true for excited state energies only if the trial function is orthogonal to the true wave function for all of the intervening states.

quantum mechanical problems. In this method, one chooses as a
trial function for a molecular orbital Ψ, a linear variation function
of the type

$$\Psi = \sum_\mu C_\mu \chi_\mu \tag{7-6}$$

where χ_μ are the appropriate atomic orbitals, and the coefficients
C_μ are the parameters that will be chosen so as to minimize the
energy. The orbitals used in the linear combination are called
basis orbitals or basis functions.

We will now illustrate a variational calculation for H_2^+. In
this, we assume that the molecular orbitals Ψ_i will be some linear
combination of hydrogen $1s$ atomic orbitals. We, thus, write

$$\Psi = C_1 \chi_A + C_2 \chi_B \tag{7-7}$$

where χ_A and χ_B are $1s$ orbitals localized on atoms A and B,
respectively. The expectation value of the energy is

$$E \equiv \langle E \rangle = \frac{(\Psi|\mathcal{H}|\Psi)}{(\Psi|\Psi)}$$

$$= \frac{C_1{}^2(\chi_A|\mathcal{H}|\chi_A) + 2C_1C_2(\chi_A|\mathcal{H}|\chi_B) + C_2{}^2(\chi_B|\mathcal{H}|\chi_B)}{C_1{}^2(\chi_A|\chi_A) + 2C_1C_2(\chi_A|\chi_B) + C_2{}^2(\chi_B|\chi_B)} \tag{7-8}$$

We take advantage of the fact that χ_A and χ_B can be taken to be
normalized, and we also introduce a shorthand notation as follows:

$$(\chi_\mu|\mathcal{H}|\chi_\nu) \equiv H_{\mu\nu} \tag{7-9a}$$
$$(\chi_\mu|\chi_\nu) \equiv S_{\mu\nu} \tag{7-9b}$$

Using the notation of Equation 7-9a and b and the normalization
condition that $(\chi_\mu|\chi_\mu) = 1$, Equation 7-8 becomes

$$E = \frac{C_1{}^2 H_{AA} + 2C_1C_2 H_{AB} + C_2{}^2 H_{BB}}{C_1{}^2 + 2C_1C_2 S_{AB} + C_2{}^2} \tag{7-10}$$

We now wish to find the values of C_1 and C_2 which make E a
minimum. To do this, we must solve the equations

$$\left(\frac{\partial E}{\partial C_1}\right)_{C_2} = 0, \left(\frac{\partial E}{\partial C_2}\right)_{C_1} = 0 \tag{7-11}$$

Going through some straightforward algebra, Equations 7-11 become

$$C_1(H_{AA} - E) + C_2(H_{AB} - S_{AB}E) = 0$$
$$C_1(H_{AB} - S_{AB}E) + C_2(H_{BB} - E) = 0 \qquad (7\text{-}12)$$

EXERCISE 7-2 Using Equations 7-10 and 7-11, derive Equations 7-12.

These equations are called secular equations. To solve them for C_1 and C_2, one makes use of the fact that, for a set of simultaneous linear equations without constant terms to have a nontrivial solution (that is, a solution other than $C_1 = C_2 = 0$), the determinant of the coefficients must vanish.[4] Thus, for Equations 7-12 to have a solution, it must be true that

$$\begin{vmatrix} H_{AA} - E & H_{AB} - SE \\ H_{AB} - SE & H_{BB} - E \end{vmatrix} = 0 \qquad (7\text{-}13)$$

where S has been used for S_{AB}. The determinant in Equation 7-13 is called a secular determinant. Since, in the present problem, χ_A and χ_B are identical and Equation 7-1 is symmetric in both nuclei, $H_{AA} = H_{BB}$, and Equation 7-13 becomes

$$(H_{AA} - E)^2 - (H_{AB} - SE)^2 = 0$$
$$H_{AA} - E = \pm (H_{AB} - SE)$$
$$E = \frac{H_{AA} \pm H_{AB}}{1 \pm S} \qquad (7\text{-}14)$$

We now write these energies separately as

$$E_+ = \frac{H_{AA} + H_{AB}}{1 + S}$$
$$E_- = \frac{H_{AA} - H_{AB}}{1 - S} \qquad (7\text{-}15)$$

and substitute them *one at a time* back into Equations 7-12. This gives the solutions

$$C_{1+} = C_{2+}$$
$$C_{1-} = - C_{2-} \qquad (7\text{-}16)$$

[4] I, pp. 313 ff.

Thus, the wave functions corresponding to the two energies E_+ and E_- are, respectively,

$$\Psi_+ = C_1\chi_1 + C_1\chi_2 = \frac{1}{(2 + 2S)^{\frac{1}{2}}} (\chi_1 + \chi_2)$$

$$\Psi_- = C_1\chi_1 - C_1\chi_2 = \frac{1}{(2 - 2S)^{\frac{1}{2}}} (\chi_1 - \chi_2)$$

(7-17)

where the functions on the right-hand side have been normalized.

EXERCISE 7-3   Show that the proper normalizing factor has been used in Equations 7-17.

Before the significance of Equations 7-15 and 7-17 is discussed, it will be useful to generalize what has been done in going from Equation 7-7 to Equation 7-17.

1. Use of an LCAO function with n orbitals and the variation principle will always lead to a set of n secular equations, each of which will contain n coefficients.

2. These secular equations will have a nontrivial solution only if the secular determinant vanishes. This secular determinant will be of dimension $n \times n$.

3. Solution of the secular determinant leads to a characteristic equation, a polynomial of degree n in E. This characteristic equation has n roots, the lowest of which is an upper bound to the energy of the lowest molecular orbital. The other roots, in increasing order, are upper bounds to the energies of higher energy *orbitals*.[5]

4. These energies are substituted back into the secular equations one at a time to find the coefficients in the LCAO function that determine the wave function that gives that particular energy. The student should memorize these general statements because this procedure will be used again in Chapter 8.

We now return to the significance of the solutions for H_2^+. The integrals, H_{AA}, H_{AB}, and S_{AB}, can all be evaluated by transforming to elliptical coordinates (see Exercise 7-4). The quanti-

---

[5] The student should be careful to distinguish between an *orbital* and a *state*. The variation principle will not allow one to make the final statement in step 3 about the excited *states* of a system with more than one electron. For a one electron system, orbital and state are synonymous and, in this case only, are the higher roots of a linear variation function upper bounds to the energies of the excited states.

ties H_{AA} and H_{AB} both turn out to be negative. The quantity H_{AA} is

$$\int \chi_A \left(-\frac{1}{2}\nabla^2 - \frac{1}{r_A} - \frac{1}{r_B} \right) \chi_A \, d\tau = E_{1s}(H) - \int \chi_A \frac{1}{r_B} \chi_A \, d\tau$$

$$(7\text{-}18)$$

In Equation 7-18 it can be seen that the integral H_{AA} (called a coulomb integral) represents the energy of an electron in a $1s$ orbital of hydrogen plus the attractive energy of nucleus B for this electron. As nuclei A and B are brought closer together the second term tends to make the energy of H_2^+ more negative and, consequently, increase the stability of the molecule. This energy stabilization is more than counteracted by the nuclear repulsion energy, however, and a plot of $\left(H_{AA} + \dfrac{1}{R_{AB}} \right)$ as a function of R_{AB} gives a curve that has the value $-\frac{1}{2}$ at $R_{AB} = \infty$ and that increases monotonically to the value ∞ at $R_{AB} = 0$. The term $\left(H_{AA} + \dfrac{1}{R_{AB}} \right)$ gives no contribution to the stability of H_2^+.

The integral H_{AB} is called the resonance or exchange integral. This integral takes into account the fact that the electron is not restricted to only a $1s$ atomic orbital on either atom A or B, but that it can exchange places between the two orbitals. The resonance integral goes to zero at large R_{AB}, and increases with the overlap as R_{AB} is made smaller. It is this integral that leads to all of the calculated binding energy in H_2^+. The significance of this integral can be rationalized in terms of the classical theory of a pair of resonating pendulums.[6]

Since both H_{AA} and H_{AB} are negative, E_+ will be the lowest energy, and E_- will be the highest. A plot of the energies E_+ and E_- as a function of internuclear distance is shown in Figure 7-3. The dotted curve in Figure 7-3 represents the exact energy. The student may obtain the plot for E_+ by working Exercise 7-4.

EXERCISE 7-4 Evaluate the integrals S_{AB}, H_{AA}, and H_{AB} as a function of the internuclear distance R (use atomic units). Transform to elliptical coordinates, and use $1 \leq \mu \leq \infty$, $-1 \leq \nu \leq +1$, $0 \leq \phi \leq 2\pi$ as the limits of integration. Make a plot of H_{AA} and E_+ versus R.

[6] See C. A. Coulson, *Valence*, Oxford University Press, London (1961) pp. 79 ff.

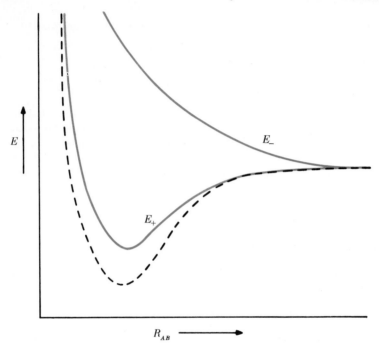

FIG. 7-3 *Energies of the states Ψ_+ and Ψ_- for $H_2{}^+$, as a function of internuclear distance R_{AB}.   The dotted curve represents the true energy. The energy of the state Ψ_- is very close to the energy of this state calculated from the exact solutions of $H_2{}^+$.*

What is the equilibrium internuclear distance?   In this approximation, what gives rise to the binding?

From a plot of E_+ *versus* R_{AB}, it can be shown that the LCAO approximation gives a binding energy of 1.76 ev and an equilibrium internuclear distance of 1.32 Å.   Comparison of these values with the experimental values of the corresponding quantities (2.791 ev and 1.37 Å) shows that the accuracy of the LCAO wave function leaves something to be desired.   The LCAO method does have many points in its favor, however.   These are,

1. The theory leads to a prediction that a stable molecule will be formed from a hydrogen atom and a proton.

2. It retains the "atoms in molecules" idea which is intuitively pleasing to the chemist.

3. The theory is computationally simple, allowing it to be applied to molecules of great complexity.

The last point is, perhaps, the greatest advantage of the LCAO-MO method.

7-3 Excited states of H_2^+

As was mentioned above in the general formulation of the LCAO method, the function Ψ_- can be regarded as an approximation to one of the excited states of H_2^+. It is a dissociative or antibonding state, however. That is, an H_2^+ molecule in the state Ψ_- is *less stable* than a hydrogen atom and a proton at all internuclear distances, and consequently, if an H_2^+ molecule could somehow be prepared in state Ψ_-, it would immediately dissociate to a hydrogen atom and a proton.

There are other excited states of H_2^+, however. The molecular orbitals that are approximations to these states may be formed from linear combinations of higher hydrogen atomic orbitals. Since these orbitals will be used to discuss the structure of more complex diatomic molecules, a nomenclature for them must be introduced. This nomenclature depends on the following characteristics:

1. The atomic orbitals from which they are formed.

2. The eigenvalue with respect to $\hat{L}_z$, the angular momentum quantum number about the internuclear axis (see Section 7-1).

3. Their property on inversion through the center of the molecule. If the orbital function does not change sign upon inversion, it is called g. If it does change sign, it is called u. This classification only applies to homonuclear diatomic molecules, such as H_2, O_2, and N_2, in which both nuclei have the same atomic number.

4. Their stability with respect to the isolated atoms. If the orbital energy is lower than the energies of the corresponding orbitals on the isolated atoms, it is called a bonding orbital. If it is less stable, it is called an antibonding orbital, and is designated by a star superscript. This latter property can also be correlated with the property of the molecular orbitals when they are reflected in a plane perpendicular to and bisecting the bond axis.

Some examples of this nomenclature are given in Table 7-1. These excited state molecular orbitals will be discussed in more detail in Section 7-6.

TABLE 7-1 SYMBOLS USED FOR SOME OF THE EXCITED MOLECULAR ORBITALS IN H_2^+. A SECOND $\pi_u 2p$ ORBITAL CAN BE FORMED FROM $2p_{-1}$ ORBITALS ON ATOMS A AND B

LCAO Function	MO Nomenclature
$1s_A + 1s_B$	$\sigma_g 1s$
$1s_A - 1s_B$	$\sigma_u^* 1s$
$2s_A + 2s_B$	$\sigma_g 2s$
$2s_A - 2s_B$	$\sigma_u^* 2s$
$2p_{0A} - 2p_{0B}$	$\sigma_g 2p$
$2p_{1A} + 2p_{1B}$	$\pi_u 2p$

EXERCISE 7-5 What are the molecular orbital symbols for the orbitals $2p_{-1A} + 2p_{-1B}$ and $2p_{0A} + 2p_{0B}$?

7-4 *The hydrogen molecule*

The hydrogen molecule occupies the same place in the theory of molecular electronic structure as the helium atom occupies in the theory of atomic structure. It is extremely important in that all of the features of the two-electron bond are present in molecular hydrogen. An understanding of this molecule gives insight into the nature of the chemical bond in more complex molecules.

The notation used for a discussion of the hydrogen molecule is shown in Figure 7-4. The Hamiltonian in atomic units is

$$\hat{\mathcal{H}} = -\frac{1}{2}\left(\nabla_1^2 + \nabla_2^2\right)$$

$$-\frac{1}{r_{A1}} - \frac{1}{r_{A2}} - \frac{1}{r_{B1}} - \frac{1}{r_{B2}} + \frac{1}{r_{12}} + \frac{1}{R_{AB}} \quad (7\text{-}19)$$

The significance of each of these terms should be familiar to the reader. The eigenvalue equation

$$\hat{\mathcal{H}}\Psi = E\Psi \quad (7\text{-}20)$$

is, like that of helium, impossible to solve in analytical form. We are, thus, forced to use an approximation method. At the lowest level of approximation, there are two methods used to describe the ground state of hydrogen. These are the molecular orbital (MO) method and the Heitler-London (HL) method. We will discuss the MO method first because it is already familiar

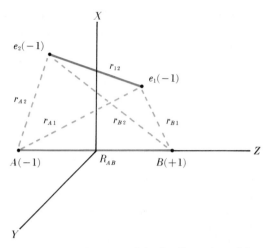

FIG. 7-4 *Distances used in the discussion of the hydrogen molecule.*

from the discussion of H_2^+. (Historically, the HL method was developed first.) After these two simple methods are introduced, various ways to improve the hydrogen molecule wave functions will be discussed. All of the results calculated below should be compared with the following experimental values:

Total energy $- 1.174$ H
Binding energy $=$ Total energy $-$ energy of 2 isolated hydrogen atoms
$\qquad = - 1.174 - (- 1.000) = - 0.174$ H
$\qquad = - 4.75$ ev
Equilibrium internuclear distance $= 0.740$ Å

In the molecular orbital method for the hydrogen molecule, we begin investigating solutions to Equation 7-20 using the approximate Hamiltonian derived from Equation 7-18 by leaving out the $1/r_{12}$ term. This Hamiltonian can be written as

$$\hat{\mathcal{H}} = - \frac{1}{2} \nabla_1{}^2 - \frac{1}{r_{A1}} - \frac{1}{r_{B1}} - \frac{1}{2} \nabla_2{}^2 - \frac{1}{r_{A2}} - \frac{1}{r_{B2}} + \frac{1}{R_{AB}}$$

$$(7\text{-}21)$$

where the order has been changed to show that the first three terms are a function only of the coordinates and momenta of electron 1, and the second three terms are a function only of the coordinates and momenta of electron 2. If $1/R_{AB}$ is both added and subtracted from Equation 7-21, this approximate Hamiltonian can be written as

$$\hat{\mathcal{K}}_0 = \hat{h}_0(1) + \hat{h}_0(2) - \frac{1}{R_{AB}} \tag{7-22}$$

where $\hat{h}_0$ is the Hamiltonian for the H_2^+ ion. Since, within the context of the Born-Oppenheimer approximation, the $1/R_{AB}$ term only contributes a constant term to the energy, we can make use of the separation of variables theorem to show that an eigenvalue equation using the Hamiltonian of Equation 7-22 is satisfied by product function of the type

$$\Psi = A\omega_i(1)\omega_i(2) \tag{7-23}$$

where ω_i are the solutions to the H_2^+ problem and A is a suitable normalizing constant.

We must now introduce electron spin into the wave function of Equation 7-23, and adjust the result so that the Pauli principle is obeyed. By applying the same kind of arguments as were used for the case of the helium atom, the student may show that the lowest energy wave function of the type of Equation 7-23 that satisfies the Pauli principle is

$$\Psi_{MO} = \omega_1(1)\omega_1(2) \frac{1}{\sqrt{2}} [\alpha(1)\beta(2) - \beta(1)\alpha(2)] \tag{7-24}$$

where the MO, ω_1, may be approximated by the LCAO function

$$\omega_1 = \frac{1}{(2 + 2S)^{\frac{1}{2}}} (1s_A + 1s_B) \tag{7-25}$$

EXERCISE 7-6 Show that Ψ_{MO} is an eigenfunction of the operator P_{12} with eigenvalue -1.

The function ψ_{MO} is an eigenfunction of an approximate Hamiltonian that is the exact Hamiltonian with the $1/r_{12}$ term omitted.

The energy is calculated in a manner similar to that for the helium atom. That is, the expectation value of E is calculated as a function of R_{AB} using Ψ_{MO} and the exact Hamiltonian. Thus,

$$
\langle E \rangle = (\Psi_{MO}|\mathcal{H}|\Psi_{MO})
$$
$$
= 2E'(R_{AB}) + \left(\Psi_{MO}\left|\frac{1}{r_{12}}\right|\Psi_{MO}\right) - \frac{1}{R_{AB}} \quad (7\text{-}26)
$$

where $E'(R_{AB})$ is the expression for the energy of H_2^+ as a function of the internuclear distance R_{AB}. To find the binding energy and the equilibrium internuclear distance, one minimizes $\langle E \rangle$ with respect to R_{AB}. If this is done, one obtains

$$
\langle E \rangle_{MO} = -1.0985 \text{ H}
$$
$$
\text{Binding energy} = \langle E \rangle - 2E(H) = -1.0985 + 1.000
$$
$$
= -0.0985 \text{ H} = -2.681 \text{ ev}
$$
$$
R_{AB}{}^0 = 0.850 \text{ Å}
$$

It is instructive to write out the MO function for hydrogen in more detail. Expanded, the space part of Equation 7-24 becomes

$$
\Psi_{MO}(\text{space part}) = \frac{1}{2 + 2S}[1s_A(1)1s_A(2)
$$
$$
+ 1s_A(1)1s_B(2) + 1s_B(1)1s_A(2) + 1s_B(1)1s_B(2)] \quad (7\text{-}27)
$$

It can be seen that the first and fourth terms represent a probability of finding both electrons close to one nucleus. This is equivalent to writing ionic structures for hydrogen of the form $H_A^+H_B^-$ and $H_A^-H_B^+$. One of the great shortcomings of the MO function is that these "ionic terms" enter into the wave function *with the same weight as the covalent terms*. This is contrary to chemical experience because chemists intuitively feel that hydrogen is a covalent compound. This feature of the MO wave function is also unsatisfactory because it predicts that, upon dissociation, one half of the hydrogen molecules should dissociate into the ions H^- and H^+. In fact, it is known that a hydrogen molecule always dissociates into two hydrogen atoms.

With these considerations in mind, one can write a second wave function for the ground state of the hydrogen molecule that only includes the "covalent" part of Equation 7-27. This is the Heitler-London wave function for hydrogen. This function is

$$
\Psi_{HL} = N[\phi_A(1)\phi_B(2)
$$
$$
+ \phi_B(1)\phi_A(2)]\frac{1}{\sqrt{2}}[\alpha(1)\beta(2) - \beta(1)\alpha(2)] \quad (7\text{-}28)
$$

where N is a normalizing constant and where ϕ_A and ϕ_B have replaced the symbols $1s_A$ and $1s_B$. The student should note that the space part of this wave function is symmetric. The spin part must be antisymmetric, therefore, to make the total wave function obey the Pauli principle. To save writing, the labels on the electrons are usually omitted with the understanding that the function for electron one is always written first, that for electron two second, etc. Using this convention, Equation 7-28 becomes

$$\Psi_{HL} = \frac{1}{N}[\phi_A\phi_B + \phi_B\phi_A]\frac{1}{\sqrt{2}}[\alpha\beta - \beta\alpha] \tag{7-29}$$

Using the exact Hamiltonian to calculate $\langle E \rangle$ one obtains

$$\langle E \rangle = -1.1160$$
$$\text{B.E.} = -0.1160 \text{ H} = -3.140 \text{ ev}$$
$$R_{AB}{}^0 = 1.67a_0 = 0.869 \text{ Å}$$

It should be noted that this calculation gives 70% of the binding energy, which is fairly good.

It can be seen from the above that the HL function gives a better value for the energy than does the MO function. It also predicts the proper behavior at large internuclear distances. It might be tempting to say that the Heitler-London method (or valence bond, VB, method as its later modifications were called) is "better" than the MO method. This conclusion is not justified, however, because both are gross approximations to the actual state of affairs in the molecule. The conclusion that *can* be drawn is that it is better to leave the ionic terms out of the wave function for hydrogen altogether than to give them equal weight with the covalent terms.

The student should be acquainted with some of the nomenclature arising from VB calculations. Using the wave function in Equation 7-29, one obtains for the energy

$$\langle E \rangle = \frac{\langle(\phi_A\phi_B + \phi_B\phi_A)|\hat{\mathcal{H}}|(\phi_A\phi_B + \phi_B\phi_A)\rangle}{\langle(\phi_A\phi_B + \phi_A\phi_B)|(\phi_A\phi_B + \phi_B\phi_A)\rangle} \tag{7-30}$$
$$= \frac{J + K}{1 + S^2}$$

where

$$J = \int \phi_A(1)\phi_B(2)\hat{\mathcal{H}}\phi_A(1)\phi_B(2) \, d\tau_1 \, d\tau_2$$
$$K = \int \phi_A(1)\phi_B(2)\hat{\mathcal{H}}\phi_B(1)\phi_A(2) \, d\tau_1 \, d\tau_2$$

and S is the overlap integral. The integral J is called a coulomb integral (not to be confused with H_{AA}) and gives the energy that a hydrogen molecule would have if its wave function were

$$\Psi = \phi_A(1)\phi_B(2)$$

that is, if the electrons were not allowed to change places. This integral leads to a shallow minimum of about 0.4 ev at an internuclear separation of 1.0 Å. The integral K is called the exchange integral. This nomenclature arises because the electrons have "changed places" in the two halves of the integrand of K. This integral leads to most of the calculated stability for the hydrogen molecule.

The generalization of the Heitler-London method to more complex molecules is known as the Heitler-London-Slater-Pauling (HLSP) or valence bond (VB) method. In the VB method, the total wave function for a molecule is made up of a product of bond eigenfunctions. For a bond formed between atoms a and b, the bond eigenfunction can be written

$$\Psi = \frac{1}{N}(ab + ba)(\alpha\beta - \beta\alpha) \tag{7-31}$$

where a and b are appropriate orbitals localized on atoms a and b, respectively. Specific examples of the use of VB theory in the treatment of complex molecules will be given in Section 7-8.

7-5 *Improvements on the wave function for* H_2

The comparison of the results from MO and VB calculations on the hydrogen molecule indicates that it is better to leave out the ionic terms altogether than to put them in with equal weight with the covalent terms. A better wave function then either might arise if the ionic terms were introduced into the wave function multiplied by a variational parameter λ. Such a wave function is called the Weinbaum function. Omitting the spin part, this function is

$$\Psi = N[(\phi_A\phi_B + \phi_B\phi_A) + \lambda(\phi_A\phi_A + \phi_B\phi_B)]$$

where λ is the arbitrary variation parameter. Minimizing the energy with respect to λ, one obtains

$$\langle E \rangle = -1.1187 \text{ H}$$
$$\text{B.E.} = -0.1187 \text{ H}$$
$$\lambda = 0.25$$

The improvement in the calculated energy in going from the HL function to the Weinbaum function is often attributed to "ionic-covalent resonance." That is, the Weinbaum function mixes in a small amount of the ionic terms $H_A{}^+H_B{}^-$, $H_A{}^-H_B{}^+$ with the covalent term H—H. Such a picture is misleading, however. As will be shown below, a better energy than that obtained with the Weinbaum function can be obtained using a completely "covalent" wave function. It should be emphasized that ideas like that of "ionic-covalent resonance" are *convenient* models in that they correlate a lot of chemical data. This makes them valuable, but they should not be thought of as necessarily giving a true picture of what the electrons are doing in molecules.

A different approach to the problem of the ground state of a hydrogen molecule was developed by Rosen. He argued that a 1*s* atomic orbital is not a good basis orbital to use because the electron distribution around a proton in a hydrogen molecule will not be the same as the distribution in an atom. In a molecule, the electron distribution would be expected to be polarized toward the other nucleus. The way to include this polarization effect is to include a little 2*p* character in the basis orbitals. Rosen, therefore, used a wave function of the form

$$\Psi_R = N[(1s_A + \kappa 2p_{zA})(1)(1s_B + \kappa 2p_{zB})(2)$$
$$+ \text{ symmetrizing terms}]$$

where κ is a variational parameter. Minimizing E with respect to κ one obtains

$$\langle E \rangle = -1.125 \text{ H}$$
$$\text{B.E.} = -0.125 \text{ H}$$

It can be seen that the Rosen wave function gives the best energy of any function so far discussed.

A method often used to improve molecular wave functions is that of introducing an effective nuclear charge or scale factors into

TABLE 7-2 THE EFFECTS OF SCALING ON THE ENERGY OF APPROXIMATE WAVE FUNCTIONS FOR H_2

Wave Function	$-E$ Unscaled		$-E$ Scaled		$-E$ exp
	au	ev	au	ev	
MO	0.0985	2.681	0.1285	3.495	
HL	0.1160	3.14	0.1391	3.784	
					0.174 au
Weinbaum	0.1187	3.229	0.14796	4.024	or
					4.75 ev
Rosen	0.125	3.400	0.1485	4.039	

the atomic orbital basis set.[7] For the hydrogen molecule, if a scale factor is introduced into the exponent of the $1s$ atomic orbital, and if the energy is then minimized with respect to this scale factor, the energies of all of the wave functions discussed above are substantially improved. This improvement can be seen in Table 7-2. It should be noted that the scaled MO function gives a better energy than the unscaled Rosen function. This shows that a wave function is improved more by scaling than by adding ionic terms or orbital polarization. The scaled Rosen function is quite good in that it gives 85% of the experimental energy. This energy is still in error by 16 kcal mole^{-1}, a substantial amount when chemical effects are being considered.

There have been many other calculations on molecular hydrogen. The best is the James-Coolidge wave function as modified by Kolos and Roothaan.[8] This function is a 50 term variation function, and the interelectron distance is explicitly included in each term. It gives a binding energy of -1.1744 H, in agreement with experiment. Unfortunately (or fortunately, depending on one's viewpoint), all concepts of atomic or molecular orbitals, exchange, coulomb, and resonance integrals have disappeared in this function.

[7] This procedure is called scaling the wave function. It usually makes a striking improvement in the calculated energy. This is because an additional parameter has been introduced into the variation function. Scaling is especially significant, however, because it ensures that the wave function satisfies the Virial theorem. For more information about this latter point, the student is referred to **III**, pp. 437 ff.

[8] Kolos and Roothaan, *Rev. Mod. Phys.*, **32**, 219 (1960).

The James-Coolidge result in 1933 satisfied many people that accurate quantum mechanical calculations were possible for molecules. Since that time, many accurate calculations have been carried out on other simple molecules (LiH, HF, etc.). It is still an open question, however, whether accurate, *ab initio*, calculations will solve many of the fundamental chemical problems associated with the structure and behavior of complex molecules.

7-6   *MO theory of more complex diatomic molecules*

A simple theory which predicts many of the properties of diatomic molecules can be developed in the same way as the independent electron theory of complex atoms was developed. To do this, one uses the molecular orbitals found for H_2^+, and places electrons in these orbitals in accordance with the Pauli principle. A schematic drawing of these independent electron MO's that indicates how their energy compares with the appropriate orbitals in the isolated atom is shown in Figure 7-5. Before discussing the electronic structure of specific diatomic molecules, the student will no doubt wish to know why the energies of the molecular orbitals shown in Figure 7-5 have the particular order indicated. First, it should be recalled from the discussion of H_2^+ that, if one forms molecular orbitals from a $1s$ orbital localized on each of two atomic centers, one ends up with two molecular orbitals. It is a general feature of the LCAO method that one always ends up with as many molecular orbitals as the number of basis orbitals used in the LCAO function. Also, at the equilibrium internuclear distance, one of the molecular orbitals is bonding and the other is antibonding. Thus, one has a lower energy, and the other has a higher energy than the sum of the energies of the corresponding orbitals in the isolated atom. These facts rationalize the number and the relative spacing of the two molecular orbitals formed from $1s$ atomic orbitals on atoms A and B. Probability contour drawings for the $\sigma_g 1s$ and $\sigma_u^* 1s$ orbitals are shown in Figure 7-6. The g and u character of these molecular orbitals is also apparent from Figure 7-6. If, in the bonding molecular orbital, $x \to -x, y \to -y, z \to -z$, the wave function still has the same sign. In the antibonding orbital, the wave function has the opposite sign at $p(x, y, z)$ as it does at $p(-x, -y, -z)$.

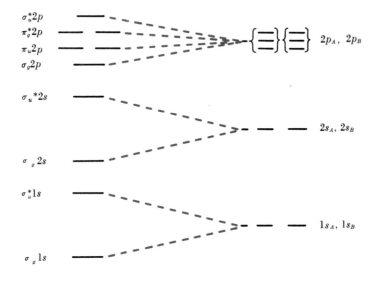

Molecular Orbital   Atomic Orbital in Isolated Atoms

FIG. 7-5 *The energies and names of the one-electron orbitals used in the simple MO treatment of diatomic molecules. The arrows represent the six electrons of the Li₂ molecule. The order shown for the orbitals $\sigma_g 2p$ through $\sigma_u^* 2p$ only holds for molecules that have large internuclear distances. Note that all the π orbitals are doubly degenerate.*

A pair of molecular orbitals exactly similar to those shown in Figure 7-6 can be formed from a linear combination of $2s$ atomic orbitals. These molecular orbitals will have a higher energy than the corresponding ones formed from $1s$ atomic orbitals because the principal quantum number of the basis orbitals has been increased.

The situation is somewhat more complicated when linear combinations of $2p$ orbitals are taken. Since there are six $2p$ orbitals on the two atomic centers, we would expect to be able to derive six molecular orbitals from them. Two different ways of combining $2p$ orbitals are shown in Figures 7-7 and 7-8. In Figure 7-7, it is seen that the two $2p_z$ orbitals can combine to form a pair of σ-orbitals—one bonding and one antibonding. The orbitals are of σ type because there is no component of angular momentum about the bond axis. In Figure 7-8, the combination of two $2p_x$ to

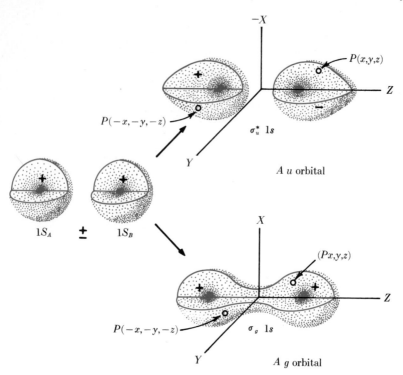

$P(x,y,z)$

$P(-x,-y,-z)$

$\sigma_u^* 1s$

$1S_A \quad \pm \quad 1S_B$

A u orbital

(Px,y,z)

$P(-x,-y,-z)$

$\sigma_g 1s$

A g orbital

FIG. 7-6   *Drawings of the $\sigma_g 1s$ and $\sigma_u^* 1s$ orbitals showing their g and u character. Note that the node in the σ_u^* orbital keeps the electrons out of the region between the two nuclei.*

form a $\pi_u 2p$ orbital is shown.   Another pair of orbitals exactly equivalent to these can be formed from a linear combination of $2p_y$ orbitals.   The $\pi_u 2p$ and $\pi_g^* 2p$ molecular orbitals will, therefore, each be doubly degenerate.   These four π orbitals plus the $\sigma_g 2p$ and $\sigma_u^* 2p$ give the required total of six molecular orbitals.

The order of energies of the molecular orbitals formed from the $2p$ atomic orbitals is a function of the internuclear distance in the diatomic molecule.   The order shown in Figure 7-5 is the one that is believed to hold at the equilibrium internuclear distance for the molecules O_2 and F_2.   How the order differs for other molecules will be discussed below.

We now place the appropriate number of electrons into this orbital scheme in accord with the Pauli principal.   Since the space

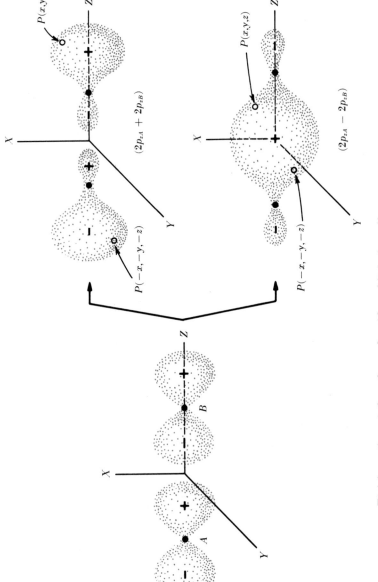

FIG. 7-7 *The formation of the $\sigma_g 2p$ and $\sigma_u^* 2p$ orbitals from linear combinations of $2p_z$ atomic orbitals. The student should see that he understands the g and u nomenclature for these orbitals.*

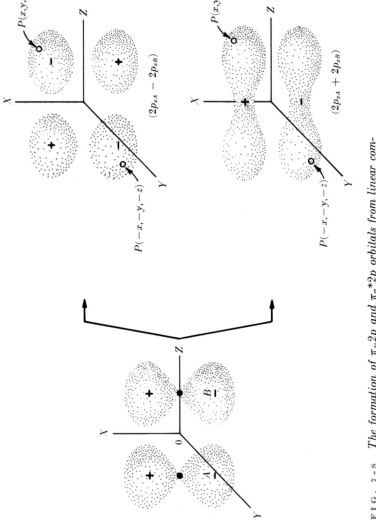

FIG. 7-8 *The formation of $\pi_u 2p$ and $\pi_g^* 2p$ orbitals from linear combinations of $2p_x$ atomic orbitals. An identical pair of molecular orbitals can be constructed from the $2p_y$ orbitals.*

part of the molecular orbital is described by three quantum numbers, only two electrons can be placed into each orbital in Figure 7-5 corresponding to the two possible values of the spin quantum numbers. The questions we hope to answer from this simple picture are:

1. Is a stable molecule formed?
2. What is the multiplicity of the ground state?
3. What are the relative values of binding energies and bond lengths in a series of stable molecules?

The first molecule that we will discuss is He_2. This molecule would have four electrons, and a consideration of Figure 7-5 shows that two electrons would have to go into each of the $\sigma_g 1s$ and σ_u*1s orbitals. Since both the bonding and antibonding orbitals formed from the hydrogen-like $1s$ atomic orbitals are filled, there will be no net stabilization of an He_2 molecule over a pair of isolated helium atoms. Therefore, He_2 will not be stable.

The Li_2 molecule has six electrons. Besides the four electrons in the $\sigma_g 1s$ and σ_u*1s orbitals, it will have two electrons in the $\sigma_g 2s$ orbital. This orbital is a bonding orbital and, therefore, Li_2 will be stable. Since the electrons must be paired, the ground state of Li_2 must be a singlet. These arguments are confirmed by experiment. The binding energy and other properties of diatomic molecules are given in Table 7-3.

The student should be able to convince himself by an argument similar to the above that Be_2 should not be stable. It isn't.

TABLE 7-3 EXPERIMENTAL DATA FOR DIATOMIC MOLECULES[a]

Molecule	Binding Energy (ev)	$R°(Å)$	Multiplicity of G.S.
Li_2	1.03	2.672	1
Be_2	not observed		—
B_2	(3.0)	1.589	3
C_2	(5.9)	1.2422	1
N_2	9.756	1.09	1
O_2	5.080	1.207	3
F_2	1.6	1.435	1

[a] Data from G. Herzberg, *Spectra of Diatomic Molecules*, D. Van Nostrand, Inc., Princeton, New Jersey (1950), Table 39.

The B_2 molecule has 10 electrons. A consideration of Figure 7-5 would indicate that the last two electrons would go into the $\sigma_g 2p$ orbital and that B_2 should, therefore, be stable and have a singlet ground state. This is only partly true. The B_2 molecule is stable, but it has a triplet ground state. As pointed out above, this discrepancy arises because the relative energies of the $\sigma_g 2p$ and the $\pi_u 2p$ orbitals are a function of internuclear distance. At short internuclear distances, the degenerate pair of $\pi_u 2p$ orbitals has a lower energy than the $\sigma_g 2p$. At long internuclear distances, the $\sigma_g 2p$ orbital has a lower energy than the pair of $\pi_u 2p$ orbitals. At some intermediate value of the internuclear distance, the $\pi_u 2p$ and $\sigma_g 2p$ orbitals have the same energy. This latter situation apparently is true for B_2 and, for this molecule, the last two electrons must go into a degenerate pair of orbitals, either the pair of $\pi_u 2p$ orbitals or into one $\pi_u 2p$ and the $\sigma_g 2p$ orbital. The state with lowest energy according to Hund's rule is the state with highest multiplicity, and the ground state is, therefore, a triplet.

For C_2, the $\pi_u 2p$ orbitals are still below the $\sigma_g 2p$ orbital in energy. This statement is based on the recent experimental work of Ramsay which shows that the ground state of C_2 is a singlet.[9] The electron configuration of the molecule must, therefore, be $(\sigma_g 1s)^2 (\sigma_u {}^* 1s)^2 (\sigma_g 2s)^2 (\sigma_u {}^* 2s)^2 (\pi_u 2p)^2 (\pi_u 2p)^2$. The first excited triplet state is only approximately 600 cm^{-1} above the ground state, however. Since the spectrum of C_2 was usually observed in flames, this excited triplet state has a high population and for a long time this was thought to be the ground state. The C_2 molecule now has four electrons in bonding orbitals that are not balanced by electrons in corresponding antibonding orbitals. It should have a greater binding energy and smaller internuclear distance than B_2. A consideration of the data in Table 7-2 shows this to be the case.

Nitrogen N_2 has all of the $2p$ bonding orbitals completely filled. It should have a singlet ground state, the largest binding energy, and the shortest internuclear distance of all the homonuclear diatomic molecules. This is borne out by the data in Table 7-3.

The discussion of the structure of O_2 and F_2 is left as an exercise for the student.

EXERCISE 7-7 Making use of the type of arguments used above, predict the multiplicity of the ground state of O_2 and F_2. Estimate the

[9] E. A. Ballik and D. A. Ramsay, *J. Chem. Phys.*, **31**, 1128 (1959).

relative order of binding energies and internuclear distances for the series N_2, O_2, F_2. Compare your results with the data in Table 7-3. The explanation of the correct multiplicity for O_2 was one of the triumphs of this simple theory.

The student may wonder what the relation is between the MO description of diatomic molecules and the classical chemical structures for these molecules. A bridge can be built between the two models by defining an effective number of bonds related to the difference in the number of bonding and antibonding electrons. We define the effective number of bonds N as

$$N_e = \frac{1}{2} \text{ (number of bonding electrons } -$$
$$\text{number of antibonding electrons)}$$

Applying this formula to calculate the effective number of bonds for the nitrogen molecule, one obtains

$$N_e = \frac{1}{2}(10 - 4) = 3$$

This result is in accord with the practice of writing a triple bond in N_2. The student may verify that this formula leads to a double bond for oxygen and a single bond for fluorine, in agreement with chemical intuition.

7-7   Excited states and electronic spectra of diatomic molecules

The excited states of a diatomic molecule are formed when an electron in the molecule is excited to a molecular orbital which has a higher energy than the orbital occupied in the ground state. The nomenclature for these states is based on the same features as the nomenclature for the one electron molecular orbitals. Similar to the procedure for atomic states, capital Greek letters designate the total angular momentum about the bond axis, and a left superscript designates the multiplicity of the state. In addition, the state is labeled with a g or a u as a right subscript depending on whether the wave function changes sign upon changing x, y, and z to $-x$, $-y$, and $-z$. This g and u designation only holds for homonuclear diatomic molecules, of course. For example, con-

**TABLE 7-4   THE STATE SYMBOLS FOR TWO ELEC-
TRONIC CONFIGURATIONS OF C_2 AND ONE FOR $N_2{}^+$**

Molecule	Electron Configuration	Symbol
C_2	$(\sigma_g 2s)^2(\sigma_u{}^*2s)^2(\pi_u 2p)^4$	$^1\Sigma_g{}^+$
	$(\sigma_g 2s)^2(\sigma_u{}^*2s)^2(\pi_u 2p)^3(\sigma_g 2p)$	$^3\Pi_u$
$N_2{}^+$	$(\sigma_g 2s)^2(\sigma_u{}^*2s)^2(\pi_u 2p)^4(\sigma_g 2p)$	$^2\Sigma_g$

sider the case of Li_2.   In the ground state, the electron configura-
tion of Li_2 is $(\sigma_g 1s)^2(\sigma_u{}^*1s)^2(\sigma_g 2s)^2$.   Since all of the electrons are in
σ orbitals, the total angular momentum about the internuclear axis
must be zero.   Furthermore, the electron spins are all paired, and
the multiplicity is one.   The $\sigma_g 2s$ orbital does not change sign upon
inversion, so the state will be g.   The ground state of the lithium
molecule is, therefore, a $^1\Sigma_g$ state.   For Σ states, an additional
right superscript is added characterizing whether the wave function
changes sign on reflection through any plane passing through the
internuclear axis.   A $+$ is used if the function does not change
sign, a $-$ is used if it does.   The complete symbol for the ground
state is, thus, $^1\Sigma_g{}^+$.   To determine whether a Σ state is plus or
minus requires an examination of each term of the determinantal
wave function for the molecule, and the subject will not be pursued
further at this point.   Some additional electron configurations and
their symbols are given in Table 7-4.   The student should try to
interpret the symbols (except for $+$ and $-$) on the basis of the
above discussion.

EXERCISE 7-8   What does the fact that the ground state of $N_2{}^+$ is
$^2\Sigma_g$ instead of $^2\Pi_u$ tell one about the ordering of the one-electron molecular
orbitals for nitrogen?

We are now in a position to talk about the excited electronic
states of the hydrogen molecule and electronic transitions that can
occur between these states.   Let us first write down some of the
possible excited states for H_2.   As mentioned above, these are
formed by exciting one electron from a $\sigma_g 1s$ molecular orbital to an
excited orbital.   Some of the possible states are listed in Table 7-5.
In this table, a bar over the orbital will indicate β spin, the lack of
a bar will indicate α spin.

We will first consider the energetics of some of these states. The $^1\Sigma_u$ and $^3\Sigma_u$ states both have one electron in a bonding and one in an antibonding orbital. The $^3\Sigma_u$ state is unstable with respect to a pair of hydrogen atoms, and it is a dissociative state. That is, if a hydrogen molecule could somehow be prepared in this state, it would immediately dissociate into a pair of hydrogen atoms. The $^1\Sigma_u$ state dissociates into a proton and a hydride ion, and it is stable.[10] The next four states can be thought of as arising from the interaction of one hydrogen atom in its ground state with an *excited* hydrogen atom with its electron in either a $2s$ or a $2p$ orbital. With respect to one normal and one excited hydrogen atom, the $^1\Sigma_u$, $^1\Pi_u$, and $^3\Pi_u$ are all stable. A potential energy curve similar to that found for the ground state will describe the energy of these states as a function of internuclear distance. A schematic picture of the ground state and the degenerate pi states is shown in Figure 7-9. A transition can take place between these two electronic states providing that it is allowed by the selection rules for electronic transitions.

In Chapter 5, it was pointed out that the intensity of a spectral transition is proportional to the square of the transition moment.

TABLE 7-5 THE GROUND AND SOME EXCITED CONFIGURATIONS OF H_2 AND THEIR STATE SYMBOLS[a]

Electron Configuration	State	Spectroscopic Notation
$(\sigma_g 1s)(\overline{\sigma_g 1s})$	$^1\Sigma_g$	X
$(\sigma_g 1s)(\overline{\sigma_u{}^*1s})$	$^1\Sigma_u$	—
$(\sigma_g 1s)(\sigma_u{}^*1s)$	$^3\Sigma_u$	—
$(\sigma_g 1s)(\overline{\sigma_g 2s})$	$^1\Sigma_g$	—
$(\sigma_g 1s)(\overline{\sigma_u{}^*2s})$	$^1\Sigma_u$	B
$(\sigma_g 1s)(\overline{\pi_u 2p})$	$^1\Pi_u$	C
$(\sigma_g 1s)(\pi_u 2p)$	$^3\Pi_u$	c

[a] In spectroscopic notation, the ground state of a molecule always is designated X. Excited singlet states are designated A, B, C · · · in order of increasing energy. Excited triplet states are likewise designated a, b, c · · · . The second three configurations in the table are not given symbols because they are either repulsive or a transition between that configuration and the ground configuration is not allowed.

[10] **III,** pp. 397 ff.

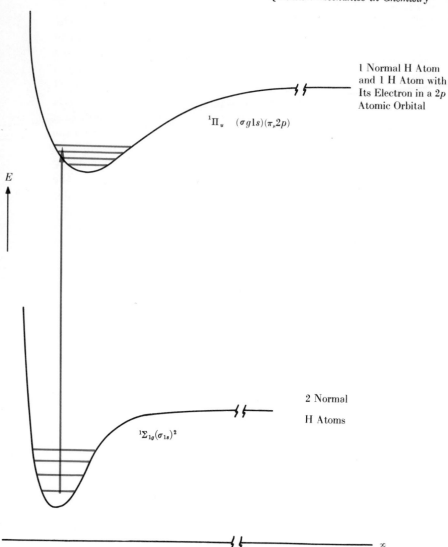

$^{1}\Pi_{u}$ $(\sigma g1s)(\pi_{\mu}2p)$

1 Normal H Atom
and 1 H Atom with
Its Electron in a $2p$
Atomic Orbital

E

2 Normal

H Atoms

$^{1}\Sigma_{1g}(\sigma_{1s})^{2}$

R_{AB} ——

x

FIG. 7-9   *The $^{1}\Sigma_{g}$ ground state and $^{1}\Pi_{u}$ excited states of H_{2}.   Several vibrational sublevels are shown for each state.   A vertical transition from the $v = 0$ vibrational level of the $^{1}\Sigma_{g}$ state to the $v = 3$ vibrational level of the $^{1}\Pi_{u}$ state is also shown.   Such a transition is called a Franck-Condon transition.*

For electronic motion in a molecule, the dipole moment operator is

$$\mu = e \sum_i Z_i \mathbf{r}_i \tag{7-32}$$

where $\mathbf{r}_i$ is the position vector of the i'th particle and Z_i is the charge on this particle. The sum i is over all electrons and nuclei in the molecule. For electronic transitions, the transition moment is then

$$\mathbf{R}^{kn} = e \left(\Psi_n^* \middle| \sum_i Z_i \mathbf{r}_i \middle| \Psi_k \right) \tag{7-33}$$

We will not explicitly evaluate any integrals like Equation 7-33, but several properties of the integrals can be derived without specifically evaluating them. First, the dipole moment operator does not contain the spin. On account of this, the transition moment will vanish if Ψ_n^* and Ψ_k have different multiplicities because spin eigenfunctions having differing eigenvalues with respect to S^2 are orthogonal (Theorem I of Chapter 6). Transitions between triplet and singlet states are, therefore, said to be spin forbidden. This is a general result which holds for all molecules.[11] Second, the vector $\mathbf{r}_i$ is an odd function of the coordinates of the i'th particle. That is, $\mathbf{r} \rightarrow -\mathbf{r}$ as $x, y, z \rightarrow -x, -y$, and $-z$, respectively. It is a general theorem that integrals over all space will vanish unless the integrand is an *even* function of all the variables. Applied to the transition moment, this means that the integral in Equation 7-33 will vanish unless the product of $\Psi_n^* \Psi_k$ is *odd*. Transitions between two g states or two u states in a diatomic molecule will not be allowed, therefore. It is said that these transitions are symmetry forbidden. It is for this reason that the two states shown in Figure 7-9 were chosen. The transition between the $^1\Sigma_g$ and $^1\Pi_u$ states is allowed.

When thinking about electronic spectra, it is important to keep in mind that in its ground and excited electronic states the molecule will also have vibrational and rotational energy. Under moderate resolution, an electronic transition will exhibit vibrational fine structure due to the fact that the electronic transition may originate at one of several possible vibrational levels of the ground state

---

[11] In some cases single-triplet transitions may become weakly allowed because of spin-orbit interaction. The spectral bands from these transitions are always very weak, however.

and terminate at one of the possible vibrational levels of the excited electronic state. Under high resolution, each of the bands due to the vibrational fine structure may sometimes be seen to be made up of lines due to transitions between different rotational levels. This rotational structure on electronic transitions can only be observed in molecules with small moments of inertia, however.

To analyze the electronic spectrum of a diatomic molecule, we first make the approximation that there is no coupling between electronic and vibrational motion. This is not a new approximation because it can be shown that this follows directly from the Born-Oppenheimer approximation. We can write the total energy for a diatomic molecule as

$$E_{tot} = E_{elec} + E_{vib} \tag{7-34}$$

and the total wave function as

$$\Psi_{tot} = \Psi_{elec} \Psi_{vib} \tag{7-35}$$

In Equations 7-34 and 7-35, the rotational energy and wave function have been neglected. In cases where rotational fine structure can be observed in an electronic transition, the rotational energies can be included in Equation 7-34 by a straightforward application of the methods used in the discussion of vibration-rotation spectroscopy.

We can now write a general expression for the frequencies observed in the electronic spectrum of a diatomic molecule. Using T_e and G to designate electronic and vibrational contributions to the energy of a state, molecules will absorb light with energy

$$\omega_{E,V} = (T_e' - T_e'') + (G' - G'') \tag{7-36}$$

Where, again, we use a single prime to designate the upper state and a double prime to designate the lower state. If we call the energy difference in cm^{-1} between the minimums of the potential energy curves of the two electronic states $\bar{\nu}_e$, and substitute the expression for an anharmonic oscillator for G, Equation 7-36 becomes

$$\omega_{E,V} = \bar{\nu}_e + \omega_e'\left(v' + \frac{1}{2}\right) - (\omega_e x_e)'\left(v' + \frac{1}{2}\right)^2$$
$$- \omega_e''\left(v'' + \frac{1}{2}\right) + (\omega_e x_e)''\left(v'' + \frac{1}{2}\right)^2 \tag{7-37}$$

In Equation 7-37, it is important to realize that ω_e' is the extrapolated fundamental vibration frequency in the *excited electronic state*. It may differ from ω_e'', the extrapolated fundamental vibration frequency in the ground state. Likewise, $(\omega_e x_e)'$ is the anharmonicity constant for the excited state. For diatomic molecules composed of first and second row atoms, only the lowest vibrational state of the ground electronic state $(v'' = 0)$ is populated. For the absorption spectrum of these molecules, the electronic band structure is given by

$$\omega_{E,V} = \bar{\nu}_e + \omega_e \left(v' + \frac{1}{2} \right) - \omega_e' X_e' \left(v' + \frac{1}{2} \right)^2 - \frac{1}{2} \omega_o'' \quad (7\text{-}38)$$

where $\omega_o'' = \omega_e'' - \frac{1}{2}\omega_e'' X_e''$ is twice the zero point vibrational energy in the ground electronic state.

There is no vibrational selection rule which limits the values which v', the vibrational quantum number in the upper electronic state, can have. Rather, the number of vibrational bands which are observed depends on the Franck-Condon principle and the overlap of vibrational wave functions in the ground and excited electronic states.

We will first discuss the Franck-Condon principle. This principle states that an electronic transition takes place so rapidly that the nuclei do not move appreciably during a transition. It should be noticed that the line corresponding to an electronic transition in Figure 7-9 was drawn vertically, that is, drawn so that the internuclear distance was the same as in the ground state. Such a transition is called a Franck-Condon transition. In general, the equilibrium internuclear distance in the excited electronic state will not be the same as that in the ground electronic state, and the two potential energy curves will be displaced from each other. Because the nuclei do not move appreciably when an electronic transition takes place, the transition must terminate at a vibrational level of the upper electronic state in which the nuclei have a high probability of having the same internuclear distance as they had in the ground state. This is shown in Figure 7-9 by the fact that the electronic transition terminates at the $v' = 3$ state.

The Franck-Condon principle can be rationalized quantum mechanically by considering the overlap of the vibrational wave functions in the ground and excited electronic states. Using the wave function of Equation 7-35 in the expression for the transition moment, we can write [12]

$$\mathbf{R} = e\left(\Psi_e'^*\Psi_v'^* \left| \sum_i Z_i\mathbf{r}_i \right| \Psi_e''\Psi_v''\right) \tag{7-39}$$

If we now divide the dipole moment operator into two parts, one depending on the electrons and the other depending on the nuclei, Equation 7-39 becomes

$$\mathbf{R} = e\{\int\Psi_e'^*\Psi_v'^*\mathbf{M}_e\Psi_e''\Psi_v'' \, d\tau_e \, d\tau_n \\ + \int\Psi_e'^*\Psi_v'^*\mathbf{M}_N\Psi_e''\Psi_v'' \, d\tau_e \, d\tau_n\} \tag{7-40}$$

where $\mathbf{M}_e$ and $\mathbf{M}_N$ are the electronic and nuclear contributions to the dipole moment and where $d\tau_e$ and $d\tau_n$ are the appropriate volume elements for the electronic and nuclear coordinates. The quantity $\mathbf{M}_N$ depends only on the nuclear coordinates. Therefore, the second integral in Equation 7-40 becomes

$$\int\Psi_e'^*\Psi_v'^*\mathbf{M}_N\Psi_e''\Psi_v'' \, d\tau_e \, d\tau_n \\ = \int\Psi_e'^*\Psi_e'' \, d\tau_e \int\Psi_v'^*\mathbf{M}_N\Psi_v'' \, d\tau_n = 0$$

because the two electronic wave functions are orthogonal (Theorem I, Section 6-6). The quantum mechanical statement of the Franck-Condon principle is that the variation of Ψ_e' and Ψ_e'' with a change in nuclear coordinates is very slow and, therefore, the first term in Equation 7-40 can be written

$$\mathbf{R} = e\{\int\Psi_e'^*\mathbf{M}_e\Psi_e'' \, d\tau_e \int\Psi_v''\Psi_v'' \, d\tau_n\} \tag{7-41}$$

where the first integral is just the electronic transition moment, and the second integral is the overlap integral between Ψ_v' and Ψ_v''. The transition probability will, therefore, be proportional to the square of the electronic transition probability and the square of the overlap integral between the appropriate vibrational levels in the ground and excited electronic states.

7-8 Localized bonds, hybrid orbitals, and directed valence

A large portion of modern chemistry has been correlated and explained by the concept of the electron pair bond. These electron pair bonds retain much of their identity regardless of what the rest

[12] The following treatment is essentially that of G. Herzberg, *Spectra of Diatomic Molecules*, D. Van Nostrand, Inc., Princeton, New Jersey (1950) pp. 200 ff.

of the molecule containing the bond is like.   This retention of bond
properties is the basic assumption that is made in the listing of
bond energies, and the successful use of these bond energies to
calculate thermodynamic properties justifies this assumption.
Further, it was pointed out in Chapter 5 that one was able to carry
over IR frequencies of bonds from molecule to molecule to a fairly
high degree of accuracy.   This is the basic feature of the organic
chemist's use of IR spectroscopy to identify an unknown compound.

The valence bond method is especially convenient for a description of the electron pair bond.   It was pointed out earlier that if
we have an orbital ϕ_A containing one electron on atom A and an
orbital ϕ_B containing one electron on atom B, then we can write
an antisymmetrized bond eigenfunction for an AB bond in the
form

$$\Psi_{AB} = N(\phi_A\phi_B + \phi_B\phi_A)(\alpha\beta - \beta\alpha) \tag{7-42}$$

As an application of the use of bond eigenfunctions in polyatomic
molecules, we will first consider the water molecule.   An oxygen
atom in the ground state has electronic configuration $1s^2 2s^2 2p^4$,
and is in a ^3P state.   We can roughly state that there is one electron in each of two $2p$ orbitals with parallel spins.   These two
electrons can be used to form bonds with other atoms that also
have a singly occupied orbital—for example, hydrogen atoms.   This
simple picture predicts oxygen to be divalent, which it is.   The
wave function for the water molecule can be thought of as a product
of two bond eigenfunctions, each of which has the form

$$\Psi_{OH} = N[\phi_{2P}(O)\phi_{1S}(H) + \phi_{1S}(H)\phi_{2P}(O)](\alpha\beta - \beta\alpha) \tag{7-43}$$

where $\phi_{2P}(O)$ is a $2p$ orbital localized on oxygen and $\phi_{1S}(H)$ is a
$1s$ orbital localized on hydrogen.   The binding energy of a water
molecule in this model is predicted to be equal to twice the energy
of an OH bond.   This is approximately correct.

This simple theory, along with one additional principle, enables
one to make predictions about the stereochemistry of molecules.
The additional principle needed is the principle of maximum overlap.   This principle was first enunciated by Pauling [13] and states

---

[13] L. Pauling, *The Nature of the Chemical Bond*, 3rd ed., Cornell University
Press, Ithaca, New York (1960) p. 108.

*Of two orbitals in an atom, the one that can overlap more with
an orbital of another atom will form the stronger bond with
that atom.   Moreover, the bond formed by a given orbital will
tend to lie in that direction in which the orbital is concentrated.*

For the case of water, the overlap between the $1s$ orbital of
hydrogen and the $2p$ orbital of oxygen will be greatest when the
hydrogen atoms are colinear with the axes of the $2p$ orbitals of
oxygen.   The bond angles in water are predicted to be 90° by this
model because 90° is the angle between the axes of a pair of $2p$
orbitals.   The actual value of the bond angle in water is 104.5°.
The quantitative agreement is not good, but the discrepancy is not
serious in view of the naïveté of the theory.

For ammonia, NH_3, a similar argument can be developed.   The
ground state of nitrogen is a ^4S state, and there is one electron in
each of the three $2p$ orbitals.   We would then predict that nitrogen
would be trivalent and should form a stable compound with three
hydrogen atoms.   Again, we predict that the bond angles in NH_3
would be 90°.   The experimental value is 108°.   The quantitative
agreement is again not good, and a troubling doubt about this
simple picture begins to appear because the agreement is getting
worse.

For carbon compounds, an additional refinement must be made
because the simple picture used above for water and ammonia no
longer predicts the correct valence.   A carbon atom has a ^3P
ground state, corresponding to two unpaired electrons, one in each
of two $2p$ orbitals.   On the basis of the arguments used above, one
would expect carbon to be divalent.   It is well known, of course,
that carbon is usually tetravalent.   Further, it is known that all
of the bonds in compounds such as CH_4 and CCl_4 are equivalent.
To revise our simple theory in order to explain these facts, we
postulate that, in order to get larger overlap and consequently
stronger bonds, atoms can make use of *hybrid orbitals*.   For carbon,
we can think of these hybrid orbitals as arising as follows.   First,
a carbon atom in its ground state is excited to the excited state
described in Equation 7-44

$$C(^3P)2s^22p2p \rightarrow C(^5S)2s2p2p2p \qquad (7\text{-}44)$$

This requires an energy of 33,735.2 cm^{-1} or 96 kcal/mole.   Next
the $2s$ orbital and the three $2p$ orbitals are combined to form four

equivalent orbitals, called sp^3 hybrids, which make angles of 109°28′ with each other. The carbon atom then utilizes the one electron in each of these hybrid orbitals to form four equivalent bonds.

The simplest form that these hybrids can take is

$$\phi_1 = \frac{1}{2}(s + p_x + p_y + p_z)$$

$$\phi_2 = \frac{1}{2}(s + p_x - p_y - p_z)$$

$$\phi_3 = \frac{1}{2}(s - p_x + p_y - p_z)$$

$$\phi_4 = \frac{1}{2}(s - p_x - p_y + p_z)$$

(7-45)

Some properties of these hybrid orbitals are calculated in the following exercise.

EXERCISE 7-9   Represent the p_x, p_y, and p_z orbitals by unit vectors along an x, y, z axis system and let these vectors point to the center of the faces of a cube. Where, in this cube, will the functions ϕ_1, ϕ_2, ϕ_3, and ϕ_4 point?

EXERCISE 7-10   Show that the four sp^3 hybrid orbitals above are mutually orthogonal.

Each bond in methane can be thought of as formed by the overlap of an sp^3 hybrid orbital on carbon with a $1s$ orbital on hydrogen, and corresponding bond eigenfunctions can be written. Apparently, the energy gained by forming four bonds instead of two is more than enough to compensate for the excitation of an electron from a $2s$ to a $2p$ orbital.

One is now in a position to explain the deviation of the bond angles in NH_3 and water from 90°. In NH_3, the bond angles are almost 109°, and one can postulate that sp^3 hybrids are used to form bonds in this compound. In H_2O, addition of a little s character to the two $2p$ orbitals would spread the bond angle to 104°.[14]

Other types of hybridization have been used to explain other types of bond geometries. A combination of a $2s$ and two $2p$

[14] For a more complete discussion of these points, see C. A. Coulson, *Valence*, Oxford University Press, London (1961) Chapter 8.

orbitals can be used to form a set of three sp^2 hybrid orbitals. These hybrids all lie in a plane and make bond angles of 120° with each other. An example of a compound utilizing sp^2 hybrid orbitals is boron trichloride, BCl_3, which is known to be planar, and have bond angles of 120°. The sp^2 hybrids are sometimes called trigonal hybrids.

A combination of a $2s$ orbital with one $2p_z$ orbital gives a set of two sp or digonal hybrid orbitals. The formation of these hybrids is shown in Figure 7-10. These hybrid orbitals are colinear. An example of a compound using sp hybrids is mercuric chloride, $HgCl_2$. This is known to be a linear molecule. This molecule further illustrates that hybridization is not restricted to the $n = 2$ atomic orbitals.

7-9   The sigma-pi description of ethylene and acetylene

The ethylene molecule is known to be planar, and all of the bond angles are close to 120°. Further, it contains unsaturation represented by a double bond in its formula. We can explain these results by assuming that the structural backbone of the molecule is composed of bonds between sp^2 hybrids on the two carbon atoms and $1s$ orbitals on the hydrogen atoms. This basic framework of the ethylene molecule is called the "sigma-bond framework." When an atom utilizes sp^2 hybrids, there is still one p orbital left over. In ethylene, these remaining p orbitals contain one electron each, and they can overlap to form a π-bond. The double bond in ethylene can be thought of, therefore, as being composed of a sigma and a pi-bond. It is the π-bond which is reactive, and, since the σ-bond framework is composed of sp^2 hybrids, the molecule would be planar and the bond angles would all be 120°.

In acetylene, the two carbon atoms must use sp hybrids in its σ-bond framework because acetylene is known to be a linear molecule. If an atom forms sp hybrids, there are two p orbitals left over on each carbon atom. These can interact to form two π-bonds at right angles to each other.

The separation of conjugated organic molecules into a σ-bond framework and a system of π electrons will be the starting point for the discussion of the unusual properties of these molecules in the next chapter.

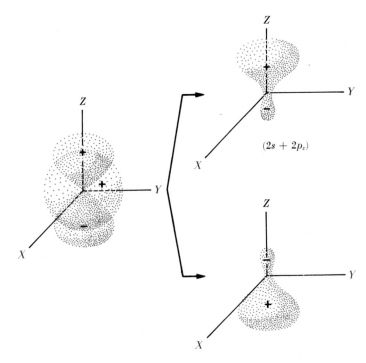

$(2s + 2p_z)$

FIG. 7-10   *Diagram showing the formation of the two sp hybrid orbitals from plus and minus linear combinations of an ns and np$_z$ orbital.*

EXERCISE 7-11   In the light of the above, discuss the structure of allene, $H_2C=C=CH_2$, in terms of bond geometry and orbital hybridization.   The three carbon atoms are colinear.

7-10   *Summary*

1. Some general features of the quantum mechanical solution to the H_2^+ problem were discussed.   Specifically, the Born-Oppenheimer approximation, which states that the electronic and nuclear motions can be treated independently, was introduced.

2. The variational method utilizing an LCAO function was applied to the calculation of the allowed energies in H_2^+.   This method is based on the variational principle which states that the energy

calculated from any appropriate approximate wave function will always be higher than the true energy of the ground state.

3. The molecular orbital and valence bond treatments of the hydrogen molecule were compared. The valence bond wave function contains no ionic terms whereas the molecular orbital wave function includes the ionic terms and covalent terms with equal weights.

4. Methods for improving the wave functions for molecular hydrogen include: adding some ionic character to the VB function, including polarization effects in the basis orbitals, and scaling.

5. A simple MO theory for complex diatomic molecules was developed that was capable of predicting molecular stability and ground state multiplicities.

6. The origin of electronic spectra of diatomic molecules was discussed, and several selection rules were derived from a consideration of the electronic transition moment. The Franck-Condon principle was introduced. This principle states that the intensity of the vibrational components of an electronic transition depends on the overlap of vibrational wave functions in the ground and excited electronic states.

7. The concept of orbital hybridization was introduced. A simple valence-bond model employing these hybrids was used to discuss the bonding and geometry of several molecules.

8. The student should be familiar with the terms, Born-Oppenheimer approximation, linear variation function, secular equations, secular determinant, characteristic equation, basis set, coulomb integral (MO), resonance integral, coulomb integral (VB), exchange integral, g and u, σ and π orbital designations, scale factor and scaling, Franck-Condon principle, hybrid orbitals, and σ-bond framework.

Chapter 8

THE ELECTRONIC
STRUCTURE OF
CONJUGATED SYSTEMS

IN THE last chapter, the localized bond model was used in the discussion of the structure of water, ammonia, methane, boron trichloride, and other molecules. It was found that this model gave a qualitatively correct picture of the energetics and stereochemistry of the compounds. The model also accounted for additivity of bond energies, the approximate constancy of the force constants, and the valence of an atom. This localized bond model becomes inadequate, however, for the description of any molecule when electrons can be delocalized over more than two atoms. The best-known example of a molecule for which the localized bond model breaks down is benzene. Using classical chemical structure theory, benzene must be represented as a "resonance hybrid" between the two limiting structures I and II:

I   II

That is, the structure of benzene cannot be adequately represented
by either structure I or II by itself.   It is somewhere between the
two.   It is the purpose of this chapter to show how these "delocalized" bonds may be treated by molecular orbital theory.

8-1   *The LCAO-MO theory for conjugated hydrocarbons*

The exact Hamiltonian for a molecule containing n electrons and
η nuclei is

$$\hat{\mathfrak{K}} = \sum_{i=1}^{n} \left(T_i - \sum_{\mu=1}^{\eta} \frac{Z_\mu}{r_{i\mu}} \right) + \sum_{i<j} \frac{1}{r_{ij}} \tag{8-1}$$

In Equation 8-1, the nuclear repulsion terms have been omitted.
For ethylene, the simplest hydrocarbon that has electron delocalization, $n = 16$ and $\eta = 6$.   Even an approximate calculation of
the allowed energies for ethylene would require considerable effort.
When dealing with conjugated organic molecules, it is usual to
simplify the calculations by first assuming that the π-electrons can
be treated independently of the σ-electrons.   In an actual calculation, we will seek a π-electron wave function Π that will be antisymmetric upon exchange of any two π-electrons and adjusted so
that the π-electron energy

$$\langle E_\pi \rangle = \frac{\langle \Pi^* | \hat{\mathfrak{K}}_\pi | \Pi \rangle}{\langle \Pi^* | \Pi \rangle} \tag{8-2}$$

is a minimum.   Performing this procedure amounts to postulating
that the total wave function for a conjugated hydrocarbon can be
written as

$$\Psi = \hat{\mathcal{Q}}_{\sigma-\pi} \Sigma \Pi \tag{8-3}$$

where Σ is an antisymmetrized wave function for the σ-electrons
and where $\mathcal{Q}_{\sigma-\pi}$ is an antisymmetrizing operator that only permutes
σ and π-electron pairs.

The Hamiltonian used in Equation 8-2 is then taken as an effective Hamiltonian.   That is, $\hat{\mathfrak{K}}_\pi$ represents the motion of the
π-electrons in the potential field of the nuclei and some kind of an

average field of the σ-electrons. It also may try to account for electron correlation between σ and π-electrons in an average way. We, therefore, write

$$\hat{\mathcal{H}}_\pi = \sum_{i=1}^{n_\pi} \hat{\mathcal{H}}_{core}(i) + \sum_{i<j=1}^{n_\pi} \frac{1}{r_{ij}} \qquad (8\text{-}4)$$

where now the sums are only over the π-electrons. In the π-electron approximation, the ethyléne molecule is reduced to a two-electron problem.

In Equation 8-4, $\hat{\mathcal{H}}_{core}$ may be thought of as including the kinetic energy of the π-electrons, the potential energy between the π-electrons and the nuclei minus the shielding effect of the σ-electrons, and any additional interaction effects between σ and π-electrons.

Implicit in this π-electron approximation is the assumption that the σ-bond framework remains the same for all π-electron states.

The student may well wonder if this approximation, which appears rather drastic, is justified. To answer this, one must appeal to the following rationalizations.

1. The distinctive chemistry of the conjugated organic molecules has been correlated by considering only the π-electron systems. This distinctive chemistry appears to be relatively independent of the σ-bond framework.

2. The characteristic spectra of these molecules can be rationalized using the π-electron approximation.

3. A large amount of other experimental data, such as ionization potentials, dipole moments, relative reactivities, etc., can be at least qualitatively described by the independent π-electron model. We, thus, once again, appeal to the fact that a theory works in order to justify its use. This does not mean that making this approximation introduces no difficulties, however. Obtaining exact quantitative agreement with experiment is fraught with many difficulties. For example, the calculated energy separation between excited singlet and triplet states of conjugated organic molecules is always too large.[1]

---

[1] For rigorous discussion of the π-electron approximation, see R. G. Parr, *Quantum Theory of Molecular Electronic Structure*, W. A. Benjamin, Inc., New York (1963) Chapter III.

We now return to the problem of treating the π-electrons by the Hamiltonian of Equation 8-4. Even if $\hat{\mathcal{K}}_{core}$ could be written exactly, eigenvalue equations using Equation 8-4 would not be exactly soluble because of the electron repulsion terms. We, therefore, must seek approximate solutions for the electrons in the same way as for diatomic molecules. The most drastic of these approximation methods is to replace the Hamiltonian in Equation 8-4 by

$$\hat{\mathcal{K}}_\pi^{\,0} = \sum_i \hat{h}_{eff}(i) \tag{8-5}$$

where $\hat{h}_{eff}(i)$ is a one-electron operator which incorporates the $\dfrac{1}{r_{ij}}$ terms into the nuclear potential in some average way. The quantity $\hat{h}_{eff}(i)$ can be written

$$\hat{h}_{eff}(i) = -\frac{1}{2}\nabla^2(i) - \sum_{\mu=1}^{N} \frac{Z_\mu'}{r_{i\mu}} \tag{8-6}$$

where the sum is over all the nuclei in the molecule and where Z_μ' is an effective nuclear charge that somehow incorporates the average screening of all of the σ-electrons as well as shielding due to the remaining π-electrons. Seeing that $\hat{h}_{eff}(i)$ is a function only of the coordinates and momenta of a single electron, we can use the separation of variables method to reduce the N π-electron problem to N *identical* one-electron problems. The final problem to be solved is thus

$$\hat{h}(i)\phi_i = \epsilon_i \phi_i \tag{8-7}$$

where ϕ_i is a one-electron molecular orbital and ϵ_i is the corresponding orbital energy. At this level of approximation, the total π-electron energy and wave function will be

$$E_\pi = \sum_{i=1}^{N} \epsilon_i \qquad \Psi_i = \prod_{i=1}^{N} \phi(i) \tag{8-8a and b}$$

Of course, electrons must be placed in the independent electron orbitals in such a way that the Pauli principle is satisfied.

8-2   The simple Hückel model

The next step in our approximate calculation of the electronic structure of conjugated hydrocarbons is to assume that the ϕ_i can be written as a linear combination of atomic orbitals. We, thus, write

$$\phi_i = \sum_{\mu=1}^{N} C_{i\mu}\chi_\mu \tag{8-9}$$

where χ_μ is a $2p_z$ orbital localized on atom μ, and where the sum extends over all atoms in the conjugated molecule.   We now apply the variation method to find the best values of the energy for the ground and excited one-electron orbitals. The student should review the outline of this procedure in Chapter 7 if he has forgotten it.   Minimizing the energy with respect to the $C_{i\mu}$ leads to a set of N linear equations in N unknowns.   These, in turn, have a non-trivial solution only if the secular determinant

$$|H_{\mu\nu} - \epsilon_i S_{\mu\nu}| = 0 \tag{8-10}$$

The features that distinguish the Hückel method from other LCAO methods are the following approximations used to simplify the determinant in Equation 8-10.   These are

1. All $H_{\mu\mu}$ are equal and are set equal to a coulomb integral α.
2. All $H_{\mu\nu} = \beta$ if atoms μ and ν are bonded.
   $= 0$ if atoms μ and ν are not bonded.
3. All $S_{\mu\nu} = 1$ if $\mu = \nu$
   $= 0$ if $\mu \neq \nu$.

Use of this method will now be illustrated in calculations of the π-electronic structure for ethylene and butadiene.

8-3   Ethylene

The ethylene calculation is a two atom and two electron problem. The nomenclature is shown in Figure 8-1.   The LCAO function is

$$\phi_i = C_{i1}\chi_1 + C_{i2}\chi_2 \tag{8-11}$$

The secular equations are

$$(H_{11} - S_{11}\epsilon_i)C_{i1} + (H_{12} - S_{12}\epsilon_i)C_{i2} = 0 \atop (H_{12} - S_{12}\epsilon_i)C_{i1} + (H_{22} - S_{22}\epsilon_i)C_{i2} = 0 \tag{8-12}$$

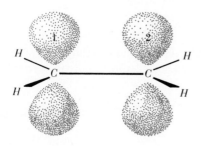

FIG. 8-1   *Labeling of the $2p_z$ orbitals used in the π-electron calculation for ethylene.*

The secular determinant is

$$\begin{vmatrix} H_{11} - S_{11}\epsilon_i & H_{12} - S_{12}\epsilon_i \\ H_{12} - S_{12}\epsilon_i & H_{22} - S_{22}\epsilon_i \end{vmatrix} = 0 \tag{8-13}$$

Applying the Hückel approximations, this becomes

$$\begin{vmatrix} \alpha - \epsilon_i & \beta \\ \beta & \alpha - \epsilon_i \end{vmatrix} = 0 \tag{8-14}$$

The solutions of Equation 8-14 are

$$(\alpha - \epsilon_i)^2 - \beta^2 = 0$$
$$\epsilon_i = \alpha \pm \beta$$

It should be noted that these solutions are identical in form to the solutions for H_2^+ except that the overlap integrals have been set equal to zero.   The two orbital energies and wave functions are thus

$$\epsilon_1 = \alpha + \beta \qquad \phi_1 = \frac{1}{\sqrt{2}}(\chi_1 + \chi_2)$$
$$\epsilon_2 = \alpha - \beta \qquad \phi_2 = \frac{1}{\sqrt{2}}(\chi_1 - \chi_2) \tag{8-15}$$

The student should recall that both α and β are negative quantities so that ϵ_1 is the lowest energy.   The total π-electron wave function is obtained by putting the *two* π-electrons into ϕ_1 with their spins paired.   Thus, for ethylene,

$$\Pi = \phi_1\phi_1 \frac{1}{\sqrt{2}}(\alpha\beta - \beta\alpha) \tag{8-16a}$$

$$E_\pi = 2\epsilon_1 = 2\alpha + 2\beta \tag{8-16b}$$

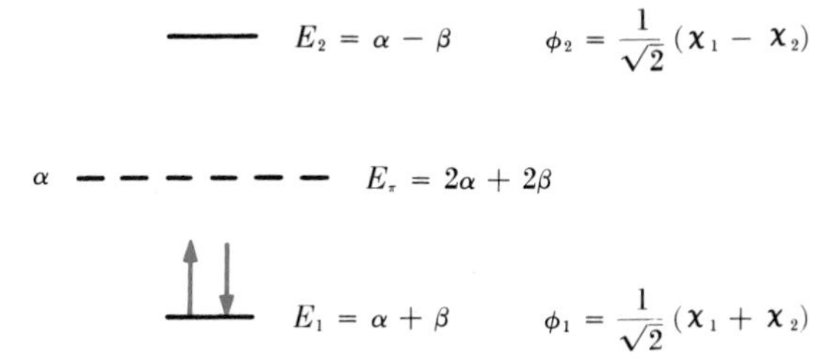

$$\underline{\qquad} \quad E_2 = \alpha - \beta \qquad \phi_2 = \frac{1}{\sqrt{2}}(\chi_1 - \chi_2)$$

$$\alpha \quad \text{-- -- -- -- --} \quad E_\tau = 2\alpha + 2\beta$$

$$\underline{\overset{\uparrow\downarrow}{\qquad}} \quad E_1 = \alpha + \beta \qquad \phi_1 = \frac{1}{\sqrt{2}}(\chi_1 + \chi_2)$$

FIG. 8-2 *Energy level diagram for the π-electrons in ethylene. The two π-electrons have been placed in the orbital ϕ_1 with antiparallel spins. The total π-electron energy is equal to the sum of the orbital energy of each electron.*

In the Hückel approximation, the integrals α and β are never evaluated. This avoids the embarrassing problem of specifying the exact form of $\hat{h}_{eff}$. Rather, the quantities α and β are given empirical values to make the theory fit experiment. A wide range of β values have been given in the literature.[2] One chooses a β value derived to fit the particular experimental data of interest. Several types of data (spectral and polarographic reduction potentials for example) are fit by a value of 2.37 to 2.39 ev. The quantity α can be identified with the energy of a p-electron on an isolated carbon atom, and is usually taken as the zero of energy. Our π-electron calculation on ethylene can be summarized by the diagram shown in Figure 8-2.

8-4 Butadiene, $CH_2\!=\!CH\!-\!CH\!=\!CH_2$

The calculation of the π-electronic structure for butadiene is somewhat more complex than that for ethylene. Butadiene exists in *cis* and *trans* forms, but in simple Hückel theory there will be no difference in the energy of the two forms because nonnearest neighbor interactions are neglected. For purposes of calculation, therefore, we can regard the molecule as linear. The numbering of the atomic orbitals is shown in Figure 8-3. The molecular

[2] A Streitwieser, Jr., *Molecular Orbital Theory for Organic Chemists*, John Wiley & Sons, Inc., New York (1961).

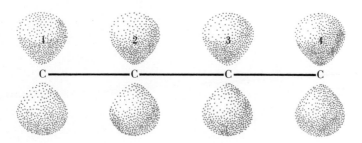

FIG. 8-3 *Labeling of the atomic orbitals used in the π-electron calculati on for butadiene. The hydrogen atoms in butadiene are not show n.*

orbitals will have the form

$$\phi_i = \sum_{\mu=1}^{4} C_{i\mu}\chi_\mu \qquad (8\text{-}17)$$

Since there are four orbitals in the basis set, there will be a set of four secular equations and a 4×4 secular determinant. Using the Hückel approximations, the student should verify that the secular determinant is

$$\begin{vmatrix} \alpha - \epsilon_i & \beta & 0 & 0 \\ \beta & \alpha - \epsilon_i & \beta & 0 \\ 0 & \beta & \alpha - \epsilon_i & \beta \\ 0 & 0 & \beta & \alpha - \epsilon_i \end{vmatrix} = 0 \qquad (8\text{-}18)$$

To simplify the solution to Equation 8-18, we divide each row of the determinant by β and make the substitution

$$x = \frac{\alpha - \epsilon_i}{\beta}$$

The secular determinant then becomes

$$\begin{vmatrix} x & 1 & 0 & 0 \\ 1 & x & 1 & 0 \\ 0 & 1 & x & 1 \\ 0 & 0 & 1 & x \end{vmatrix} = 0 \qquad (8\text{-}19)$$

If Equation 8-19 is evaluated by the method of minors, one obtains the characteristic equation

$$x^4 - 3x^2 + 1 = 0 \tag{8-20}$$

EXERCISE 8-1 Evaluate the determinant in Equation 8-19 and show that it leads to the characteristic equation given in Equation 8-20.

Usually the roots to an equation of this type would have to be found by an iterative method such as the Newton-Raphson method.[3] In this case, however, it turns out that Equation 8-20 is factorable. Thus,

$$x^4 - 3x^2 + 1 = (x^2 + x - 1)(x^2 - x - 1) = 0 \tag{8-21}$$

and, therefore

$$\begin{aligned} x^2 + x - 1 &= 0 \\ x^2 - x - 1 &= 0 \end{aligned} \tag{8-22}$$

The four roots of the secular determinant are, therefore

$$x = \frac{1 + \sqrt{5}}{2} = +1.618 \qquad \epsilon = \alpha - 1.618\beta$$

$$x = \frac{1 - \sqrt{5}}{2} = -0.618 \qquad \epsilon = \alpha + 0.618\beta$$

$$\tag{8-23}$$

$$x = \frac{-1 + \sqrt{5}}{2} = +0.618 \qquad \epsilon = \alpha - 0.618\beta$$

$$x = \frac{-1 - \sqrt{5}}{2} = -1.618 \qquad \epsilon = \alpha + 1.618\beta$$

Using these roots, the energy diagram can be constructed. This diagram is shown in Figure 8-4.

At this point, we introduce a quantity called the delocalization energy, DE. The delocalization energy is defined as the difference between the total π-electron energy of the molecule of interest and the π-electron energy of the same number of isolated double bonds. Thus, for butadiene,

$$\begin{aligned} DE &= E_\pi(\text{Butadiene}) - 2E_\pi(\text{Ethylene}) \\ &= 2(\alpha + 1.618\beta) + 2(\alpha + 0.618\beta) - 2(2\alpha + 2\beta) \\ &= 4\alpha + 4.472\beta - 4\alpha - 4\beta \\ &= 0.472\beta \end{aligned} \tag{8-24}$$

[3] I, pp. 492 ff.

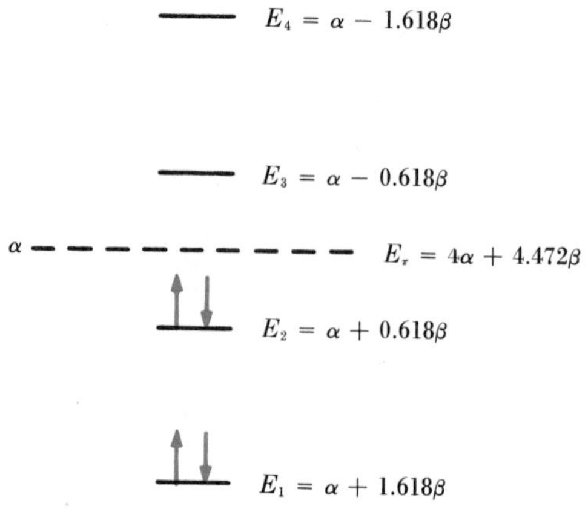

$$E_4 = \alpha - 1.618\beta$$

$$E_3 = \alpha - 0.618\beta$$

$$\alpha - - - - - - - - - \quad E_r = 4\alpha + 4.472\beta$$

$$E_2 = \alpha + 0.618\beta$$

$$E_1 = \alpha + 1.618\beta$$

FIG. 8-4 *Energy level diagram for the π-electrons in butadiene. Butadiene has four π-electrons so the two lowest energy orbitals are filled. The total π-electron energy is $2(\alpha + 1.618\beta) + 2(\alpha + 0.618\beta)$. The student should note that the orbitals are paired about the zero of energy. This is a general property of conjugated hydrocarbons containing no odd-membered rings.*

The delocalization energy is a measure of the extra stabilization that a molecule has due to the fact that electrons can move over the whole molecule. It has often been related to "resonance" energies that can be calculated from experimental data by various means.[4]

For example, Klages[5] has defined the resonance energy of a compound as follows:

$$RE = \Delta H_{Comb}^{Ref} - \Delta H_{Comb}^{Exp} \tag{8-25}$$

where ΔH_{Comb}^{Ref} is the calculated heat of combustion of a reference structure assuming isolated double bonds, and ΔH_{Comb}^{Exp} is the measured heat of combustion of the compound. To calculate ΔH_{Comb}^{Ref}, one makes use of a table of bond contributions to heats of combustion. These tables are compiled by comparing combustion

---

[4] The subject of resonance energies is a fascinating and controversial one. For more information, the student should see A. Streitwieser, Jr., *MO Theory for Organic Chemists*, John Wiley & Sons, Inc., New York (1961) Chapter 9.

[5] F. Klages, *Ber.* **82**, 358 (1949).

TABLE 8-1 SOME BOND CONTRIBUTIONS TO HEATS OF COMBUSTION OF A HYPOTHETICAL REFERENCE STRUCTURE FOR A CONJUGATED MOLECULE WHERE THE DOUBLE BONDS ARE ASSUMED TO BE LOCALIZED[a]

Bond	Contributions to ΔH_{comb}. Kcal
C—H	54.0
C—C	49.3
C=C (unsubstituted)	121.6
C=C (monosubstituted)	119.1
C=C (cis-disubstituted in a 6-membered ring)	117.4
C=C (tetrasubstituted)	112.0
correction for a 6-membered ring	+1.0

[a] The resonance energy of a compound is defined as the difference between the heat of combustion of the reference structure and the actual heat of combustion.

data for a large number of aliphatic and alicyclic compounds with no conjugated double bonds. Some of the bond contributions to resonance energies given by Klages are given in Table 8-1. Using the numbers in Table 8-1, we can calculate ΔH_{Comb}^{Ref} for butadiene. It is

$$\Delta H_{Comb}^{Ref} = 6(54.0) + 49.3 + 2(119.1) = 611.5 \text{ kcal}$$

The experimental value of the heat of combustion is 607.91 kcal.[6] The resonance energy calculated from Equation 8-25 is, therefore, 3.6 kcal. Comparing this resonance energy with the value of DE calculated for butadiene gives $\beta = 7.6$ kcal, which is much too low. This result emphasizes that the connection between resonance energies and delocalization energies calculated from MO theory is a tenuous one. In fact, Dewar has developed an alternate set of bond energies that depends on the type of σ-bond hybridization.[7] Using this set, he can "explain" most of the "resonance energy" without invoking π-electron delocalization.

The next step in a π-electron calculation on butadiene is the calculation of the coefficients of the four molecular orbitals that

[6] Selected Values of Chemical Thermodynamic Properties, National Bureau of Standards (U.S.) Circ. No. 500, 1952.

[7] M. J. S. Dewar and H. N. Schmeising, Tetrahedron, 5, 166 (1959), Ibid, 11, 96 (1960).

correspond to the four energies found above. This can be done by substituting the energies into the four secular equations, *one at a time*, and solving for the four sets of coefficients. This procedure often leads to arithmetic errors, however, and a more systematic procedure has been developed for calculating coefficients. This procedure automatically normalizes the molecular orbitals, also.

The method is based on the fact that the value of a particular coefficient is proportional to the signed minor or cofactor of the appropriate element of a row in the secular determinant (usually the first row). To use this method, one proceeds as follows:

1. Choose a row in the secular determinant, usually the first.

2. Calculate the value of the minors of each element of this row in terms of x and numbers. Give the minors the appropriate sign of $(-1)^{i+j}$, where i is the label of the row, and j is the label of the column for which the minor is evaluated.

The first two steps will be illustrated for butadiene. The four signed minors are

$$M_1 = + \begin{vmatrix} x & 1 & 0 \\ 1 & x & 1 \\ 0 & 1 & x \end{vmatrix} = x^3 - 2x \qquad (8\text{-}26a)$$

$$M_2 = - \begin{vmatrix} 1 & 1 & 0 \\ 0 & x & 1 \\ 0 & 1 & x \end{vmatrix} = -(x^2 - 1) \qquad (8\text{-}26b)$$

$$M_3 = + \begin{vmatrix} 1 & x & 0 \\ 0 & 1 & 1 \\ 0 & 0 & x \end{vmatrix} = x \qquad (8\text{-}26c)$$

$$M_4 = - \begin{vmatrix} 1 & x & 1 \\ 0 & 1 & x \\ 0 & 0 & 1 \end{vmatrix} = -1 \qquad (8\text{-}26d)$$

Once this has been done, the following steps should be carried out.

3. Calculate the values of the minors for the roots taken one at a time.

4. Square each value obtained in Step 3, and sum the squares.

5. Take the square root of the sum of the squares, and divide each value obtained in 3 by this quantity.

6. The resulting numbers will be the appropriate coefficients. If this procedure is done in tabular form, it is an easy matter to

TABLE 8-2 ILLUSTRATIVE CALCULATION OF THE CO-EFFICIENTS IN THE LOWEST ENERGY MOLECULAR ORBITAL IN BUTADIENE. THE FINAL COEFFICIENTS MAY ALL BE MULTIPLIED BY -1 WITHOUT CHANGING THE WAVE FUNCTION. ALL COEFFICIENTS WOULD THEN BE POSITIVE

μ	M_μ	$M_\mu{}^2$	$C_\mu = M_\mu/(\Sigma M^2)^{\frac{1}{2}}$
1	-1	1.000	-0.371
2	-1.618	2.618	-0.600
3	-1.618	2.618	-0.600
4	-1	1.000	-0.371
		$\Sigma M_\mu{}^2 = 7.236$	

check for errors, and one is less likely to make an error in the first place.

Steps 3 to 6 for butadiene are illustrated in Table 8-2 for the root $x = -1.618$. This procedure is only learned by practice which is the reason for the following exercise.

EXERCISE 8-2 Calculate the coefficients for the orbitals which correspond to the other three roots for butadiene.

The wave functions and energies for butadiene are summarized in Table 8-3.

In many respects, the coefficients of the atomic orbitals are of more interest than the orbital energies because, from the coefficients, additional quantities that are related to the π-electron dis-

TABLE 8-3 A SUMMARY OF THE ENERGIES AND CO-EFFICIENTS OF THE FOUR MOLECULAR ORBITALS OF BUTADIENE. THE STUDENT SHOULD VERIFY THAT THE NUMBER OF NODES IN THE MOLECULAR ORBITALS INCREASES FROM 0 TO 3 AS THE ENERGY OF THE OR-BITALS INCREASES

i	ϵ_i	$\phi_i = \sum\limits_{\mu=1}^{\mu} C_{i\mu}\chi_\mu$
1	$\alpha + 1.618\beta$	$0.371\chi_1 + 0.600\chi_2 + 0.600\chi_3 + 0.371\chi_4$
2	$\alpha + 0.618\beta$	$0.600\chi_1 + 0.371\chi_2 - 0.371\chi_3 - 0.600\chi_4$
3	$\alpha - 0.618\beta$	$0.600\chi_1 - 0.371\chi_2 - 0.371\chi_3 + 0.600\chi_4$
4	$\alpha - 1.618\beta$	$0.371\chi_1 - 0.600\chi_2 + 0.600\chi_3 - 0.371\chi_4$

tribution in the molecule can be defined. We will be interested in three such quantities: the electron densities, bond orders, and free valency indices. These are defined as follows:

1. The electron density on atom μ, q_μ. This is the probability of finding a π-electron on atom μ. It is defined as

$$q_\mu = \sum_i N_i C_{i\mu}{}^2 \tag{8-27}$$

where N_i is the number of electrons in the i'th *molecular orbital* (N_i can have the values 0, 1, or 2), and where $C_{i\mu}$ is the coefficient of *atomic* orbital μ in the i'th molecular orbital. To illustrate, q_1 for butadiene will be calculated

$$q_1 = 2C_{11}{}^2 + 2C_{21}{}^2 + OC_{31}{}^2 + OC_{41}{}^2$$
$$= 2(0.371)^2 + 2(0.600)^2 = 1.000$$

The net charge on atom, ξ_μ, is defined as

$$\xi_\mu = 1 - q_\mu \tag{8-28}$$

For atom 1 in butadiene, the net charge is zero.

EXERCISE 8-3 Suppose that one of the π-electrons in butadiene was ionized to give the butadiene positive ion. What would the net charge on atom 1 be in this positive ion?

2. The bond order of bond $\mu\nu$. This quantity is a measure of the amount of multiple bond character in a bond. Bond orders have been correlated with bond lengths and with vibrational force constants. The bond order is defined as

$$P_{\mu\nu} = \sum_i N_i C_{i\mu} C_{i\nu} \tag{8-29}$$

To illustrate, P_{12} for butadiene will be calculated

$$P_{12} = 2(0.371)(0.600) + 2(0.600)(0.371) + 0 = 0.894$$

The bond order for ethylene is 1.000, so the above result indicates that the 1,2 bond in butadiene is not quite a double bond.

3. The free valency index of atom μ, F_μ. This quantity is less useful than the other two, but it is sometimes used as a measure of free radical reactivity. It is defined as

$$F_\mu = \sqrt{3} - \text{Sum of bond orders of all bonds to atom } \mu \tag{8-30}$$

The $\sqrt{3}$ arises because it is the maximum value which the sum of the bond orders to a single carbon atom can have. To illustrate, F_1 for butadiene is

$$F_1 = 1.732 - 0.894 = 0.838$$

The free valency index is a quantitative expression of Thiele's idea of "residual valence."

EXERCISE 8-4 Calculate the remaining electron densities, bond orders, and free valency indices for butadiene.

8-5 The use of symmetry to simplify quantum mechanical calculations

It is, no doubt, obvious to the student that, as the number of atoms in a conjugated molecule increases, the labor and time spent in a simple Hückel calculation becomes large. If the molecule possesses some symmetry, it is possible to reduce this computational labor.

A symmetry operation is any operation performed on a molecule that leaves the molecule indistinguishable from its original configuration. Examples of symmetry operations are reflection in a plane, inversion through a center, rotation about an axis of symmetry, etc. Since, after a symmetry operation is carried out, the molecule is indistinguishable from its original configuration, the Hamiltonian for a molecule must be invariant upon any symmetry operations. In mathmatical language, this means that the Hamiltonian and an operator corresponding to any symmetry operation commute.

Symmetry is used to simplify quantum mechanical problems as follows:

1. Linear combinations of the atomic orbital basis set are found that are eigenfunctions of the appropriate symmetry operators for a molecule.

2. These "symmetry orbitals" are then used as a new basis set for a Hückel calculation.

3. Use can be made of the quantum mechanical theorem in Chapter 6 to set all matrix elements of the form $(\Psi_i|\mathcal{H}|\Psi_j) = 0$ if Ψ_i and Ψ_j belong to different eigenvalues of a symmetry operator.

This procedure will now be illustrated for butadiene. For butadiene, it will be sufficient to regard the molecule as having

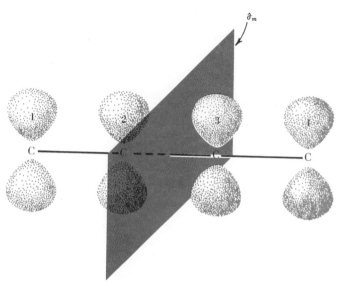

FIG. 8-5 *The mirror plane in butadiene. The mirror plane operator is only appropriate for cis-butadiene; trans-butadiene has a center of inversion, however, which leads to the same results as the mirror plane.*

a plane of symmetry passing through the middle of the central bond. This plane of symmetry is shown in Figure 8-5. We introduce the mirror plane operator $\hat{\sigma}_m$ that requires one to reflect the orbital following the operator in this plane. A consideration of Figure 8-5 shows that the operator $\hat{\sigma}_m$ has the following effect on the atomic orbitals

$$
\begin{aligned}
\hat{\sigma}_m \chi_1 &= \chi_4 \\
\hat{\sigma}_m \chi_2 &= \chi_3 \\
\hat{\sigma}_m \chi_3 &= \chi_2 \\
\hat{\sigma}_m \chi_4 &= \chi_1
\end{aligned}
\tag{8-31}
$$

Using these results, a set of four eigenfunctions of $\hat{\sigma}_m$ can be constructed by inspection. Since operating on χ_1 and χ_4 with $\hat{\sigma}_m$ gives χ_4 and χ_1, respectively, a function which gives the same function back again upon operation with $\hat{\sigma}_m$ must contain *both* χ_1 and χ_4 with coefficients of equal magnitude. A similar argument holds for χ_2 and χ_3. The four symmetry functions and their eigenvalues,

λ, with respect to $\acute{\sigma}_m$ are, therefore,

$$S_1 = \frac{1}{\sqrt{2}} (\chi_1 + \chi_4), \qquad \lambda = +1$$

$$S_2 = \frac{1}{\sqrt{2}} (\chi_2 + \chi_3), \qquad \lambda = +1$$

$$S_3 = \frac{1}{\sqrt{2}} (\chi_2 - \chi_3), \qquad \lambda = -1$$

$$S_4 = \frac{1}{\sqrt{2}} (\chi_1 - \chi_4), \qquad \lambda = -1$$

(8-32)

The student should verify the fact that these four functions are eigenfunctions of $\acute{\sigma}_m$ with the eigenvalues given.

Using the symmetry functions as the basis set and applying Theorem III of Chapter 6, we can immediately write the secular determinant. It is

$$\begin{vmatrix} H'_{11} - E & H'_{12} & 0 & 0 \\ H'_{12} & H'_{22} - E & 0 & 0 \\ 0 & 0 & H'_{33} - E & H'_{34} \\ 0 & 0 & H'_{34} & H'_{44} - E \end{vmatrix} = 0 \qquad (8\text{-}33)$$

where the primes indicate that these matrix elements are integrals over the *symmetry* orbitals. Whenever a determinant can be written so that two or more blocks are connected only by zeros, the determinant is said to be factorable. This means that the determinant above can be written as the product of a pair of 2 by 2 determinants

$$\begin{vmatrix} H'_{11} - E & H'_{12} \\ H'_{12} & H'_{22} - E \end{vmatrix} \begin{vmatrix} H'_{33} - E & H'_{34} \\ H'_{34} & H'_{44} - E \end{vmatrix} = 0 \qquad (8\text{-}34)$$

and, therefore, that each factor equals zero.

$$\begin{vmatrix} H'_{11} - E & H'_{12} \\ H'_{12} & H'_{22} - E \end{vmatrix} = 0, \quad \begin{vmatrix} H'_{33} - E & H'_{34} \\ H'_{34} & H'_{44} - E \end{vmatrix} = 0$$

(8-35)

The important point to notice is that a 4 by 4 secular determinant has been reduced to a pair of 2 by 2 secular determinants, and this

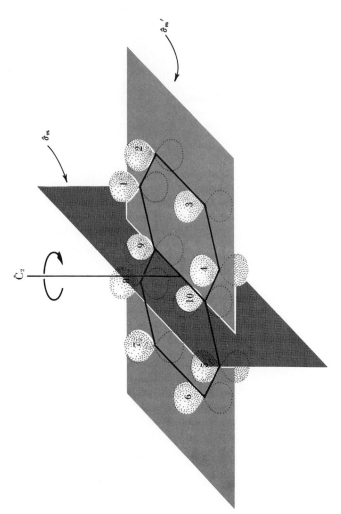

FIG. 8-6   The symmetry operations for naphthalene.   The $\hat{C}_2$ operator is a rotation of 180° about the twofold axis.   The $\hat{\sigma}_m$ and $\hat{\sigma}_m'$ operators are reflections in the appropriate planes.   The plane of the molecule is also a reflection plane, but all p orbitals must have eigenvalue −1 with respect to reflection in this plane.

greatly simplifies the work of finding the energies and coefficients. Exercise 8-5 illustrates the completion of the problem and the fact that the same results are obtained using the symmetry orbitals as were obtained using the original atomic orbital basis set.

EXERCISE 8-5 Evaluate the matrix elements $H_{\mu\nu}$, for μ, $\nu = 1 - 4$ using the symmetry orbitals as basis functions. Show that the characteristic equations that one obtains are the same as Equation 8-21. Calculate the coefficients of the two symmetry orbitals S_1 and S_2 using the root $x = -1.618$. Show that the MO that is obtained is the same as ϕ_1.

The use of symmetry becomes more important for large molecules. For example, a Hückel calculation on naphthalene using the atomic orbital basis set would involve solving a 10×10 secular determinant and evaluating ten 9×9 minors to calculate the coefficients. We can greatly reduce the amount of work needed for the π-electron calculation on naphthalene by making use of the fact that naphthalene has three symmetry operations that leave the molecule indistinguishable from its original configuration. These symmetry operations are two mirror planes, $\acute{\sigma}_m$, $\acute{\sigma}_m{'}$, and a twofold axis of rotational symmetry, $\hat{C}_2$. These symmetry elements and the numbering of the atoms in naphthalene are shown in Figure 8-6. The molecular plane is also a symmetry element, but its use does not result in any simplification of the problem since all $2p_z$ orbitals are already antisymmetric with respect to reflection in the molecular plane.

The problem, then, is reduced to constructing a set of simultaneous eigenfunctions of the three symmetry operators, $\hat{C}_2$, $\acute{\sigma}_m$, and $\acute{\sigma}_m{'}$. In this case, it is more difficult to construct the appropriate symmetry orbitals by inspection than it was for butadiene. A systematic procedure for constructing these orbitals is available, however, and a brief outline of this procedure will now be given.

The effects of symmetry on the atomic orbitals of naphthalene can be summarized by specifying the possible eigenvalues of symmetry orbitals with respect to four symmetry operators. The four operators are the three shown in Figure 8-6 plus the identity operator $\hat{E}$ that requires one to leave the molecule alone. The only possible eigenvalue with respect to $\hat{E}$ is $+ 1$, but we will see below that symmetry orbitals can be constructed with eigenvalues ± 1 with respect to the other three operators. The possible combinations of eigenvalues are listed in Table 8-4.

TABLE 8-4 POSSIBLE EIGENVALUES WITH RESPECT
TO THE FOUR SYMMETRY OPERATORS FOR THE NAPH-
THALENE MOLECULE. EACH SET OF EIGENVALUES IS
LABELED TO FACILITATE DISCUSSION

	E	C_2	σ_m	$\sigma_m{}'$
A_1	1	1	1	1
A_2	1	1	-1	-1
B_1	1	-1	1	-1
B_2	1	-1	-1	1

The student will no doubt notice that some combinations are missing from Table 8-4, for example, the set of eigenvalues $+1$, -1,
-1, -1. A consideration of Figure 8-6 shows why such a set of
eigenvalues would be impossible. The student can see that $\hat{C}_2$
converts χ_1 into χ_5; however, the same result can be obtained by
reflecting χ_1 first in $\acute{\sigma}_m$, and then $\acute{\sigma}_m{}'$. We can, thus, say mathematically that $\hat{C}_2$ is equal to $\acute{\sigma}_m\acute{\sigma}_m{}'$. To have eigenvalue -1
with respect to $\hat{C}_2$ then requires that the product of the eigenvalues
with respect to $\acute{\sigma}_m$ and $\acute{\sigma}_m{}'$ be minus also. This is not true if the
eigenvalues with respect to σ_m and $\sigma_m{}'$ are both -1.[8]

Each of the sets of eigenvalues in Table 8-3 is labeled to facilitate
talking about them. By convention, sets containing the eigenvalue $+1$ with respect to $\hat{C}_2$ are labeled with A, those containing
the eigenvalues -1 with respect to $\hat{C}_2$ are labeled with a B.
Symmetry orbitals can now be constructed by taking the atomic
orbitals one at a time, performing the operations $\hat{E}$, $\hat{C}_2$, $\acute{\sigma}_m$, and
$\acute{\sigma}_m{}'$, and then multiplying the results by the appropriate eigenvalue
from Table 8-3. For example, if we take χ_1 and the set of eigenvalues A_1, we can obtain the symmetry orbital

$$\chi_1(A_1) \rightarrow \chi_1 + \chi_5 + \chi_8 + \chi_4 \tag{8-36}$$

since

$$\begin{aligned}
\hat{E}\chi_1 &= \chi_1 \\
\hat{C}_2\chi_1 &= \chi_5 \\
\acute{\sigma}_m\chi_1 &= \chi_8 \\
\acute{\sigma}_m{}'\chi_1 &= \chi_4
\end{aligned} \tag{8-37}$$

[8] For a good discussion of relations between the sets of eigenvalues in
Table 8-4, see F. A. Cotton, *Chemical Applications of Group Theory*, Interscience Publishers, Inc., New York, 1963, Chapter 4.

Likewise, a symmetry orbital with a B_1 set of eigenvalues formed from atomic orbital χ_2 would be

$$\chi_2(B_1) \rightarrow \chi_2 - \chi_3 - \chi_6 + \chi_7 \tag{8-38}$$

By following this procedure, using different atoms with each set of eigenvalues, the student can construct the set of 10 symmetry orbitals which are given in Table 8-5.

An eigenfunction with a set of eigenvalues given by any row of Table 8-4 is said to belong to the *representation* indicated by the symbol in the left hand column of the table. Thus, the eigenfunction $\chi_2 - \chi_3 - \chi_6 + \chi_7$ is said to belong to the representation B_1.

It should be remembered that all of the symmetry operations commute with each other and with the Hamiltonian. This means that, if we apply Theorem III of Chapter 6, all integrals of the type $(S_1|\mathcal{H}|S_2)$ will vanish unless S_1 and S_2 have identical eigen-

TABLE 8-5 SYMMETRY ORBITALS FOR NAPHTHALENE[a]

A_1	A_2
$S_1 = \dfrac{1}{2}(\chi_1 + \chi_4 + \chi_5 + \chi_8)$	$S_4 = \dfrac{1}{2}(\chi_1 - \chi_4 + \chi_5 - \chi_8)$
$S_2 = \dfrac{1}{2}(\chi_2 + \chi_3 + \chi_6 + \chi_7)$	$S_5 = \dfrac{1}{2}(\chi_2 - \chi_3 + \chi_6 - \chi_7)$
$S_3 = \dfrac{1}{\sqrt{2}}(\chi_9 + \chi_{10})$	

B_1	B_2
$S_6 = \dfrac{1}{2}(\chi_1 - \chi_4 - \chi_5 + \chi_8)$	$S_9 = \dfrac{1}{2}(\chi_1 + \chi_4 - \chi_5 - \chi_8)$
$S_7 = \dfrac{1}{2}(\chi_2 - \chi_3 - \chi_6 + \chi_7)$	$S_{10} = \dfrac{1}{2}(\chi_2 + \chi_3 - \chi_6 - \chi_7)$
$S_8 = \dfrac{1}{\sqrt{2}}(\chi_9 - \chi_{10})$	

[a] Note that the atomic orbitals χ_9 and χ_{10} only appear in the A_1 and B_1 sets. This is because these orbitals must have eigenvalue $+1$ with respect to $\hat{\sigma}'_m$. The student should verify that the numerical factor in each orbital ensures that it is normalized.

values with respect to *all four* symmetry operators. Thus, all matrix elements between orbitals in different groups in Table 8-5 will vanish. The original 10×10 determinant for the naphthalene calculation using atomic orbitals will then factor into two 3×3 and two 2×2 determinants when symmetry orbitals are used. This factoring results in a considerable saving of effort in the calculation. The completion of the calculation of the π-electron energies and wave functions for naphthalene makes an excellent exercise to test the students understanding of the material in this chapter.

EXERCISE 8-6 Calculate the π-electron energies and wave functions for naphthalene using the symmetry orbitals in Table 8-5. Also calculate the electron densities, bond orders, and free valency indices. The orbital energies and coefficients are given in Table 8-6.

As the student no doubt suspects, the above discussion has been an introduction to the use of group theory to simplify quantum mechanical calculations. The student interested in further work in group theory should consult the reference given in footnote 7.

TABLE 8-6 ORBITAL ENERGIES AND COEFFICIENTS OBTAINED FROM A HÜCKEL CALCULATION ON NAPHTHALENE[a]

i	ϵ_i	$C_1, C_4,$ C_5, C_8	$C_2, C_3,$ C_4, C_7	C_9, C_{10}	Representation
1	$\alpha + 2.303\beta$	0.3006	0.2307	0.4614	A_1
2	$\alpha + 1.618\beta$	0.2629	0.4253	0.0000	B_2
3	$\alpha + 1.303\beta$	0.3996	0.1735	0.3471	B_1
4	$\alpha + 1.000\beta$	0.0000	-0.4083	0.4083	A_1
5	$\alpha + 0.618\beta$	0.4253	0.2629	0.0000	A_2
6	$\alpha - 0.618\beta$	0.4253	-0.2629	0.0000	B_2
7	$\alpha - 1.000\beta$	0.0000	-0.4083	0.4083	B_1
8	$\alpha - 1.303\beta$	0.3996	-0.1735	-0.3471	A_1
9	$\alpha - 1.618\beta$	0.2629	-0.4253	0.0000	A_2
10	$\alpha - 2.303\beta$	0.3006	-0.2307	-0.4614	B_1

[a] The coefficients are arranged in groups that have the same numerical value. The relative signs of the coefficients within each group are determined by the representation to which the molecular orbital belongs. Thus, for ϕ_2 which belongs to B_2, $C_1 = C_4 = -C_5 = -C_8$.

8-6   The electronic spectra of conjugated systems

The basic principles necessary for the understanding of the electronic spectra of π-electron systems are similar to those treated in Chapter 7 in the discussion of the electronic spectra of diatomic molecules. There are several differences in detail, however. One difference comes about because conjugated molecules are usually quite large with large moments of inertia and many vibrational degrees of freedom. This means that rotational fine structure is almost never resolved in the electronic spectra of these molecules. In fact, only the highest frequency vibrations give rise to vibrational fine structure. The electronic spectrum of a conjugated molecule, therefore, usually contains several quite broad bands, some of which may have additional vibrational fine structure.

At first thought it might seem foolish to embark on a calculation of the energies of π-electron transitions. After all, use of the LCAO method for the hydrogen molecule gave a binding energy that was in error by 43%. How can we expect good agreement for more complex molecules when we are making even more drastic assumptions than were made for molecular hydrogen? The situation turns out to be not so hopeless as the above statements would indicate, however. Although it is true that no π-electron theory yet developed can give exact quantitative agreement with experiment, it is also true that many of the qualitative features of the electronic spectra of conjugated molecules can be rationalized by such a theory.

The *cis*-butadiene molecule will be used as an example in the calculation of π-electron spectral quantities. This molecule is chosen for two reasons: the one-electron energies and wave functions have already been given in Section 8-4, and the molecule shares some of the symmetry operations already discussed for naphthalene.

The symmetry properties of a molecule are extremely important in a discussion of electronic spectra. The student should recall that one was able to derive electronic selection rules for diatomic molecules on the basis of symmetry arguments alone. A similar procedure can be used for the selection rules in symmetric conjugated hydrocarbons except that the arguments are a little more complicated.

The *cis*-butadiene molecule, a suitable coordinate system, and

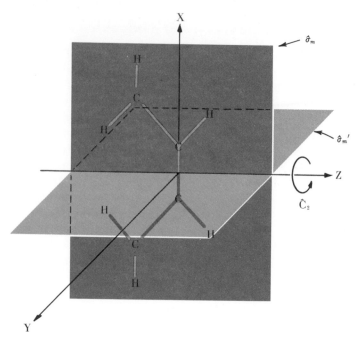

FIG. 8-7   *The symmetry operations for the cis-butadiene molecule.   The molecule lies in the XZ plane.   By convention, the Z axis is always taken along $\hat{C}_2$.   To show how the coordinate x transforms, consider what happens to a unit vector along the X axis when it is operated on by the three symmetry operators.*

the appropriate symmetry operations are shown in Figure 8-7. By convention, the Z axis is taken along $\hat{C}_2$. The Y axis is perpendicular to the plane of the molecule. There are four possible symmetry operations for butadiene: the identity operation $\hat{E}$, a twofold axis $\hat{C}_2$, and two mirror planes $\hat{\sigma}_m$ and $\hat{\sigma}_m'$. In this case $\hat{\sigma}_m$ is the plane of the molecule. The possible sets of simultaneous eigenvalues are given in Table 8-7. Such a table is also called a character table for the C_{2v} group. In the first column of the table, the symmetry labels are given as well as the coordinate, if any, which belongs to that particular representation. The remainder of the table is identical to that used in the discussion of naphthalene.

Our first job is to see to which group of eigenvalues or to which

TABLE 8-7 **POSSIBLE SETS OF EIGENVALUES FOR THE FOUR SYMMETRY OPERATORS IN cis-BUTADIENE. THE STUDENT MAY SHOW THAT THE COORDINATES x, y, AND z BELONG TO THE REPRESENTATION SHOWN BY CONSIDERING THE BEHAVIOR OF A UNIT VECTOR ALONG EACH AXIS WHEN IT IS OPERATED ON BY THE SYMMETRY OPERATORS**

	E	C_2	σ_m	σ_m'
$A_1; z$	1	1	1	1
A_2	1	1	-1	-1
$B_1; x$	1	-1	1	-1
$B_2; y$	1	-1	-1	1

representation the four molecular orbitals of butadiene belong. This can be done by operating on each of the molecular orbitals in turn by the four symmetry operators and finding the eigenvalue with respect to each. It should immediately be clear that, since all p orbitals are antisymmetric with respect to the molecular plane, all four molecular orbitals must belong to either the A_2 or B_2 representations. By recalling the results of Section 8-5, where the eigenvalue with respect to $\acute{\sigma}_m'$ was used to simplify the calculation, the representations of the four orbitals can immediately be written down. They are

$$\phi_1, \quad b_2; \qquad \phi_3, \quad b_2$$
$$\phi_2, \quad a_2; \qquad \phi_4, \quad a_2$$

where the convention has been introduced that small letters will be used to indicate the symmetry of one-electron orbitals. (Capital letters will indicate the symmetry of a state or configuration.)

Within the one-electron approximation, the ground state wave function for butadiene is

$$\Psi_0 = N\phi_1(1)\bar{\phi}_1(2)\phi_2(3)\bar{\phi}_2(4) \tag{8-39}$$

where, as before, N is a normalizing factor and the bar indicates β spin. The symmetry of this ground state wave function is the product of the symmetries of the one-electron orbitals. The set of eigenvalues characterizing Ψ_0 is, thus,

$$E = (1)^2 \cdot (1)^2 = 1 \qquad \sigma_m = (-1)^2 \cdot (-1)^2 = 1$$
$$C_2 = (-1)^2 \cdot (1)^2 = 1 \qquad \sigma_m' = (1)^2 \cdot (-1)^2 = 1$$

and the symmetry of Ψ_0 is, therefore, A_1.

TABLE 8-8 THE WAVE FUNCTIONS AND SYMMETRIES OF THE GROUND STATE AND SOME EXCITED CONFIGU-RATIONS OF BUTADIENE

State	Wave Function	Symmetry
Ψ_0	$\phi_1(1)\bar{\phi}_1(2)\phi_2(3)\bar{\phi}_2(4)$	A_1
Ψ_1	$\phi_1(1)\bar{\phi}_1(2)\phi_2(3)\bar{\phi}_3(4)$	B_1
Ψ_2	$\phi_1(1)\bar{\phi}_1(2)\phi_2(3)\bar{\phi}_4(4)$	A_1
Ψ_3	$\phi_1(1)\bar{\phi}_2(2)\phi_2(3)\bar{\phi}_3(4)$	A_1
Ψ_4	$\phi_1(1)\bar{\phi}_2(2)\phi_2(3)\bar{\phi}_4(4)$	B_1

We next consider some of the excited states of butadiene. These can be thought of as arising from the excitation of one of the electrons in ϕ_1 or ϕ_2 to either ϕ_3 or ϕ_4. Some of these excited state wave functions and their symmetries are given in Table 8-8. The symmetries of these excited states can be obtained in the same way as those for the ground state.

We will next use this simple model to calculate the excitation energies and selection rules for π-electron transitions. The excitation energies are the differences between the appropriate orbital energies. Thus,

$$E(0 \rightarrow 1) = \epsilon_3 - \epsilon_2 = -0.618\beta - 0.618\beta$$
$$= -1.236\beta$$
$$E(0 \rightarrow 2) = E(0 \rightarrow 3) = \epsilon_4 - \epsilon_2 = -2.236\beta$$
$$E(0 \rightarrow 4) = \epsilon_4 - \epsilon_1 = -3.236\beta$$

It should be noted that, because of the pairing properties of the orbital energies, the $E(0 \rightarrow 2)$ and the $E(0 \rightarrow 3)$ transitions have the same energy at this level of approximation. The selection rules are derived by considering the symmetry of the integrand in the transition moment. If the position vector of the i'th electron is written out in terms of its components, then

$$\mathbf{R}^{ok} = e(\Psi_k{}^*|x\mathbf{i} + y\mathbf{j} + z\mathbf{k}|\Psi_0) \qquad (8\text{-}40)$$

To evaluate the selection rules, the symmetry of the excited state and of each of the terms x, y, and z must be considered. If the integral $\mathbf{R}^{ok}$ is not to vanish, the integrand must be totally symmetric or belong to the A_1 representation (see Section 7-7). The Ψ_2 and Ψ_3 states are of A_1 symmetry; therefore, only the z component of the transition moment is nonvanishing. This is because only the z coordinate has A_1 symmetry, and the product of the A_1 representation with any other representation will not give an integrand with A_1 symmetry. The states Ψ_1 and Ψ_4 have B_1 symmetry, and the products $\Psi_0\Psi_1$ and $\Psi_0\Psi_4$, therefore, have B_1 symmetry. As a consequence, only the x term in the transition moment for these transitions is nonvanishing because a function of B_1 symmetry multiplied by either z or y will not give an integrand which has A_1 symmetry. We, therefore, find that all of the transitions discussed above will be allowed. We can further predict the spectroscopic behavior of oriented molecules when polarized light is used. If the plane of polarization of a light wave is defined as the plane of oscillation of the electric field vector, then transitions $\Psi_0 \to \Psi_1$ and $\Psi_0 \to \Psi_4$ will be observed only when the light beam is Z-axis polarized. Likewise, the transitions $\Psi_0 \to \Psi_2$ and $\Psi_1 \to \Psi_3$ will be observed only for X-axis polarized light. For this reason, the transitions $\Psi_0 \to \Psi_4$ and $\Psi_1 \to \Psi_4$ are said to be Z-axis polarized and the transitions $\Psi_0 \to \Psi_2$ and $\Psi_0 \to \Psi_3$ are said to be X-axis polarized. Comparison of the above calculations with experiment is difficult. The *cis*-butadiene molecule is unstable with respect to the *trans* form and is difficult to study. Because of this, the experimental data is quite sparse. In addition, the lowest energy transition that has been observed is at 2170 Å. Any other transition will be in vacuum ultraviolet, and experimental studies in this region are rather difficult. The absorption at 2170 Å corresponds to an energy of 5.7 ev or 131 kcal/mole. If this energy is assigned to the $\Psi_0 \to \Psi_1$ transition, and if it is compared with the transition energy calculation above from simple Hückel theory, the value of β must be 4.6 ev or 110 kcal/mole. This value is much too high when compared with values of β used in more refined calculations on spectra and other properties. The polarization of this lowest energy absorption band is not yet known so it is not even absolutely certain that the lowest energy excited state has B_1 symmetry.

The above calculation does not really tell one if a simple Hückel treatment is adequate for a discussion of the electronic spectra of conjugated hydrocarbons. It does, however, illustrate the basic procedure for calculating spectral properties. Furthermore, the treatment given above serves in many cases as the starting point for more refined calculations of π-electron spectra. These refined calculations have been highly successful in calculating the details of the electronic spectra of many conjugated molecules.[9]

8-7 Summary

1. The approximations inherent in the π-electron approximation for treating the electronic structure of conjugated molecules were discussed.

2. The general features of the molecular orbital method for treating these molecules were introduced. The secular equation arising from this treatment was simplified using the approximations first introduced by Hückel.

3. Examples of simple MO calculations on ethylene and butadiene were given. The discussion of butadiene included a systematic way to calculate the coefficients of the molecular orbitals.

4. Resonance energies were defined as the difference between the experimental heat of combustion and the heat of combustion calculated for a reference structure assuming localized double bonds. These resonance energies were related to the delocalization energies calculated from Hückel theory.

5. The π-electron bond orders, electron densities, and free valence indices were defined.

6. The use of symmetry to simplify quantum mechanical calculations was discussed, and the idea of a symmetry operator was introduced. The use of symmetry was illustrated in calculations on butadiene and naphthalene.

7. The method used to calculate spectral properties of π-electron systems was illustrated by a calculation for *cis*-butadiene. The symmetry of the molecule was used to derive electronic selection rules and the polarization properties of the possible transitions.

8. The student should be familiar with the terms, delocalization energy, bond order, charge density, free valence index, resonance energy, symmetry operation, identity operator, representation, character table, and polarization of a transition.

[9] For a general discussion of the spectra of conjugated molecules see Sandorfy, *Electronic Spectra and Quantum Chemistry*, Prentice-Hall, Inc., Englewood Cliffs, New Jersey, 1964 and J. N. Murrell, *The Theory of the Electronic Spectra of Organic Molecules*, John Wiley & Sons, Inc., New York, 1963.

Chapter 9

ELECTRON AND
NUCLEAR MAGNETIC
RESONANCE SPECTROSCOPY

IT WAS pointed out in Chapter 6 that an intrinsic spin angular momentum had to be postulated for the electron in order to account for many experimental results. Nuclei, also, have such an intrinsic spin angular momentum, and it is characterized by a nuclear spin quantum number, I. Nuclei differ from electrons in that there are a large number of different values which the nuclear spin quantum number can have. The electron spin quantum number, it should be recalled, is restricted to the value $\frac{1}{2}$. Nuclear spin quantum numbers range in half integral units from 0 to 6. Unless he wishes to study nuclear structure, the chemist must accept the nuclear spin quantum number for any given nucleus as a matter of empirical fact, but there are at least some rules which divide nuclei into classes according to their mass number, A, and their charge number, Z. These rules are:

1. If the mass number A is odd, the nuclear spin I is half integral.

2. If the mass number A and the charge number Z are both even, the spin is zero.

3. If the mass number A is even, but the charge number Z is odd, the spin is integral.

Thus, ^{1}H, ^{19}F, and ^{31}P have nuclear spin $I = \frac{1}{2}$. The nuclei ^{16}O and ^{12}C have $I = 0$, and ^{2}H (deuterium), ^{6}Li, and ^{14}N have $I = 1$. We will only be concerned with nuclei which have spin $\frac{1}{2}$ in this chapter. This enables us to treat these nuclei and electrons with the same nomenclature.

The properties of nuclear spin angular momentum are essentially the same as those for electron spin angular momentum except that, for most nuclei, the nuclear magnetic moment is parallel to the spin vector and not antiparallel as with electrons (^{15}N, $I = \frac{1}{2}$, is an exception). That is, for nuclei with spin $\frac{1}{2}$, there are two functions, α and β, each of which is an eigenfunction of both $\hat{I}^2$ and $\hat{I}_z$, where $\hat{I}$ is the nuclear spin operator and $\hat{I}_z$ is the operator for the z-component of nuclear spin. The functions α and β have the property that

$$
\begin{aligned}
\hat{I}^2\alpha &= \frac{1}{2}\left(\frac{1}{2}+1\right)\alpha & \hat{I}_z\alpha &= \frac{1}{2}\alpha \\
\hat{I}^2\beta &= \frac{1}{2}\left(\frac{1}{2}+1\right)\beta & \hat{I}_z\beta &= -\frac{1}{2}\beta
\end{aligned}
\tag{9-1}
$$

For these nuclei, there is a corresponding magnetic moment operator $\hat{\mu}$ equal to

$$
\hat{\mu} = g_N\beta_N\hat{I}
\tag{9-2}
$$

where g_N is the nuclear g factor that is characteristic of each nucleus, and β_N is the nuclear magneton equal to 5.0505×10^{-24} erg gauss^{-1}. The student will notice that Equation 9-2 is identical to Equation 6-57 for the magnetic moment due to electron spin except that the minus sign is missing. The operators for nuclear spin angular momentum combine and commute in the same way as do those for electron spin angular momentum.

9-1   The interaction of an isolated
spin $\frac{1}{2}$ particle with an applied magnetic field

If a spin $\frac{1}{2}$ particle is placed in a static magnetic field, the two states α and β no longer have the same energy.   The classical energy of interaction between a magnetic dipole $\mathbf{\mu}$ and a static field $\mathbf{H}$ is given by

$$E = - \mathbf{\mu} \cdot \mathbf{H} \tag{9-3}$$

The corresponding magnetic Hamiltonian operator for this interaction is, therefore

$$\hat{\mathcal{K}}_e = - (- g_0 \beta \hat{\mathbf{S}}) \cdot \mathbf{H} = g_0 \beta \hat{\mathbf{S}} \cdot \mathbf{H} \text{ (electrons)} \tag{9-4a}$$
$$\hat{\mathcal{K}}_N = - g_N \beta_N \hat{\mathbf{I}} \cdot \mathbf{H} \text{ (nuclei)} \tag{9-4b}$$

The student should recall (Section 1-4) that the dot product of two vectors $\hat{\mathbf{S}}$ and $\mathbf{H}$ is equal to the length of $\mathbf{H}$ times the length of the projection of $\hat{\mathbf{S}}$ on $\mathbf{H}$.   Since the direction of $\mathbf{H}$ defines the Z axis, the projection of $\hat{\mathbf{S}}$ on $\mathbf{H}$ is $\hat{S}_z$.   Equations 9-4 then become

$$\hat{\mathcal{K}}_e = g_0 \beta H \hat{S}_z \tag{9-5a}$$
$$\hat{\mathcal{K}}_N = - g_N \beta_N H \hat{I}_z \tag{9-5b}$$

The energies of the states α and β are found from the eigenvalue equations

$$\begin{aligned} \hat{\mathcal{K}}\alpha &= E_\alpha \alpha \\ \hat{\mathcal{K}}\beta &= E_\beta \beta \end{aligned} \tag{9-6}$$

The student can easily verify that

$$E_\alpha = \pm \frac{1}{2} g_i \beta_i H$$
$$E_\beta = \mp \frac{1}{2} g_i \beta_i H \tag{9-7}$$

where the upper sign is for electrons and the lower sign is for nuclei, and where the appropriate values of g and β are used.   The quantity H is the magnitude of the magnetic field.   Thus, the energy of the states α and β diverges as H increases.   A plot of the

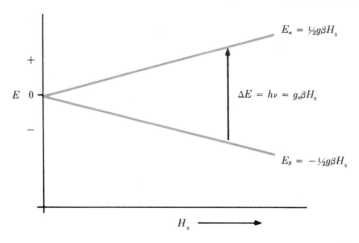

FIG. 9-1 *A plot of the energy of the states α and β for an isolated electron in an applied magnetic field. A similar plot holds for protons except that the α and β states must be exchanged, and the appropriate values of g and β must be used. Transitions between these two states are studied in magnetic resonance experiments. The transition frequency ν is equal to $g\,\beta H_0/h$.*

energy of the states α and β for electrons is shown in Figure 9-1. A similar plot holds for spin $\frac{1}{2}$ nuclei except that the labeling of the states is reversed and the appropriate values of g and β must be used.

The phenomena of electron and nuclear magnetic resonance are based upon the fact that transitions are possible between the two states α and β. These transitions occur when an electromagnetic wave of frequency ν is applied to the sample under the condition that

$$h\nu = g_i\beta_iH \tag{9-8}$$

Equation 9-8 is called the resonance condition.

EXERCISE 9-1 Calculate the resonance frequency for a sample containing unpaired electrons in a magnetic field of 3300 gauss. Use the Boltzmann distribution law to calculate the population ratio of the α and β states at room temperature (300°K).

9-2   *Electron spin resonance[1] spectroscopy— hyperfine interactions*

For ESR spectroscopy, the experimental conditions that are usually used to satisfy Equation 9-8 are a magnetic field strength of about 3300 gauss, and an rf frequency of approximately 9500 Mc. For an atom or a molecule to have an ESR spectrum, it must have one or more unpaired electrons. In quantum mechanical language, the wave function for the atom or molecule must have a nonzero eigenvalue with respect to the operator $\hat{S}^2$. In general, there are three main situations in which such atoms or molecules occur. These are:

1. Paramagnetic ions in solution and in crystals such as Fe^{+3}, Mn^{+2}, etc.
2. Organic and inorganic free radicals in solution.
3. Radiation-produced fragments in crystals.

Most of the discussion in this chapter will be concerned with case 2.

If the interaction discussed in Section 9-1 were the only one present, ESR spectroscopy would not be very interesting. All atoms or molecules that contained unpaired electrons would give an ESR spectrum consisting of a single absorption at the frequency satisfying the condition described by Equation 9-8. Fortunately, there are several interactions between unpaired electrons and their environment, and it is these interactions which make ESR fascinating to those interested in the details of molecular electronic structure.

The actual magnetic field which an unpaired electron experiences is the vector sum of the applied field and the *internal* fields of the molecule. Some important types of internal fields are:

1. Fields due to other unpaired electrons in the molecule or ion.
2. Fields due to magnetic nuclei in the molecule.
3. Fields due to unpaired electrons in surrounding molecules or ions.

In addition, there may be a contribution to the magnetic moment of the electron from its *orbital* angular momentum. This latter

[1] Electron spin resonance (ESR) is sometimes called electron magnetic resonance (EMR) or electron paramagnetic resonance (EPR). The terms are synonymous.

effect has profound effects on the frequency of an ESR absorbtion because it changes the g value from the free spin value.

In what follows, it will be assumed that there is no contribution to the magnetic moment of the electron from its orbital angular momentum, and that the only source of internal magnetic fields are magnetic nuclei in the molecule. There are then two types of interaction between the unpaired electrons and magnetic nuclei. These are:

1. The dipole-dipole interaction. This is analogous to the classical interaction of a pair of magnetic dipoles. The only difference is that the dipole moment of the unpaired electron must be calculated quantum mechanically because an electron is, in fact, distributed over space. This interaction is anisotropic. That is, it depends on the relative orientations of the applied magnetic field and the spin vector of the magnetic nucleus. This interaction is an important source of information in single crystal studies, but it is averaged to zero in liquids because of the rapid tumbling motion of the molecules. The mathematics involved in discussing the dipole-dipole interaction are somewhat complicated and this interaction will not be discussed.

2. The isotropic or Fermi-contact interaction. This is a quantum mechanical interaction and has *no classical analogue*. It arises when there is a nonzero probability of finding the unpaired electron *at* the magnetic nucleus in question. In the orbital approximation, s orbitals are the only ones that do not vanish at the nucleus. If the wave function for the odd electron has some orbital s character which is centered on a magnetic nucleus, an isotropic hyperfine interaction will be observed. In fact, this is the only kind of interaction observed for free radicals in solution.

To illustrate the effects of the isotropic hyperfine interaction on an ESR spectrum, consider the case of a system of gaseous hydrogen atoms. In the ground state, the electron in a hydrogen atom has no angular momentum, and also, the dipole-dipole interaction vanishes for electrons in s orbitals. The only interaction that must be considered is the isotropic hyperfine interaction between the odd electron and the proton that has spin $I = \frac{1}{2}$. If an ESR experiment is done in very large magnetic fields, both the electron and proton will have their magnetic moments quantized along the direction of the applied field. This gives rise to four different states, each with a slightly different energy. These states are

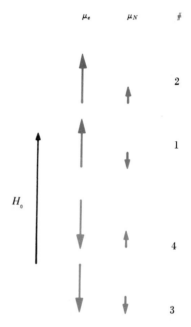

F I G . 9 - 2 *Drawing of the possible arrangements of the electron and proton magnetic moment vectors for a hydrogen atom in a strong magnetic field. The numbers of the states correspond to the numbers of the wave functions used later in the quantum mechanical description. The sizes of the electron and nuclear spin vectors are not to scale. The electron spin vector is actually ∼ 1000 times larger than the proton spin vector.*

shown schematically in Figure 9-2. A consideration of the selection rules shows that the only transitions that are allowed are those for which the nuclear spin quantum number does not change. Thus, transitions between states 3 and 1, and between states 4 and 2, would occur. The ESR spectrum would, therefore, consist of two lines corresponding to these two transitions. The spacing between the two lines is the proton hyperfine coupling constant, a.

The above has been a qualitative discussion. To show how the energy levels work out in detail, we must calculate them quantum mechanically. The spin part of the Hamiltonian operator for a hydrogen atom in a magnetic field is

$$\hat{\mathcal{K}}_{sp} = - g_0\beta\hat{\mathbf{S}} \cdot \mathbf{H} + g_N\beta_N\hat{\mathbf{I}} \cdot \mathbf{H} + ha\hat{\mathbf{S}} \cdot \hat{\mathbf{I}} \qquad (9\text{-}9)$$

In Equation 9-9, the first two terms represent the interaction of the electron and nuclear spins with the applied field, and the third term represents the electron-nuclear hyperfine interaction, a being the hyperfine coupling constant just defined and h being Planck's constant. Equation 9-9 assumes that all dipole-dipole interactions are zero, and that there is no contribution from electron orbital angular momentum. As mentioned above, both of these assumptions are true for hydrogen atoms. For strong magnetic fields[2] the Hamiltonian 9-9 takes the simple form

$$\hat{\mathcal{K}}_{sp} = g_0\beta H \hat{S}_z - g_N\beta_N H \hat{I}_z + ha\hat{S}_z\hat{I}_z \tag{9-10}$$

The spin functions appropriate for this problem are the proper product functions of single electron and nuclear spin functions. These are

$$\Psi_1 = \alpha(e)\alpha(p) \tag{9-11a}$$
$$\Psi_2 = \alpha(e)\beta(p) \tag{b}$$
$$\Psi_3 = \beta(e)\alpha(p) \tag{c}$$
$$\Psi_4 = \beta(e)\beta(p) \tag{d}$$

It can be readily seen, by operating on the functions 9-11 with the Hamiltonian 9-10, that all are already appropriate eigenfunctions. The eigenenergies can immediately be written down and are

$$E_1 = \frac{1}{2} g_0\beta H - \frac{1}{2} g_N\beta_N H + \frac{1}{4} ha \tag{9-12a}$$

$$E_2 = \frac{1}{2} g_0\beta H + \frac{1}{2} g_N\beta_N H - \frac{1}{4} ha \tag{b}$$

$$E_3 = -\frac{1}{2} g_0\beta H - \frac{1}{2} g_N\beta_N H - \frac{1}{4} ha \tag{c}$$

$$E_4 = -\frac{1}{2} g_0\beta H + \frac{1}{2} g_N\beta_N H + \frac{1}{4} ha \tag{d}$$

In a typical magnetic resonance experiment, the sample interacts with the oscillating magnetic field of an electromagnetic wave. This oscillating magnetic field is applied perpendicular to the applied field. The appropriate transition moment for calculating

[2] In this case, strong magnetic fields are defined by the condition that $g_0\beta H, g_N\beta_N H \gg a$. For a hydrogen atom in a 10,000 gauss field, $g_0\beta H \approx 20$ k mc, $g_N\beta_N H \approx 42$ mc, and $a \approx 1400$ mc. Thus, the condition $g_0\beta H \gg a$ holds, but not $g_N\beta_N H_0 \gg a$. The above calculation for hydrogen is, therefore, an approximate one. For the organic radicals discussed later, the approximation $g_N\beta_N H > a$ is fairly good, and the simplified form of the Hamiltonian can be used. For an example of a more complete calculation, the reader is referred to the article "Hyperfine Interactions in X-Irradiated Magnesium Phosphite Hexahydrate," M. W. Hanna and L. J. Altman, *J. Chem. Phys.*, **36**, 1788 (1962).

intensities is

$$R_{ij} = (\Psi_i|\hat{\mu}_\perp|\Psi_j) = g_0\beta(\Psi_i|\hat{S}_\perp|\Psi_j) \tag{9-13}$$

where $\hat{\mu}_\perp$ is the operator for the component of electronic spin angular momentum perpendicular to the applied field and $\hat{S}_\perp = \hat{S}_x + i\hat{S}_y = \hat{S}_+$. The intensity of the ESR transitions is proportional to

$$g_0{}^2\beta^2|(\Psi_i|\hat{S}_\perp|\Psi_j)|^2$$

Applying Equation 9-13 to calculate the various R_{ij}, it can be shown, using the methods of Chapter 6, that

$$\begin{aligned} R_{13} &= R_{24} = g_0{}^2\beta^2 \\ R_{12} &= R_{14} = R_{23} = R_{34} = 0 \end{aligned} \tag{9-14}$$

Thus, only the transitions $3 \rightarrow 1$ and $4 \rightarrow 2$ are allowed, and these have energies

$$E_1 - E_3 = g_0\beta H + \frac{1}{2}ha$$

$$E_2 - E_4 = g_0\beta H - \frac{1}{2}ha \tag{9-15}$$

There will, therefore, be two lines in the ESR spectrum of atomic hydrogen centered at $g_0\beta H$ and separated by ha. The student can see that all of the results of the qualitative treatment given first are confirmed by the quantum mechanical calculation.

EXERCISE 9-2   The student should work through all of the details of Equations 9-12 through 9-15 by carrying out the appropriate operations.

Calculation of the ESR spectrum of more complicated radicals is a straightforward, but time consuming, extension of the principles described above. It is more convenient, for these more complex radicals, to use the qualitative picture first discussed. As a further example, consider the ESR spectrum of the methyl radical $\cdot CH_3$. This radical is probably planar with bond angles of $120°$. In any case, the three protons are magnetically equivalent because they are related to one another by a symmetry operation of the molecule. Figure 9-3 shows the possible alignment of the three nuclear moments for a single electron moment alignment. It can be seen that there are *four* possible internal fields due to the three protons, depending on how the proton moments are aligned. The

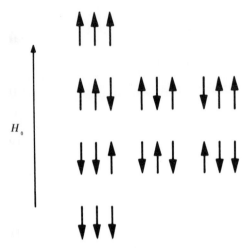

H_0

FIG. 9-3 *Possible alignments of the nuclear moments in the methyl radical. Any of these combinations can occur with any of the two possible electron moment alignments. In a large sample of methyl radicals, the odd electrons will experience four slightly different fields from the nuclear moment alignments.*

energy differences between nuclear spin levels (see below) are extremely small, and, consequently, all of the configurations shown in Figure 9-3 will have equal populations. The ESR spectrum of a large number of methyl radicals will appear as though each electron spin configuration sees *four* different internal magnetic fields since the nuclear spin configuration in each molecule will be a different one of the four in Figure 9-3. These states will be weighted in the ratio of $1:3:3:1$ since there are three times as many ways for the nuclei to give the middle fields in Figure 9-3 as there are for them to give the end fields. The energy level diagram for a methyl radical will, therefore, look like that of Figure 9-4. It should be pointed out that transitions in Figure 9-4 are represented by arrows of constant length since, in ESR spectrometers, the frequency is held constant and the magnetic field is varied. The ESR spectrum of the methyl radical is, therefore, made up of four equally spaced lines. The spacing between these lines is independent of H_0 (except in very weak fields) and is, again, equal to the hyperfine coupling constant a.

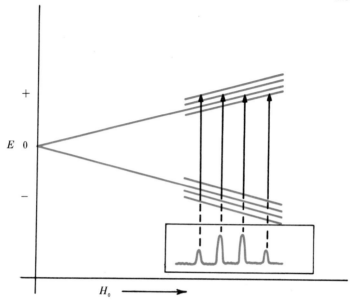

FIG. 9-4 *The energy level diagram and* ESR *spectrum of the methyl radical. In* ESR *experiments, the magnetic field is varied and the frequency is held constant. Because of this, the transitions are represented as arrows with constant length. The lines in the spectrum are separated by the hyperfine coupling constant a = 23 gauss.*

In general, for a molecule which has N equivalent protons, there will be $N + 1$ hyperfine lines in the ESR spectrum. The relative intensities of these lines will be in the same ratio as the binomial coefficients of the N'th order binomial expansion. If these coefficients are not familiar to the student, they can be calculated by making use of the magic triangle shown in Table 9-1.

TABLE 9-1 FIRST FIVE LINES OF THE MAGIC TRIANGLE FOR FINDING RELATIVE INTENSITIES OF HYPERFINE LINES IN ESR SPECTRA. WHAT IS THE NEXT LINE?

N	Relative Intensities of $N + 1$ Lines							
0					1			
1				1		1		
2			1		2		1	
3		1		3		3		1
4	1		4		6		4		1

For molecules with nonequivalent protons, the ESR spectrum can be constructed as follows:

1. Divide the protons in the molecule into equivalent groups according to the symmetry of the molecule. Assign each group a coupling constant, a_i.

2. Starting with a single line on a piece of graph paper, construct the spectrum that would be expected if only the group of protons with the largest splitting constant were present. (One must use chemical intuition to decide which group this is if the a_i are not known.)

3. Use each of the lines obtained in step 2 and divide them according to the number of protons in the group with the next largest splitting constant.

4. Continue the process until all of the groups of protons have been used.

The above procedure will be illustrated for the ethyl radical $\cdot CH_2CH_3$. This radical was observed by doing an ESR experiment on liquid ethane while it was being irradiated with a beam of electrons from a van de Graaff generator. If the protons on the radical center are called σ protons and the methyl protons are called π protons, then the splitting constants are [3]

$$a_\sigma = 22.38 \text{ gauss}$$
$$a_\pi = 26.87 \text{ gauss}$$

A construction of the theoretical spectrum of the ethyl radical using the above rules is shown in Figure 9-5. There are three π protons and two σ protons, and the initial ESR line will be split first into a $1:3:3:1$ quartet with spacing a_π. Each of these lines will then be split into a $1:2:1$ triplet with spacing a_σ to give the final spectrum. This final calculated spectrum should be compared with the experimental spectrum shown in Figure 9-6.

In practice, the experimentalist usually has a pretty good idea of what free radical he has, but he has no knowledge of the coupling constants. To analyze an ESR spectrum, a reverse procedure to that described above is used. That is, the experimentalist constructs several trial spectra using different ratios of coupling constants for the radical that he thinks he has. These coupling constant ratios are guessed at from chemical intuition and past experi-

[3] R. W. Fessenden and R. H. Schuler, *J. Chem. Phys.*, **39**, 2147 (1963).

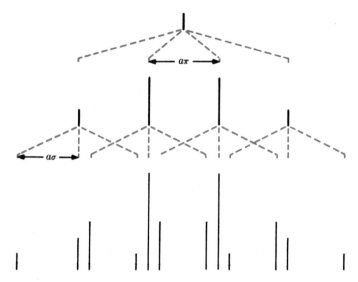

FIG. 9-5 *Construction of the ESR spectrum of the ethyl radical. A ratio of $a_\pi : a_\sigma$ of 13:11, which is close to the experimental ratio, was used in construction. This spectrum looks enough like the experimental spectrum (Figure 9-6) that the lines can be assigned and coupling constants measured.*

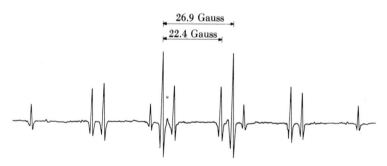

FIG. 9-6 *Experimental spectrum of the ethyl radical. By comparing this spectrum with the theoretical spectrum in Figure 9-5, accurate values of the coupling constants can be measured. For example, the spacing between the two most intense lines is equal to a_π, the spacing between the two end lines is a_σ. (Courtesy of R. W. Fessenden and the American Institute of Physics.)*

ence.   A calculated spectrum that looks like the observed spectrum
is finally obtained, and the actual coupling constants are measured
from the observed spectrum.   A large amount of coupling constant
data on conjugated organic radicals is now available for guidance
in this process.[4]

9-3   *Coupling constants and molecular electronic structure*

Isotropic hyperfine coupling constants are important in studying
the electronic structure of large conjugated organic radicals.   It
was pointed out above that the isotropic hyperfine coupling constant measures the amount of s character in the odd electron wave
function about the nucleus in question.   This fact immediately
raises an important question.   In conjugated aromatic radicals,
one observes hyperfine structure from the protons attached to the
aromatic ring.   Yet the unpaired electron in these radicals is in a
π-molecular orbital, and these molecular orbitals vanish in the
molecular plane since they are constructed from linear combinations of $2p_z$ atomic orbitals (see Chapter 8).   The explanation for
this paradox that is now accepted is that there is a small amount of
mixing between the σ and π orbitals.   That is, the σ-π interactions
that were neglected in the discussion of π-electronic structure in
Chapter 8 are important when talking about hyperfine interactions.   Using this idea, McConnell[5] showed that the hyperfine
coupling constant was related to the unpaired spin density on the
adjacent carbon by the relation

$$a_\mu = Q\rho_\mu \tag{9-16}$$

where a_μ is the observed coupling constant for proton μ, ρ_μ is the
spin density on the carbon atom to which proton μ is attached, and
Q is a semiempirical constant equal to 23–27 gauss.   The importance of Equation 9-16 is that it gives an experimental means of
determining the odd electron distribution in conjugated molecules.
This experimentally determined electron distribution can then be
compared with the results of various theoretical calculations.   For

[4] A. Carrington, *Quart. Rev.*, **17**, 67 (1963).
[5] H. M. McConnell, *J. Chem. Phys.*, **24**, 764 (1956).   See, also, Ref. 4 for a
good discussion of this relationship.

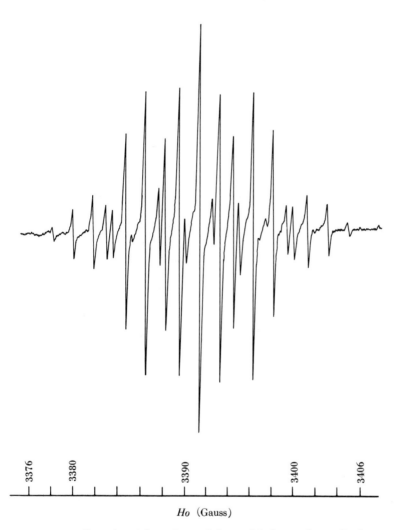

Ho (Gauss)

FIG. 9-7 *Experimental spectrum of the naphthalene anion radical. This is a first derivative spectrum taken at the University of Colorado. The magnetic field strengths are given at the bottom of the figure in gauss. For students interested in calculating the g value of the radical, the cavity frequency was 9503 Mc.*

example, in a simple Hückel calculation, the spin density at any carbon atom can be very easily calculated.   For carbon atom μ, it is equal to $c_{i\mu}^2$ where $c_{i\mu}$ is the coefficient of atom μ *in the molecular orbital i in which the odd electron resides*.   Thus, for the naphthalene anion radical, for example, the unpaired electron would be in the lowest unoccupied orbital of the neutral molecule, and the odd electron densities can readily be calculated.

Comparison of these calculated spin densities with the experimental values calculated from ESR spectra with the aid of Equation 9-16 gives important information about the adequacy of various theoretical models.

EXERCISE 9-3   In Figure 9-7 is shown an experimental spectrum of the naphthalene anion radical.   Using the methods described above, analyze the spectrum to find the values of the two hyperfine coupling constants a_1 and a_2.   Because of the nature of the detection methods used in ESR, the spectrum in Figure 9-7 is the *first derivative* of the absorption spectrum.   The point where the derivative crosses the baseline corresponds to the maximum in an absorption spectrum.   The coupling constants should come out close to 5.0 and 1.8 gauss.

EXERCISE 9-4   Using the results of Exercise 8-5, calculate the spin densities at 1 and 2 positions of naphthalene.   Compare these values and their ratio with the corresponding quantities determined from the experimental spectra in Exercise 9-3 and Equation 9-16.   Use $Q = 24$ gauss.

9-4   *Nuclear magnetic resonance spectroscopy — the chemical shift*

The resonance condition for spin $\frac{1}{2}$ nuclei is analogous to Equation 9-8 except that the nuclear magneton and nuclear g factor must be used.   Thus, for nuclei

$$h\nu = g_N \beta_N H \tag{9-17}$$

In many books, nuclear magnetic resonance is discussed classically rather than quantum mechanically.   This is possible because the spacing between nuclear spin levels is much smaller than kT at room temperature.   In this classical description, the macroscopic magnetic moment of the sample is thought of as precessing about the applied field with an angular frequency ω_0 called the Larmor precession frequency. The quantity ω_0 is related to the ν of Equation 9-17 by the relations

$$\omega_0 = 2\pi\nu = \gamma H_0 \qquad\qquad (9\text{-}18)$$

where γ is called the gyromagnetic ratio of the nucleus. By comparing Equations 9-17 and 9-18, the student can see that

$$\gamma \equiv \frac{\gamma}{2\pi} = \frac{g_N\beta_N}{h}, \qquad \text{or} \qquad \gamma = \frac{g_N\beta_N}{\hbar}$$

EXERCISE 9-5 For protons in a magnetic field of 10,000 gauss, resonance is observed at a frequency of 42.576 Mc. Calculate g_N and γ for protons.

EXERCISE 9-6 A manufacturer has recently marketed a 100 Mc proton nmr. What magnetic field strength is used in this instrument?

EXERCISE 9-7 For a 60 Mc spectrometer, calculate the relative population of the α and β states of a sample of protons at 25°C.

Since most of the chemical applications of NMR involve proton resonance spectroscopy, the discussion that follows will be restricted to protons.

In NMR, the actual field at a given nucleus is, once again, not merely the applied field, but is the vector sum of the applied field and internal fields. For liquid samples, there are two major contributions to this internal field. The first contribution can be rationalized from the fact that nuclei are magnetically screened due to the diamagnetic circulation of electrons.[6] This source of internal fields gives rise to the phenomenon called the "chemical shift." The second contribution comes from the nonvanishing field at each nucleus due to the magnetic moments of neighboring nuclei. This effect gives rise to "spin-spin splittings." The chemical shift will be discussed in the remainder of this section, and spin-spin splittings will be discussed in the next section.

It is well known that if a molecule with no unpaired electrons is placed in an applied field, the electrons will circulate in such a way

---

[6] The student unfamiliar with magnetic susceptibilities should see P. W. Selwood, "The Determination of Magnetic Susceptibilities," Chapter XLIII in *Technique of Organic Chemistry*, edited by A. Weissburger, Vol. I, Interscience Publishers, Inc., New York (1960).

as to induce a magnetic field in the molecule opposed to the applied field. This is the same phenomenon as that responsible for the diamagnetic susceptibility of a molecule. Thus, in any molecule, each nucleus will experience an internal field that opposes the applied field due to this circulation of electrons. Furthermore, the strength of this opposing field is proportional to the applied field. We can, thus, write that the magnetic field at nucleus j is

$$H_j = H_0(1 - \sigma_j) \tag{9-19}$$

where σ_j is called the screening constant of nucleus j. Our transition frequency then becomes

$$\nu = \chi H_0(1 - \sigma_j) \tag{9-20}$$

For protons, σ_j is of the order of 0–10 ppm, but its absolute value cannot be measured. The reason for this is that, to measure σ_j, one would have to make independent measurements of both frequency and magnetic field to better than 1 ppm. It is possible to measure frequencies to this accuracy, but the most accurate way to measure magnetic fields is to use an NMR probe and measure the frequency necessary to induce resonance. Thus, it is not possible to determine H_0 accurately enough to measure σ_j. All chemical shifts are, therefore, measured with respect to the shift in a reference compound. Unfortunately, there has been no general agreement on referencing procedures, so that the literature is filled with chemical shift values using different references. Most modern work uses tetramethylsilane (TMS) as a reference compound, however.

The chemical shift for a given nucleus is defined as follows:

$$\delta_j = \frac{H_s - H_r}{H_r} \times 10^6 \text{ ppm} \tag{9-21}$$

where H_s is the value of the magnetic field at the sample absorption peak and H_r is the value of the magnetic field at the reference absorption peak. Fields are used because it is more convenient to run an NMR experiment at constant frequency and vary H_0 slightly than it is to vary the frequency at constant H_0. To make matters more confusing for the novice, however, field strengths are often expressed in frequency units. The two are equivalent since, for a given nucleus, field is directly proportional to frequency through the gyromagnetic ratio. Substituting Equation 9-19 into 9-21, and using the fact that $\sigma_R \lll 1$, one obtains

$$\delta(\text{dimensionless}) = \frac{\gamma H_0(1 - \sigma_s) - \gamma H_0(1 - \sigma_r)}{\gamma H_0(1 - \sigma_r)} \times 10^6$$

$$= \frac{\sigma_r - \sigma_s}{1} \quad (9\text{-}22)$$

$$= \frac{\nu_s - \nu_r}{\text{spectrometric frequency}} \times 10^6$$

Using this convention, δ is positive if the reference is more screened than the sample, that is, if the reference signal occurs at a *higher* value of H_0 than the sample signal. A chemical shift scale using this convention assigns the protons in TMS the value 0.00. The quantity δ then measures the shift *downfield* from a TMS reference of the protons of interest. A second scale commonly used is the τ scale. In this scale, the protons in TMS are assigned the value 10.000; the chemical shift in τ units is then

$$\tau = 10.000 - \delta$$

There is, at present, some disagreement as to which of these scales is the best.

The chemical shift is an important parameter in NMR spectroscopy because, in general, nuclei in different chemical environments will have different screening constants. Thus, in the best cases, there will be one absorption in an NMR spectrum for each group of chemically distinct protons. The relative areas under each of these absorption peaks also give the relative number of protons in each equivalent group. These features have proved valuable in using NMR to identify unknown compounds. For example, suppose one has a compound with known empirical formula C_4H_6. Its NMR spectrum shows two peaks at roughly 4.0 τ and 7.7 τ with relative heights of one and two, respectively. What is the structure of the compound? There are four possible compounds that can be written that have the correct molecular formula. They are

$$CH_3CH_2C\equiv CH$$
I
ethylacetylene

$$CH_2=CH-CH=CH_2$$
II
butadiene

$$\begin{array}{c} HC-CH_2 \\ \parallel \quad | \\ HC-CH_2 \end{array}$$
III
cyclobutene

$$\begin{array}{c} CH_2 \\ \parallel \\ C \\ \diagup \quad \diagdown \\ CH_2———CH_2 \end{array}$$
IV
methylenecyclopropane

The NMR spectrum immediately rules out compound I because it should have three different kinds of protons. Compounds II, III, and IV would all be consistent with the number and relative intensities of the lines in the spectrum, however. The chemical shift difference between the two kinds of protons is quite large, however, and in compound II one would not expect much difference in shielding of the six protons because they are all attached to a double bond. Compound II can, therefore, be ruled out. To make a final decision between compounds III and IV, one must be aware of an empirical fact that protons in a cyclopropane ring would be expected to occur at abnormally high τ values.[7] Knowing this, compound IV can be ruled out, and the unknown substance has been identified as compound III with only its empirical formula and NMR spectrum.[8]

There is now a great deal of empirical information such as that used in the above discussion about the relation between proton chemical shifts and molecular structure. The interested student should consult the monograph by Jackman [9] for an excellent discussion of some of these relationships.

[7] L. M. Jackman, *Applications of NMR Spectroscopy to Organic Chemistry*, Pergamon Press, Inc., New York (1959) p. 52.

[8] For a set of interesting structural problems, including the one discussed here, see J. D. Roberts, *Nuclear Magnetic Resonance*, McGraw-Hill Book Company, Inc., New York (1959) Appendix C.

[9] L. M. Jackman, *Applications of NMR Spectroscopy to Organic Chemistry*, Pergamon Press, Inc., New York (1959) Chapter 4.

9-5   *Nuclear magnetic resonance—*
spin-spin splittings

Using the information presented above, one would expect the NMR spectrum of ethyl alcohol, CH_3CH_2OH, to consist of three lines with relative intensities $3:2:1$ corresponding to the three types of protons in the molecule, three methyl protons, two methylene protons, and one hydroxyl proton. This is, in fact, what is observed if the spectrum is observed under *low resolution* (Figure 9-8a).   If the spectrum is observed under high resolution, and if the alcohol has not been specially purified, additional splittings appear in the spectrum as shown in Figure 9-8b.   These additional splittings have several characteristic features.   These are:

1. The spacing between lines in the CH_2 quartet is exactly the same as the spacing between lines in the CH_3 triplet.

2. The spacings of the lines in the CH_2 quartet and the CH_3 triplet are independent of the magnetic field strength used in the experiment.   The spacing between the CH_2 and CH_3 multiplets (arising from the chemical shift) is directly proportional to the field strengths.

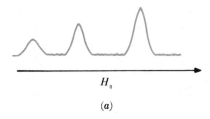

H_0

(a)

FIG. 9-8   *Proton resonance spectrum of ethyl alcohol under (a) low resolution, (b) high resolution.   The relative areas under the three peaks are $1:2:3$, and this serves to identify them. The OH peak has no spin-spin splittings in (b) because of chemical exchange.   The separations between peaks is not to scale.*

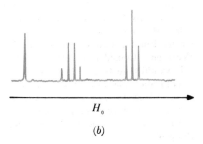

H_0

(b)

This additional structure arises from the second source of internal magnetic fields mentioned above. Splittings arising from this source are called spin-spin splittings, and the spacing between two lines in the multiplet is called the spin-spin splitting constant, J.[10] The number and relative intensities of the lines within a multiplet can be rationalized by a qualitative picture similar to that used for calculating the number and intensity of the hyperfine components in an ESR spectrum. That is, there is a magnetic interaction of *each* equivalent group of protons with the protons (or other magnetic nuclei) on *adjacent* atoms. For example, if we observe the resonance of the methylene protons in ethyl alcohol, there are four different fields at which resonance can occur, depending on how the methyl protons are aligned in that particular molecule. These four fields arise from the same nuclear configurations that were responsible for the hyperfine splittings in the methyl radical (see Figure 9-3). In a sample with a large number of alcohol molecules, the resonance of the methylene protons on different molecules will occur at any of four slightly different fields. Since there are three times as many ways to get the middle configuration in Figure 9-3 as there are the end configurations, the middle lines in the methylene quartet will be three times as intense as the end lines.

A similar argument can be used to explain why the methyl protons are split into a triplet with relative intensities 1:2:1. There are three possible configurations of the two methylene protons, so that the protons on CH_3 group will experience three slightly different fields in a sample of ethyl alcohol molecules, with a statistical distribution of 1:2:1.

---

[10] The existence of spin-spin interactions implies that a given proton has a way of "knowing" how the protons on adjacent atoms are oriented in the applied magnetic field. The interaction cannot be a magnetic dipole-dipole coupling because such a coupling would be averaged to zero in non-rigid molecules by the rapid rotational and vibrational motions within the molecule. Ramsey and Purcell (*Phys. Rev.*, **85**, 143 (1962)) have suggested a mechanism for this interaction that involves an indirect coupling *via* the electrons. Consider the case of HF (F^{19} has spin $\frac{1}{2}$). The oriented proton spin would tend to give the electron in the HF bond closest to it a preferred orientation. Because of the Pauli principle, the electron in the HF bond farthest from the proton would have the opposite orientation. This electron, in turn, would give the F^{19} nuclear spin a preferred orientation. Thus, the F^{19} experiences a small internal field which depends on the orientation of the proton.

For cases where the chemical shift between two types of nuclei is much larger than the spin-spin splitting constant, the following rules enable one to calculate the spin-spin splitting pattern:

1. Divide the magnetic nuclei into groups of equivalent nuclei.

2. No spin-spin splittings are observed between members of the same group of equivalent nuclei.

3. The number and intensity of lines from one equivalent group of protons will depend on the number of *groups* of equivalent nuclei on *adjacent* atoms and on the number of nuclei in each group.

4. A group of N equivalent nuclei on an adjacent atom will give rise to $N + 1$ lines in the spectrum of the group being observed.

5. The intensities of these lines are in the ratios of the binomial coefficients of the expansion $(a + b)^N$, and these ratios can be found using the magic triangle in Table 9-1.

6. For cases where a nucleus is coupled to more than one group of equivalent nuclei with different J's, the spin-spin multiplet must be constructed like a complex hyperfine splitting pattern. That is, one begins with the splittings due to the group with the largest spin coupling constant, and constructs the pattern for coupling with that group alone. Each of the resulting lines is then coupled to the group of protons with next largest coupling constant, etc.

E X E R C I S E 9 - 8 An analysis of the NMR spectrum of pure 2,3,3,4,4-pentafluorocyclobutene can be analyzed by assuming that the proton has spin coupling constants of 9.5, 6.9 and 1.5 cps with the cross ring fluorines, vinyl fluorine, and adjacent fluorines, respectively. Construct the multiplet pattern for this compound.

The student will, no doubt, have noticed that there is nothing in the above prescription for constructing spin-spin multiplets that explains the absence of any spin-spin splittings from or on the OH proton in the ethanol spectrum. For very pure ethanol samples, such spin-spin splittings are observed. That is, the OH resonance is a triplet, and the CH_2 resonance is a *pair* of quartets. This is exactly the behavior predicted on the basis of the above rules. In the absence of special purification procedures, most ethanol contains traces of an acid or base, and these substances catalyze the exchange of the OH proton between different molecules. If this chemical exchange is fast enough, the OH proton will experience only an average magnetic field, and a single line results.   Similarly, the effects of spin-spin splitting of the OH proton on the CH_2 group also disappears.

In instances where the difference in chemical shifts between two groups of magnetically distinct nuclei becomes of the same order of magnitude as the spin-coupling constant, the spectrum becomes much more complicated.   To interpret such spectra, a complete quantum mechanical analysis must be done.   No new principles are involved in such a calculation, but a detailed discussion of the techniques for this analysis is beyond the scope of this text.   The interested student is referred to the excellent treatment of this subject by Roberts.[11]

9-6 *Line widths, relaxation times, and the uncertainty principle*

Compared with other kinds of spectroscopy, the spacing between nuclear spin levels is very small.   That is, ΔE for proton spin states in a 14,000 gauss field is much less than kT at room temperature.   The two spin states will be almost equally populated with a slight excess of nuclei in the lower state (see Exercise 9-7).

When the spectrometer is swept through the resonance condition, this slight excess of population of the lower state is destroyed unless there are mechanisms by which nuclei in the upper state can "relax" back to the ground state, and, thus, maintain the Boltzmann distribution.   Such relaxation mechanisms are called spin-lattice relaxation (sometimes longitudinal relaxation), and are characterized by a spin-lattice relaxation time, T_1.   If T_1 is very long, nuclei cannot relax back to the lower state when excited in a resonance experiment; the Boltzmann excess in the lower state is destroyed, and the absorption signal disappears.   This phenomenon is called saturation.   If T_1 is very short, the energy of both the upper and lower states will become uncertain because of the uncertainty principle, and line broadening will result.

Spin-lattice relaxation arises from random fluctuations of the internal field of the sample.   These fluctuations arise from the tumbling motion of other molecules that possess magnetic nuclei and from the rotational and vibrational motion of other magnetic

[11] J. D. Roberts, *An Introduction to Spin-Spin Splittings in NMR Spectroscopy*, W. A. Benjamin, Inc., New York (1961).

nuclei in the same molecule. There is a component of this randomly fluctuating field at the resonance frequency, and it is this component which causes spin-lattice relaxation.

Besides this fluctuating field, at any instant of time there will be an internal field that has *zero* frequency with respect to a given proton. In general, this zero frequency component will be slightly different for protons of the same type in different molecules. This internal field will give rise to an additional source of line broadening in addition to the uncertainty broadening discussed above. Since the width of an NMR line is measured in cps, the reciprocal of a line width has units of time (sec). The actual line width of an NMR signal is characterized by an empirical time called the spin-spin relaxation time (or transverse relaxation time) and is designated T_2. In many cases in liquids, $T_1 = T_2$ and the line width is completely due to uncertainty broadening.

The form of the uncertainty principle to be used in this discussion is

$$\overline{\Delta E} \, \overline{\Delta t} \geq \hbar \tag{9-23}$$

This states that the product of the uncertainty in the energy of a state times its lifetime (the maximum uncertainty in time) must be equal or greater than $\hbar$. The quantity $\overline{\Delta E}$ can be written as $h \, \overline{\Delta \nu}$, however, and substituting this into Equation 9-23 gives

$$h \, \overline{\Delta \nu} \, \overline{\Delta t} \geq \frac{h}{2\pi}$$

$$\overline{\Delta \nu} \, \overline{\Delta t} \geq \frac{1}{2\pi} \geq 0.159 \tag{9-24}$$

This means that the uncertainty in the frequency of a spectral line times the uncertainty in the lifetime of one or both of the states involved must be equal to or larger than 0.159. For NMR spectroscopy, the quantity relating to $\Delta \nu$ is the width of the line at one half the maximum position. The reciprocal of this width in radians sec^{-1} is defined as $2/T_2$. Thus,

$$(\Delta \omega)_{\frac{1}{2}\max} = 2\pi(\Delta \nu)_{\frac{1}{2}\max} \equiv 2/T_2 \tag{9-25}$$

and T_2 can, therefore, be measured directly from the NMR spectrum. The spin-lattice relaxation time, T_1, is more difficult to measure. The most accurate method uses a pulsed NMR technique.[12]

An understanding of relaxation phenomena is becoming more and more important in NMR experiments. For example, in several recent studies, measurements of the longitudinal relaxation time (T_1) for water have been used to study metal ion binding in biological systems. These studies are based on the observation that the presence of certain paramagnetic ions drastically shortens the T_1 for solvent water. Such a T_1 shortening is reasonable because the presence of the unpaired electrons on a rapidly tumbling ion in solution produces strong oscillating fields at the protons in water and, therefore, provides an efficient relaxation mechanism. When a large biological molecule is added to the system, the paramagnetic ion may be bound onto it. If this happens, the rotational motion of the ion will be slowed and this will change its effect on the T_1 for water. A careful examination of these changes can give important information on enzyme-metal ion-substrate interactions.[13]

9-7   *Summary*

1. The energy levels of a system of independent spin $\frac{1}{2}$ particles in a magnetic field were derived. Transitions between these levels give rise to electron and nuclear magnetic resonance phenomena.

2. The origin of hyperfine interactions in the solution ESR spectra of free radicals was discussed. The ESR spectrum for gaseous hydrogen atoms, methyl radicals, and ethyl radicals were described.

3. Hyperfine coupling constants from aromatic radicals were used to calculate odd electron densities by McConnell's relationship $a_i = Q\rho_i$. These experimental odd electron densities can be compared with densities calculated by various theoretical methods to test the adequacy of the theory.

4. The chemical shift in NMR spectroscopy was shown to be due to the screening effect of the electrons in a molecule. This screening effect will be different for nuclei in different chemical environments and the chemical shift is, therefore, a sensitive indicator of molecular electronic structure.

---

[12] H. Y. Carr and E. M. Purcell, *Phys. Rev.*, **94**, 630 (1954).
[13] A. S. Mildvan and M. Cohn, *Biochem.* **2**, 910 (1963).

5. Spin-spin coupling gives rise to multiplet patterns in NMR spectroscopy that are formally the same as hyperfine coupling patterns in ESR spectroscopy. The appropriate spin-spin multiplets were calculated for the groups of protons in ethyl alcohol.

6. The two relaxation times of importance in NMR and ESR were introduced and the relationship between line widths, the uncertainty principle, and the magnitudes of the relaxation times were discussed.

7. The student should be familiar with the terms, dipole-dipole interaction, Fermi-contact interaction, hyperfine coupling constant, spin density, Larmor precession frequency, diamagnetic susceptibility, chemical shift, spin-spin coupling constant, tau scale, delta scale, T_1, T_2, longitudinal relaxation time, transverse relaxation time, and saturation.

BIBLIOGRAPHY

A. The following three books give broad coverage of topics of interest to chemists. These three books have been used extensively as references in this book and every student should be somewhat familiar with their contents.

 I. H. Margenau and G. M. Murphy, *The Mathematics of Physics and Chemistry*, D. Van Nostrand, Princeton, New Jersey, 1943.
 II. H. Eyring, J. Walter, and G. E. Kimball, *Quantum Chemistry*, John Wiley & Sons, Inc., New York, 1949.
III. W. Kauzmann, *Quantum Chemistry*, Academic Press, Inc., New York, 1957.

B. The following are undergraduate physical chemistry texts which have discussions of quantum phenomena. The first four books listed are likely to be the most useful.

1. G. Barrow, *Physical Chemistry*, McGraw-Hill Book Company, Inc., New York, 1961.
2. D. F. Eggers, Jr., N. W. Gregory, G. D. Halsey, Jr., and B. S. Rabinovitch, *Physical Chemistry*, John Wiley & Sons, Inc., New York, 1964.
3. W. J. Moore, *Physical Chemistry*, Third Edition, Prentice-Hall, Inc., Englewood Cliffs, New Jersey, 1962.
4. A. J. Rutgers, *Physical Chemistry*, Interscience Publishers, Inc., New York, 1954.
5. G. H. Duffy, *Physical Chemistry*, McGraw-Hill Book Company, Inc., New York, 1962.

6. W. F. Sheehan, *Physical Chemistry*, Allyn and Bacon, Inc., Boston, 1961.

C. The following two books have excellent discussions of classical mechanics. The second book also has a good discussion of quantum mechanics.

1. N. Davidson, *Statistical Mechanics*, McGraw-Hill Book Company, Inc., New York, 1962.
2. R. C. Tolman, *The Principles of Statistical Mechanics*, Oxford University Press, London, 1955.

D. The following two books are nonmathematical discussions of quantum mechanics and valence theory. The book by Coulson is especially recommended for beginning students.

1. C. A. Coulson, *Valence*, Second Edition, Oxford University Press, London, 1961.
2. L. Pauling, *The Nature of the Chemical Bond*, Third Edition, Cornell University Press, Ithaca, New York, 1960.

E. The books under this heading are all treatments of quantum mechanics more from the viewpoint of the physicist. This list includes only those that the author is somewhat familiar with and is not meant to be complete.

1. D. R. Bates, Ed., *Quantum Theory, I. Elements*, Academic Press, New York, 1961. The first three chapters give precise, but brief, discussions of many of the subjects covered in this book.
2. P. A. M. Dirac, *The Principles of Quantum Mechanics*, Fourth Edition, Oxford University Press, London, 1958. An advanced and very general treatment of quantum mechanics. The first chapter is interesting reading on the relation between quantum theory and experimental measurements.
3. L. Harris and A. L. Loeb, *Introduction to Wave Mechanics*, McGraw-Hill Book Company, New York, 1963. Contains a good introduction to classical wave theory and shows how quantum mechanics can be developed by pressing the analogy between Ψ functions and standing waves.
4. P. T. Matthews, *Introduction to Quantum Mechanics*, McGraw-Hill Book Company, Inc., New York, 1963. A brief and concise statement of some of the fundamental principles of quantum mechanics.
5. A. Messiah, *Quantum Mechanics*, Two Volumes, John Wiley & Sons, Inc., New York, 1961. A definitive and advanced treatment of quantum mechanics. Recommended for people going on for advanced work in quantum mechanics.

6. V. Rojansky, *Introductory Quantum Mechanics*, Prentice-Hall, Inc., Englewood Cliffs, New Jersey, 1938. A classic beginning physics text in quantum mechanics.

7. L. D. Landau and E. M. Lifshitz, *Quantum Mechanics, Non Relativistic Theory*, Addison-Wesley Publishing Company, Inc., Reading, Massachusetts, 1958. An excellent, but difficult, book for chemists wishing to do advanced work in chemical physics.

F. Books on atomic and molecular spectroscopy.

1. G. Barrow, *Introduction to Molecular Spectroscopy*, McGraw-Hill Book Company, Inc., New York, 1962. Good treatment of rotation and vibration spectra.

2. L. J. Bellamy, *The Infrared Spectra of Complex Molecules*, John Wiley & Sons, Inc., New York, 1958.

3. G. Herzberg, *Atomic Spectra and Atomic Structure*, Dover Publications, New York, 1944.

4. G. Herzberg, *Spectra of Diatomic Molecules*, D. Van Nostrand, Princeton, New Jersey, 1950. The definitive text in this field. Contains tables of spectroscopic data in the back.

5. G. Herzberg, *Infrared and Raman Spectra*, D. Van Nostrand, Princeton, New Jersey, 1945.

6. H. H. Jaffé and M. Orchin, *Theory and Applications of Ultraviolet Spectroscopy*, John Wiley & Sons, Inc., New York, 1962. Good discussion of electronic spectra of organic molecules. Much experimental data is included and rationalized.

7. G. W. King, *Spectroscopy and Molecular Structure*, Holt, Rinehart, & Winston, Inc., New York, 1964. Discusses rotational, vibrational, and electronic spectroscopy.

8. J. N. Murrell, *The Theory of the Electronic Spectra of Organic Molecules*, John Wiley & Sons, Inc., New York, 1963. An excellent discussion of the theory of electronic spectra in conjugated organic molecules.

9. C. Sandorfy, *Electronic Spectra and Quantum Chemistry*, Prentice-Hall, Inc., Englewood Cliffs, New Jersey, 1964. Emphasis on calculation of electronic spectra of conjugated systems.

10. E. B. Wilson, Jr., J. C. Decius, and P. C. Cross, *Molecular Vibrations*, McGraw-Hill Book Company, Inc., New York, 1955. An advanced and theoretical treatment of vibrational spectroscopy.

G. The following two books are mainly about the use of molecular orbital theory to calculate properties of π-electron systems.

1. R. Daudel, R. Lefebvre, and C. Moser, *Quantum Chemistry Methods and Applications*, Interscience Publishers, Inc., New York, 1959.

2. A. Streitwieser, Jr., *Molecular Orbital Theory for Organic Chemists*, John Wiley & Sons, Inc., New York, 1961.

H. Books on Magnetic Resonance Spectroscopy.

1. L. M. Jackman, *Nuclear Magnetic Resonance Spectroscopy*, Pergamon Press, New York, 1959. An excellent, qualitative introduction to NMR.
2. J. D. Roberts, *Nuclear Magnetic Resonance*, McGraw-Hill Book Company, Inc., New York, 1959. This book is at the same level as Jackman, but does not contain as much empirical information. It does contain a good discussion of NMR studies of reaction kinetics and a number of fascinating problems.
3. J. D. Roberts, *An Introduction to Spin-Spin Splittings in NMR Spectroscopy*, W. A. Benjamin Inc., New York, 1961. This book gives detailed instructions for calculating spin-spin splitting patterns when the chemical shifts and spin coupling constants are of the same order of magnitude.
4. J. A. Pople, W. G. Schneider, and H. J. Bernstein, *High Resolution Nuclear Magnetic Resonance*, McGraw-Hill Book Company, Inc., New York, 1959. This is the best monograph on NMR available for chemists. It gives a complete coverage of both theory and experiment up to 1959. It is at a more advanced level than books H-1 and H-2.
5. D. J. E. Ingram, *Free Radicals*, Academic Press, New York, 1958. This is about the only book on ESR suitable for chemists. It is a good introductory book and surveys the field through 1957.

I. Miscellaneous books.

1. F. A. Cotton, *Chemical Applications of Group Theory*, John Wiley & Sons, Inc., New York, 1963. A good introductory text on group theory.
2. R. G. Parr, *Quantum Theory of Molecular Electronic Structure*, W. A. Benjamin, Inc., New York, 1963. A good book to supplement the present volume. Contains a critical discussion of the problems involved in molecular calculations as well as a collection of key reprints on the subject.
3. L. Pauling and E. B. Wilson, Jr., *Introduction to Quantum Mechanics*, McGraw-Hill Book Company, Inc., New York, 1935. Good for its applications to problems of chemical interest such as spectroscopy; many electron, atomic, molecular, and valence bond calculations.
4. K. Pitzer, *Quantum Chemistry*, Prentice-Hall, Inc., Englewood Cliffs, New Jersey, 1953. Good as a reference to calculation of properties of macroscopic systems.
5. J. C. Slater, *Quantum Theory of Molecules and Solids*, Volume 1. *Electronic Structure of Molecules*, McGraw-Hill Book Company, Inc., New York, 1963. Excellent discussion of refined calculations on small molecules.

INDEX